THE OXFORD ENGINEERING SCIENCE SERIES

GENERAL EDITORS

F. W. CRAWFORD, A. L. CULLEN, J. W. HUTCHINSON,
W. H. WITTRICK, L. C. WOODS

GU01005717

NON-LINEAR OSCILLATIONS

BY

PETER HAGEDORN

TRANSLATED AND EDITED
BY
WOLFRAM STADLER

CLARENDON PRESS · OXFORD

Oxford University Press, Walton Street, Oxford OX2 6DP

London Glasgow New York Toronto
Delhi Bombay Calcutta Madras Karachi
Kuala Lumpur Singapore Hong Kong Tokyo
Nairobi Dar es Salaam Cape Town
Melbourne Auckland
and associates in
Beirut Berlin Ibadan Mexico City Nicosia

Oxford is a trade mark of Oxford University Press

First published by Akademische Verlag 1978
Translation published by the Clarendon Press 1981
First issued in paperback 1982

Published in the United States of America
by Oxford University Press, New York

British Library Cataloguing in Publication Data
Hagedorn, Peter
Non-linear oscillations. — (Oxford engineering
science series)
1. Nonlinear oscillations
I. Title   II. Stadler, Wolfram
III. Nichtlineare Schwingungen, English
531'.322   QA867.5
ISBN 0-19-856156-3

Library of Congress Cataloging in Publication Data
Hagedorn, Peter.
Non-linear oscillations.

(Oxford engineering science series)
Translation of: Nichtlineare Schwingungen.
Includes bibliographies and indexes.
1. Nonlinear oscillations.   2. Differential
equations, Nonlinear.   I. Stadler, Wolfram.
II. Title.   III. Series.
QA867.5H3313   1982   531'.322   82-14243
ISBN 0-19-856156-3 (pbk.)

Printed in Great Britain by
The Thetford Press Limited, Thetford, Norfolk

Dedicated to my father

TRANSLATOR'S PREFACE

All too often undergraduate education tends to create the impression of a world governed entirely by linear differential equations. With the exception of a few first-order non-linear equations and at most an elliptic integral arising from the solution of the pendulum equation, few topics on non-linear ordinary differential equations are included in undergraduate courses.

This book will be of use in bridging the gap in undergraduate education by providing a text on non-linear oscillations at an intermediate rather than a graduate level. The mathematical demands of the book are such that a senior or a first-year graduate student in engineering or the sciences should be able to deal with the subject matter. The large number of worked-out examples is ideal for a course oriented toward the computational aspects of non-linear differential equations; simultaneously, the reader should find the book to be a quick reference on procedures and solution methods for non-linear oscillation problems.

San Francisco, California   Wolfram Stadler
August, 1980

PREFACE

In this book, systems described in terms of non-linear ordinary differential equations are treated; that is, it concerns the subject of *Non-linear oscillations*. The material corresponds approximately to a one-semester graduate course as offered by the author at the Technical University in Darmstadt during the winter semesters 1975–6 and 1976–7. In each case, this course was preceded by two-semester courses on the linear oscillations of discrete and of continuous systems, so that there was no need to deal with a presentation of the characteristics of linear systems.

The present work differs from other books on *Theory of oscillations* and on *Analysis of non-linear systems* mainly in the selection of the topics covered; the subject is so broad that the aims and the research interests of the authors tend to produce quite a variety of books on the subject. The presentations thus span the range from Cesari's work, *Asymptotic behaviour and stability problems in ordinary differential equations* (Springer, Berlin, 1959) to Klotter's *Technische Schwingungslehre* (*Applied oscillation theory*, Springer, Berlin, 1951 (Vol. 1) and 1960 (Vol. 2)), and beyond to Hayashi's *Nonlinear oscillations in physical systems* (McGraw-Hill, New York, 1964) or to Blaquière's *Nonlinear system analysis* (Academic Press, New York, 1966).

Here, an attempt is made to convey to engineers and physicists alike the basic ideas of the dynamic behaviour of non-linear systems. The book is meant to provide the reader with some insight into the most important phenomena and solution methods in non-linear oscillations with no attempt at presenting a complete treatment of the subject. As a consequence of the author's personal inclinations, a relatively thorough treatment of stability theory is given. Furthermore, the inclusion of a chapter on optimal control in a book on non-linear systems appears to be a novelty. This is all the more surprising since the differential equations arising in this subject often yield to a treatment based on the methods used in the theory of oscillations.

In Chapter 1 the mathematical pendulum is used to provide a survey of free and forced oscillations in damped and undamped systems. This simple model is used to provide illustrations for and comparisons between the various approximation schemes. A brief treatment of the existence of periodic solutions, of subharmonic oscillations, and of combined resonance is given. The idea for such an introduction involving the example of the pendulum stems from the excellent book by Blaquière; however, somewhat different methods are used in part. The corresponding exercises involve differential equations which are of the Duffing type, or similar to it.

Chapter 2 is a summary of Liapounov stability theory. The first and the second method of Liapounov are explained for autonomous as well as for non-autonomous systems. Here, a fundamental familiarity with the theory of linear oscillations is assumed. La Salle's theorem about the stability of invariant domains is explained in terms of some illustrative examples.

Chapter 3 is devoted to self-excited oscillations and contains the theorems by Poincaré-Bendixson, by Liénard, and by Levinson and Smith, among others. Various methods are used to obtain approximations for the limit cycles.

Chapter 4 is a survey of the theory of canonical perturbations in Hamiltonian mechanics.

An introduction to optimal control theory is given in Chapter 5. It is shown how the canonical perturbation theory of classical mechanics may be used in optimal control problems.

At the end of each chapter, exercises which are also treated in the text are presented; hints for their solution may be found at the end of the book.

Furthermore, the end of each chapter contains a bibliography which is augmented by a name index at the end of the book. Because of the large amount of technical literature, no attempt at completeness is made here either. Generally, the citations consist of a few of the earlier fundamental works in the area—quite often worthy of study, based on past experience—some classical and modern texts and monographs and a selection of articles of current vintage. The intent is to provide the reader with the connection to the newest research results. Naturally, the selection is strongly influenced by personal taste.

During the lectures, the analytical approximation results were frequently checked with an analogue computer—as it turned out, a valuable experience from a didactic viewpoint.

The author is grateful to Dr H. Kühl and B. Schäfer for working out the solutions to the exercises, to W. Teschner, K. G. Krapf, and B. Schäfer for the thorough reading of the manuscript and subsequent proof-reading thereof, and, finally, to Mrs. R. Popp for the careful typing of the manuscript. Also, my thanks to the publisher for a good working relationship and the appealing format of the book.

Darmstadt   P. Hagedorn
May 1977

CONTENTS

PREFACE   vi

INTRODUCTION   1

1. THE MATHEMATICAL PENDULUM AS AN ILLUSTRATION OF
   LINEAR AND NON-LINEAR OSCILLATIONS: SYSTEMS WHICH
   ARE SIMILAR TO A SIMPLE LINEAR OSCILLATOR   3
   1.1. Undamped free oscillations of the pendulum   3
        1.1.1. Perturbation methods   5
        1.1.2. The method of harmonic balance   11
        1.1.3. The Ritz method   12
        1.1.4. Method of equivalent linearization   14
        1.1.5. The exact solution   16
   1.2. Damped free oscillations   21
        1.2.1. The influence of small damping terms   22
        1.2.2. The method of slowly changing phase and amplitude   25
   1.3. Forced oscillations   29
        1.3.1. The existence of periodic solutions   29
        1.3.2. Undamped forced oscillations   35
        1.3.3. The influence of damping and the jump phenomenon   39
        1.3.4. Subharmonic oscillations   49
        1.3.5. Combination frequencies   52
   1.4. General comments   53
   References   54
   Exercises   56

2. LIAPOUNOV STABILITY THEORY   60
   2.1. The concept of Liapounov stability   60
   2.2. The direct method of Liapounov   70
   2.3. Supplementary remarks concerning the direct method of Liapounov   80
   2.4. Stability by the first approximation (autonomous case)   84
   2.5. Stability by the first approximation (periodic case)   96
   2.6. Stability by the first approximation (aperiodic case)   107
   2.7. Additional comments concerning stability   110
   References   111
   Exercises   113

3. SELF-EXCITED OSCILLATIONS   117
   3.1. Basic concepts   117
   3.2. Self-excited oscillations in mechanical and electrical systems   119
   3.3. Analytical approximation methods for the computation of
        self-excited oscillations   131
        3.3.1. Perturbation methods   131

    3.3.2. Slowly changing phase and amplitude   135
    3.3.3. Method of equivalent linearization   136
3.4. Analytical criteria for the existence of limit cycles   139
3.5. Forced oscillations in self-excited systems   143
3.6. Self-excited oscillations in systems with several degrees of freedom   145
3.7. Additional comments concerning self-excited oscillations   150
References   151
Exercises   152

4. HAMILTONIAN SYSTEMS   154
4.1. Hamiltonian differential equations in mechanics   154
4.2. Canonical transformations   160
4.3. The Hamilton–Jacobi differential equation   167
4.4. Canonical transformations and the motion   174
4.5. Canonical perturbation theory   176
4.6. Additional comments concerning Hamiltonian systems   180
References   181
Exercises   182

5. INTRODUCTION TO THE THEORY OF OPTIMAL CONTROL   184
5.1. Control problems, controllability   184
5.2. The Pontryagin maximum principle   187
5.3. Transversality conditions and problems with target sets   198
5.4. Canonical perturbation theory in optimal control   201
5.5. Additional comments concerning the theory of optimal control   206
References   207
Exercises   208

SOLUTIONS FOR THE EXERCISES   211

NAME INDEX   285

SUBJECT INDEX   287

INTRODUCTION

Why a treatment of *Non-linear oscillations*? Primarily because the descriptive differential equations for physical systems generally are linear only as first approximations. Since the treatment of non-linear differential equations is a good deal more complicated than that of linear ones, one limits oneself, whenever possible, to linear models. As it turns out, linearization often results in an accurate representation of the characteristics of the system and provides a description which suffices for the practical needs of the engineer. There are cases, however, where the investigation of the linearized system does not yield a sufficiently accurate representation — thus, for example, in large-amplitude oscillations of elastic systems. Also, under certain conditions, the non-linear approach may lead to completely new phenomena which are not possible at all in linear systems. This is the case, for example, for subharmonic and ultraharmonic forced oscillations or for the existence of a limit cycle (an isolated periodic oscillation of a self-excited system).

In modern engineering with its continuous refinement of instrumentation, its improved computational capabilities, and the more narrow tolerances, the theory of non-linear oscillations is gaining more and more practical meaning. Applications of the theory of non-linear oscillations may not only be found in classical mechanics but also in electronics, communications, quantum mechanics, biology, and in many other branches of science.

Apart from some very few exceptions, it is generally not possible to provide analytical closed-form solutions for the differential equations occurring in non-linear oscillations. Naturally, a numerical solution may be obtained when the motion corresponding to certain initial conditions is to be determined. It is, however, of little use if one wishes to obtain a survey of the possible solution types and of their dependence on the individual parameters.

Two different approaches will be used here: general theorems from the theory of non-linear differential equations about the existence of periodic solutions, about stability, and so forth, and methods for the analytical computation of approximate solutions. The two methods supplement each other, since we may expect that the approximation methods provide approximations of a periodic solution if its existence is assured *a priori*. Error estimates for the approximations often cannot be given without difficulty, even though experience shows that the methods yield good results in many cases.

A large part of the methods used in the analysis of non-linear systems derives from celestial mechanics, where perturbation theory — probably the most important approximation method — was originally developed (Poincaré 1957). The origin of modern stability theory (Liapounov 1892) was also closely related to that of analytical mechanics, and today it finds application in dynamical systems of every kind. However, only a relatively small number of general theorems about the existence of periodic solutions is known. Important inceptions of such a theory may be found in the work of Poincaré and Birkhoff (1927), for example. Practical applications, however, are dominated by *ad hoc* methods, generally some variant of a perturbation approach. A good survey of the modern methods of perturbation theory may be found in the fine book by Nayfeh (1973).

The ill repute in which perturbation theory is often held becomes understandable if one considers that Delaunay (1816-72) in a seventh-order approximation to the moon's orbit obtained an equation which covered 170 (printed) pages. Thank God those times are past! Today, the analytic approximation methods have a different meaning from that before the computer age. For given initial conditions and specified parameters, ordinary differential equations today may be numerically integrated with considerably more speed and accuracy than was feasible only a few decades ago. If some insight into the character of the solution and its dependence on certain parameters is to be obtained, then the numerical calculation must be repeated for many differing parameter combinations. The sheer quantity of data then may get so large that even relatively simple general relationships may be recognized only with great difficulty. The analytical approximation methods, however, make it possible to comprehend simple relationships approximately by means of analytical expressions. They often lead to easily surveyed and quite useful results. The accuracy may increase with an increase in the number of terms of an analytical approximation, but the perspicuity will suffer. All approximations here will thus be restricted to only a few terms.

In contrast to lectures on ordinary differential equations, the proofs of general theorems here are pushed into the background and are usually not completely presented. Here ordinary differential equations will be treated which may serve as models for a variety of physical systems, and these mathematical models will then be attacked with the various tools of the trade. The derivation of differential equations from given mechanical, electrical, and other physical models will only be a peripheral occupation. It is assumed that the reader is familiar therewith. Even in the presumably known theory of linear systems, one generally obtains non-linear differential equations initially which are then transformed to linear equations by applying linearization procedures.

References

Birkhoff, G.D. (1927). *Dynamical systems.* American Mathematical Society, Providence, Rhode Island.
Nayfeh, A.H. (1973). *Perturbation methods.* John Wiley, New York.
Poincaré, H. (1957). *Les méthodes nouvelles de la mécanique céleste* [*New methods in celestial mechanics*], Vols. 1–3. Dover, New York. [First edn 1892].

THE MATHEMATICAL PENDULUM AS AN ILLUSTRATION OF LINEAR AND NON-LINEAR OSCILLATIONS: SYSTEMS WHICH ARE SIMILAR TO A SIMPLE LINEAR OSCILLATOR

1.1. Undamped free oscillations of the pendulum

Many of the mathematical methods employed in non-linear oscillations may be successfully tested on one of the simplest mathematical systems: the mathematical pendulum. When friction is neglected, the differential equation governing the free oscillation of the mathematical pendulum is given by

$$ml\ddot{x} + mg \sin x = 0 \tag{1}$$

or

$$\ddot{x} + \omega_0^2 \sin x = 0. \tag{2}$$

Here m is the mass, l the length of the pendulum, g the gravitational acceleration, and $\omega_0^2 = g/l$; the angle x designates the deviation from the (stable) vertical

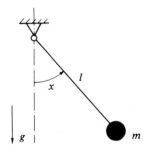

Fig. 1.1. The mathematical pendulum.

equilibrium position (see Fig. 1.1). For the linearized system, the approximation $\sin x \approx x$ is used; that is, only the first term of the Taylor series

$$\sin x = x - \frac{x^3}{3!} + \frac{x^5}{5!} - \frac{x^7}{7!} + \dots$$

is taken into consideration; for small x this should lead to good results. The non-linear differential equation (2) then is replaced by

$$\ddot{x} + \omega_0^2 x = 0 \tag{3}$$

with the general solution

$$x = A \sin \omega_0 t + B \cos \omega_0 t, \tag{4}$$

where A and B are the constants of integration yet to be determined from the initial conditions. The natural circular frequency ω_0 does not depend on the amplitude of oscillation. As is known from linear oscillations, this is a general characteristic of linear systems. If the initial values of x and $\dot{x}$ at the time $t = 0$ are given by x_0 and $\dot{x}_0$, respectively, then

$$x = \frac{\dot{x}_0}{\omega_0} \sin \omega_0 t + x_0 \cos \omega_0 t \tag{5}$$

and

$$\dot{x} = \dot{x}_0 \cos \omega_0 t - x_0 \omega_0 \sin \omega_0 t \tag{6}$$

follow immediately. The 'phase-plane diagram' in the $x, \dot{x}$-plane consists of the family of ellipses given by

$$x^2 + \frac{\dot{x}^2}{\omega_0^2} = x_0^2 + \frac{\dot{x}_0^2}{\omega_0^2}, \tag{7}$$

as may easily be deduced by eliminating t from (5) and (6), or of a family of circles, if one uses $x, \dot{x}/\omega_0$ instead of $x, \dot{x}$ as coordinate axes (Fig. 1.2). All these circles or ellipses are traversed in the same time, $T = 2\pi/\omega_0$. These facts are familiar from the theory of linear oscillations.

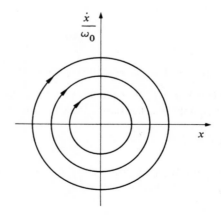

Fig. 1.2. Phase diagram of the linear oscillator.

Clearly, the linear representation fails completely for large angles x. In fact, the differential eqn (2) even has an additional 'equilibrium position' $x = \pi$, $\dot{x} = 0$, whereas the 'linearized' differential eqn (3) only has a single critical point at $x = 0$, $\dot{x} = 0$! One would expect to obtain a better representation of the behaviour of the solutions of (2) by keeping not only the first term in the Taylor series but also as many terms of higher order as possible. Although (2) may be solved exactly, various approximation schemes will be used before giving the exact solution to the problem.

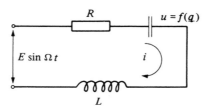

Fig. 1.3. Non-linear electric circuit.

With few exceptions, the equations treated in this chapter will be of the type $\ddot{x} + h(x)\dot{x} + f(x) = p(t)$, of which (2) is a special case (with $h(x) \equiv 0, p(t) \equiv 0$). Herein, $p(t)$ is an 'excitation' — generally periodic — and $h(x)\dot{x}$ with $h(x) \geqslant 0$ is a 'damping term'. Differential equations of this type not only occur in numerous vibration problems in mechanics but also occur frequently in other fields. Thus, for example, the electrical circuit of Fig. 1.3 is described by the differential equations $L \ (\mathrm{d}i/\mathrm{d}t) + Ri + f(q) = E \sin \Omega t$ or $L\ddot{q} + R\dot{q} + f(q) = E \sin \Omega t$. Here, i is the current, $L > 0$ the (linear) inductance, $R \geqslant 0$ the (linear) Ohmian resistance, $u = f(q)$ is the potential of the non-linear condenser with charge q, and $E \sin \Omega t$ is the alternating voltage with circular frequency Ω specified at the terminals. In this analogy, the pendulum of Fig. 1.1 corresponds to the closed circuit ($E = 0$) with $R = 0$. In the remainder of this chapter, the physical realization of this differential equation will be ignored, but for brevity it will generally be referred to as the 'pendulum'.

1.1.1. Perturbation methods

The expression $\sin x \approx x - x^3/6$ should certainly be a closer approximation than $\sin x \approx x$; as a result, one obtains

$$\ddot{x} + \omega_0^2 x - \frac{\omega_0^2}{6}x^3 = 0 . \tag{8}$$

In order to give a somewhat more general treatment, the investigation will be based on the Duffing equation

$$\ddot{x} + \omega_0^2 x + \mu x^3 = 0 \tag{9}$$

where μ is a 'small parameter'. One may now try to obtain a solution in the form

$$x(t) = x_0(t) + \mu x_1(t) + \mu^2 x_2(t) + \ldots + \mu^m x_m(t) + \ldots \qquad (10)$$

where the $x_i(t)$, $i = 0, 1, 2, \ldots$ are functions yet to be determined. The substitution of (10) in (9) yields

$$\ddot{x}_0 + \omega_0^2 x_0 + \mu(\ddot{x}_1 + \omega_0^2 x_1 + x_0^3) + \mu^2(\ddot{x}_2 + \omega_0^2 x_2 + 3\,x_0^2 x_1) + o(\mu^2) = 0 \qquad (11)$$

when ordered in terms of the powers of μ.† This results in the system of equations

$$\ddot{x}_0 + \omega_0^2 x_0 = 0, \qquad (12)$$

$$\ddot{x}_1 + \omega_0^2 x_1 = -x_0^3, \qquad (13)$$

$$\ddot{x}_2 + \omega_0^2 x_2 = -3\,x_0^2 x_1, \qquad (14)$$

and so on,

which may then be solved recursively. The general solution of (12) is given by (4); it may also be written in the form

$$x_0(t) = C \sin(\omega_0 t + \gamma) \qquad (15)$$

with new constants of integration C and γ.

The substitution of (15) into (13) results in

$$\ddot{x}_1 + \omega_0^2 x_1 = -C^3 \sin^3(\omega_0 t + \gamma). \qquad (16)$$

In order to solve this equation in as simple a manner as possible, the right-hand side is written as a sum of trigonometric functions:

$$\ddot{x}_1 + \omega_0^2 x_1 = -\frac{3}{4}C^3 \sin(\omega_0 t + \gamma) + \frac{1}{4}C^3 \sin(3\omega_0 t + 3\gamma). \qquad (17)$$

---

†The symbol $o(s)$ here has its usual meaning: one has $\lim_{s\to 0} \{o(s)/s\} = 0$. One distinguishes between $o(s)$ and $O(s)$. Whereas $o(s)$ represents terms which are small in comparison to s, $O(s)$ is used to represent terms of the order of magnitude of s, that is, $\lim_{s\to 0} \{O(s)/s\}$ is finite.

The solution now is

$$x_1(t) = \frac{3t}{8\omega_0} C^3 \cos(\omega_0 t + \gamma) - \frac{1}{32\omega_0^2} C^3 \sin(3\omega_0 t + 3\gamma) +$$

$$+ C_1 \sin(\omega_0 t + \gamma_1) \tag{18}$$

with additional constants of integration, C_1 and γ_1. The solution (18) consists of a superposition of the free oscillations with the two forced oscillations with circular frequencies ω_0 and $3\omega_0$; this holds because (17) is again a linear differential equation.

In the successive solutions of (14) and of the following differential equations, further constants of integration $C_2, C_3, \ldots, \gamma_2, \gamma_3, \ldots$ arise, all of which must be determined from the initial conditions. However, since only two initial conditions are available, there are a number of approaches to the evaluation of these constants; two approaches are especially close at hand:

1. The initial conditions

$$\left. \begin{aligned} x(0) &= x_0(0) + \mu x_1(0) + \mu^2 x_2(0) + \ldots, \\ \dot{x}(0) &= \dot{x}_0(0) + \mu \dot{x}_1(0) + \mu^2 \dot{x}_2(0) + \ldots \end{aligned} \right\} \tag{19}$$

are imposed in the 'zeroth approximation'; that is, for a given $x(0), \dot{x}(0)$ the constants C and γ in (15) are chosen so as to satisfy $x_0(0) = x(0), \dot{x}_0(0) = \dot{x}(0)$; in addition, one specifies $x_i(0) = 0, \dot{x}_i(0) = 0$ for $i = 1, 2, \ldots$.

However, rather than treating the general case with arbitrary $x(0)$ and $\dot{x}(0)$, only the solutions corresponding to $x(0) = A$ and $\dot{x}(0) = 0$ will be determined (in fact, the general solution may easily be deduced from this particular case). With

$$\left. \begin{aligned} x_0(0) &= A, \ \dot{x}_0(0) = 0, \\ x_i(0) &= 0, \ \dot{x}_i(0) = 0, \ i = 1, 2, \ldots \end{aligned} \right\} \tag{20}$$

eqn (15) then results in $C = A$, and $\gamma = \frac{1}{2}\pi$ and for $i = 1$ one hence obtains

$$\frac{1}{32} \frac{C^3}{\omega_0^2} + C_1 \sin \gamma_1 = 0,$$

$$C_1 \cos \gamma_1 = 0,$$

in conjunction with (18). These expressions yield $\gamma_1 = \frac{1}{2}\pi$ and $C_1 = -C^3/32\omega_0^2$ along with

$$x(t) = C\cos\omega_0 t + \mu\frac{1}{32}\frac{C^3}{\omega_0^2}[\cos 3\omega_0 t - \cos\omega_0 t - 12\omega_0 t\sin\omega_0 t] +$$

$$+ o(\mu). \tag{20a}$$

The constants which arise in the higher-order approximations may be determined in a similar manner.

2. All of the C_i, $i = 1, 2, \ldots$, are set equal to zero (the γ_i remain arbitrary) and C and γ are not determined directly from the initial conditions for $x_0, \dot{x}_0$ but from (19), since the initial conditions for $x_i, \dot{x}_i$ ($i = 1, 2, \ldots$) also depend on C and γ. If one again insists on $\dot{x}(0) = 0$, then one now has

$$\dot{x}(0) = 0 = C\omega_0\cos\gamma + \mu\left[\frac{3}{8}\frac{C^3}{\omega_0}\cos\gamma - \frac{3}{32\omega_0}C^3\cos 3\gamma\right] + \ldots,$$

which is satisfied with $\gamma = \frac{1}{2}\pi$. The solution is given by

$$x(t) = C\cos\omega_0 t + \mu\frac{1}{32}\frac{C^3}{\omega_0^2}[\cos 3\omega_0 t - 12\omega_0 t\sin\omega_0 t] + o(\mu), \tag{20b}$$

and

$$x(0) = A = C + \mu\frac{1}{32}\frac{C^3}{\omega_0^2} + o(\mu)$$

follows. Note that the amplitude $A = x(0)$ is no longer equal to C!

If the perturbation computations are continued in this same manner, one eventually obtains $x(0)$ and, in the case of a periodic solution, also the amplitude, in the form

$$x(0) = C + \mu A_1(C) + \mu^2 A_2(C) + \ldots. \tag{21}$$

If only the first-order terms in μ are kept in the series (20a) and (20b), then there occurs an unbounded term, increasing linearly with time, with the seeming implication that no periodic solution exists! It is known from observation, however, that periodic solutions are to be expected. Nevertheless, this series expansion is quite useful for small time intervals, large errors resulting only when 'large' times are being considered. The terms 'large' and 'small' here are meant in comparison with the period, $T = 2\pi/\omega_0$. In celestial mechanics, where this type of perturbation approach was first used, even a century may still be considered to be a 'small' interval. This latter fact gave rise to the designation 'secular terms' for terms growing beyond all bounds with time.

In fact, the solutions of (9) are periodic, but this is no longer apparent from the series which has been truncated after a finite number number of terms. Recall that the same comment applies to the Taylor expansion of the periodic function $\sin(\omega_0 + \mu)t$ with respect to μt:

$$\sin(\omega_0 + \mu)t = \sin \omega_0 t + \mu t \cos \omega_0 t - \frac{\mu^2 t^2}{2!} \sin \omega_0 t -$$

$$- \frac{\mu^3 t^3}{3!} \cos \omega_0 t + \ldots,$$

a series which converges for all μt, but not uniformly for $t \in (0, \infty)$!†

It thus becomes desirable to adjust the perturbation approach in such a manner that the periodicity of the solution may already be recognized after a finite number of terms and, if possible, in such a way that one obtains a remainder which is uniformly small in t. An approach proposed by Lindstedt (1883) is used, together with what is known from past experience, namely, that the circular frequency of a non-linear oscillation is a function of the amplitude.

Consequently, one writes

$$\omega^2 = \omega_0^2 + \mu e_1(C) + \mu^2 e_2(C) + \ldots \tag{22}$$

or

$$\omega_0^2 = \omega^2 - \mu e_1(C) - \mu^2 e_2(C) + o(\mu^2). \tag{23}$$

These expressions together with (10) are substituted in (9) and the result is again arranged according to powers of μ to yield

$$\ddot{x}_0 + \omega^2 x_0 + \mu(\ddot{x}_1 + \omega^2 x_1 + x_0^3 - e_1 x_0) +$$

$$+ \mu^2(\ddot{x}_2 + \omega^2 x_2 + 3 x_0^2 x_1 - e_2 x_0 - e_1 x_1) + o(\mu^2) = 0. \tag{24}$$

---

†The series $\sum\limits_{\nu = 1}^{\infty} f_\nu(x)$ is said to converge to $g(x)$, $x \in (a,b)$, if for every $\epsilon > 0$ there exists a number $N(\epsilon,x)$ such that $|g(x) - \sum\limits_{\nu = 1}^{n} f_\nu(x)| < \epsilon$ for every $n > N(\epsilon,x)$. The series is uniformly convergent for $x \in (a,b)$ if for every $\epsilon > 0$ there exists a number $N(\epsilon)$, *depending only on* ϵ, such that $|g(x) - \sum\limits_{\nu = 1}^{n} f_\nu(x)| < \epsilon$ for every $n > N(\epsilon)$ and for every $x \in (a,b)$, where (a,b) denotes the open interval $a < x < b$.

This equation is satisfied by setting the coefficients of the powers of μ equal to zero, resulting in

$$\ddot{x}_0 + \omega^2 x_0 = 0, \tag{25}$$

$$\ddot{x}_1 + \omega^2 x_1 = -x_0^3 + e_1 x_0, \tag{26}$$

$$\ddot{x}_2 + \omega^2 x_2 = -3 x_0^2 x_1 + e_2 x_0 + e_1 x_1, \tag{27}$$

. . . .

The substitution of $x_0(t) = C \sin(\omega t + \gamma)$ in eqn (26) yields:

$$\ddot{x}_1 + \omega^2 x_1 = -C^3 \sin^3(\omega t + \gamma) + e_1 C \sin(\omega t + \gamma)$$

and hence

$$\ddot{x}_1 + \omega^2 x_1 = -\frac{3}{4} C^3 \sin(\omega t + \gamma) + \frac{1}{4} C^3 \sin(3\omega t + 3\gamma) +$$

$$+ e_1 C \sin(\omega t + \gamma). \tag{28}$$

In order to ensure that no secular terms appear in the solution of (28), resonance must be avoided. To do so, the function $e_1(C)$, unspecified until now, is chosen as

$$e_1(C) = \frac{3}{4} C^2. \tag{29}$$

As a consequence of (22), one has

$$\omega^2 = \omega_0^2 + \mu \frac{3}{4} C^2 + o(\mu) \tag{30}$$

and

$$x_1(t) = C_1 \sin(\omega t + \gamma_1) - \frac{1}{32\omega^2} C^3 \sin(3\omega t + 3\gamma). \tag{31}$$

For simplicity, the integration constant C_1 is set equal to zero, yielding

$$x(t) = C \sin(\omega t + \gamma) - \frac{\mu}{32\omega^2} C^3 \sin(3\omega t + 3\gamma) + o(\mu) \tag{32}$$

(note again that C no longer corresponds to the amplitude of $x(t)$). If one takes account of the second-order terms in a similar manner, one obtains

$$x(t) = C \sin (\omega t + \gamma) - \mu \frac{1}{32\omega^2} C^3 \sin (3\omega t + 3\gamma) +$$

$$+ \mu^2 \frac{1}{1024\omega^4} C^5 \{\sin (5\omega t + 5\gamma) - 3 \sin (3\omega t + 3\gamma)\} + o(\mu^2), \tag{33}$$

$$\omega^2(C) = \omega_0^2 + \frac{3\mu}{4} C^2 + \frac{3\mu^2}{128} \frac{C^4}{\omega^2} + o(\mu^2). \tag{34}$$

Naturally, ω^2 on the right-hand side of (34) may be replaced by ω_0^2.

Note that the non-linear term in (9) gives rise to harmonic terms of odd order in $x(t)$ and that the frequency of free oscillation thus becomes dependent on the amplitude.

It is generally difficult to prove that a given non-linear differential equation has solutions which may be written in the power series form which was used here; in addition, error estimates are exceedingly difficult to obtain (see Cesari 1959; Nayfeh 1973).

1.1.2. The method of harmonic balance

It is now assumed that (8) has a solution which may be approximated by

$$x(t) = C \sin \omega t \tag{35}$$

but where the circular frequency $\omega(C)$ may depend on the amplitude. With

$$x^3 = C^3 \sin^3 \omega t = C^3 \left(\frac{3}{4} \sin \omega t - \frac{1}{4} \sin 3 \omega t \right)$$

one obtains

$$\ddot{x} + \omega_0^2 \left(x - \frac{x^3}{6} \right) = \left(\omega_0^2 - \omega^2 - \omega_0^2 \frac{C^2}{8} \right) C \sin \omega t +$$

$$+ \omega_0^2 \frac{C^3}{24} \sin 3 \omega t, \tag{36}$$

which naturally is not equal to zero in general. The right-hand side of (36) would have to vanish if $x(t)$ were to be a solution of (8). One may, however, at least assure the vanishing of the factor of $\sin \omega t$ by setting

$$\omega^2 = \omega_0^2 \left(1 - \frac{C^2}{8} \right). \tag{37}$$

If it is further assumed that C^3 is small, then the right-hand side of (36) is 'nearly zero' and (8) is approximately satisfied. Note that the expression (37) coincides with (30) if one sets $\mu = -\omega_0^2/6$ in the latter. Naturally, for small C one may also write

$$\omega = \omega_0 \left(1 - \frac{C^2}{16} \right). \tag{38}$$

A better approximation is obtained if the method of harmonic balance is based on an estimate containing higher harmonics,

$$x(t) = C \sin \omega t + \sum_{n=2}^{m} C_n \sin n\omega t + \sum_{n=2}^{m} D_n \cos n\omega t \tag{39}$$

instead of the estimate (35). This estimate now is introduced in (8) and the right-hand side of the differential equation is written as a sum of trigonometric functions. The differential equation then is approximately satisfied by setting the coefficients of $\sin \omega t$, $\sin n\omega t$, $\cos n\omega t$, $n = 2, 3, \ldots, m$ equal to zero in this sum. This results in $2m - 1$ algebraic equations for the unknowns ω, C_2, $C_3, \ldots, C_m, D_2, D_3, \ldots, D_m$ in terms of C. Evidently, only the coefficients $C_3, C_5, C_7, \ldots$ are non-zero. Although it is generally not possible to give a satisfactory mathematical justification for this procedure, it is nevertheless quite useful in many practical applications (see Hayashi 1964).

1.1.3. The Ritz method

The method of Ritz, which has found especially frequent use in the solution of boundary-value problems in the mechanics of elastic systems, may also be used in non-linear oscillation problems. The unknown function $x(t)$ is written as a linear combination of suitable functions $\psi_i(t), i = 1, 2, \ldots$, that is,

$$x(t) = \sum_{i=1}^{m} C_i \psi_i(t), \tag{40}$$

where m may also tend to infinity. The coefficients $C_i, i = 1, 2, \ldots$ are to be determined in such a way that the error due to the substitution of the approximate solution for the exact solution is made as small as possible. If one writes

$$\ddot{x} + \omega_0^2 \left(x - \frac{x^3}{6} \right) = \sum_{i=1}^{m} C_i \ddot{\psi}_i(t) +$$

$$+ \omega_0^2 \left\{ \sum_{i=1}^{m} C_i \psi_i - \frac{1}{6} \left(\sum_{i=1}^{m} C_i \psi_i \right)^3 \right\} = e(t), \tag{41}$$

and demands that the mean square error over a given time interval,

$$\frac{1}{b-a} \int_a^b e^2(t)\,dt,$$

be as small as possible — in other words, it is to be minimized subject to the constraint (40) — then

$$\frac{\partial}{\partial C_j} \int_a^b e^2(t)\,dt = 2 \int_a^b e \frac{\partial e}{\partial C_j}\,dt = 0, \; j = 1, 2, \dots \tag{42}$$

yields a system of algebraic equations from which the C_i, $i = 1, 2, \dots$ may be determined. For example, the choice of

$$\psi_1(t) = \sin \omega t, \; \psi_2(t) = \dots = \psi_m(t) = 0, \tag{43}$$

yields

$$e(t) = \left(\omega_0^2 - \omega^2 - \frac{\omega_0^2}{8} C_1^2 \right) C_1 \sin \omega t + \frac{\omega_0^2}{24} C_1^3 \sin 3\omega t \tag{44}$$

and with $a = 0, b = T = 2\pi/\omega$,

$$\int_0^T e \frac{\partial e}{\partial C_1}\,dt = \int_0^T \left\{ \left(\omega_0^2 - \omega^2 - \frac{\omega_0^2}{8} C_1^2 \right) C_1 \sin \omega t + \right.$$

$$\left. + \frac{\omega_0^2}{24} C_1^3 \sin 3\omega t \right\} \left\{ \left(\omega_0^2 - \omega^2 - \frac{3\omega_0^2}{8} C_1^2 \right) \sin \omega t + \right.$$

$$\left. + \frac{\omega_0^2}{8} C_1^2 \sin 3\omega t \right\} dt = 0. \tag{45}$$

Besides the trivial solution $C_1 = 0$, one also obtains the algebraic equation

$$\omega^4 - 2\left(1 - \frac{1}{4}C_1^2\right)\omega_0^2\,\omega^2 + \omega_0^4\left(1 - \frac{1}{2}C_1^2 + \frac{5}{96}C_1^4\right) = 0 \quad (46)$$

with the two roots

$$\omega^2 = \omega_0^2\,\{1 + (-\,0.25 \pm 0.10)\,C_1^2\} \qquad\qquad (47)$$

as long as it is assumed that the amplitude remains small and that C_1^4 is negligible. It is easy to show that the plus sign in (47) corresponds to the minimum of $\int_0^T e^2\,\mathrm{d}t$, whereas the minus sign yields the maximum thereof. Note that the circular frequency ω as computed here is somewhat below that given by eqn (37). Still better approximations would be obtained if additional functions such as $\psi_3(t) = \sin 3\omega t$ were to be admitted beside $\psi_1(t) = \sin \omega t$ in expression (42).

In comparison to the previously treated methods, convergence (in the sense of the L_2-norm) may be more easily proven for this procedure, and error estimates often may also be obtained without too much difficulty. In spite of the non-linearity, the convergence of the Ritz method is apparent in the present case. The method of Galerkin, which finds frequent use in the solution of boundary-value problems in elastomechanics, need not yield the same results here; the convergence of the method is not necessarily assured.

1.1.4. Method of equivalent linearization

Here, the non-linear differential equation

$$\ddot{x} + \omega_0^2 \sin x = 0$$

is replaced by the linear differential equation

$$\ddot{x} + \omega^2 x = 0 \qquad\qquad (48)$$

where ω^2, however, may still depend on the initial conditions, that is, on the amplitude. There are several criteria available for choosing ω. It is probably closest at hand to replace the 'non-linear spring' by a linear spring such that the stored energies are equal for the same amplitude, that is,

$$\omega_0^2 \int_0^C \sin x \, \mathrm{d}x = \omega^2 \frac{C^2}{2},$$

which results in

$$\omega^2 = 2\omega_0^2 \frac{1 - \cos C}{C^2}\;.$$

The use of $\cos C \approx 1 - (C^2/2!) + (C^4/4!)$ results in

$$\omega^2 \approx \omega_0^2 \left(1 - \frac{C^2}{12}\right),$$

a relatively poor approximation.

Better results are obtained with Blaquière's (1966) 'optimal linearization method'. An error

$$e = \omega^2 x - \omega_0^2 \sin x \qquad (49)$$

is defined, which represents the difference between the linear and the non-linear restoring term. Here e is a function of ω^2 and x or of ω^2 and t if a solution for $x(t)$ is assumed in the form

$$x(t) = C \sin \omega t.$$

The function $\omega^2(C)$ now is determined in such a way that the mean square error

$$\frac{1}{T} \int_0^T e^2(\omega^2, t) \, dt$$

is minimized for fixed T. Consequently, one has the condition

$$\frac{\partial}{\partial \omega^2} \int_0^T e^2(\omega^2, t) \, dt = \int_0^T 2e \frac{\partial e}{\partial \omega^2} \, dt = 0. \qquad (50)$$

The use of equation (49) results in

$$\int_0^T (\omega^2 x^2 - \omega_0^2 x \sin x) \, dt = 0 \qquad (51)$$

and hence

$$\omega^2 = \omega_0^2 \frac{\int_0^T x \sin x \, dt}{\int_0^T x^2 \, dt}. \qquad (52)$$

If the solution $x(t) = C \sin \omega t$ is substituted in the linear equation, then the integrals may be computed with $T = 2\pi/\omega$:

$$\int_0^T C \sin \omega t \, \sin \, (C \sin \omega t) \, \mathrm{d}t \; = \; 2\frac{\pi}{\omega} \, CJ_1(C) \,,$$

which then results in

$$\omega^2 \; = \; \omega_0^2 \frac{2\,J_1(C)}{C}. \tag{53}$$

Here, J_k is the kth order Bessel function of the first kind. If only the first two terms of the Taylor series of the Bessel function J_1 are considered, that is,

$$J_1(x) = \frac{1}{2}x - \frac{1}{16}x^3 + \frac{1}{384}x^5 - \dots \,,$$

then one again obtains $\omega^2 \; = \; \omega_0^2 \left(1 - \frac{1}{8}C^2 \right).$

1.1.5. The exact solution

First, a more general approach is used in order to investigate just how one may obtain an analytical solution of the differential equation

$$m\ddot{x} + f(x) = 0 \tag{54}$$

where m is a constant and where $f(x)$ is an arbitrary integrable function.

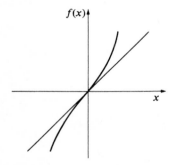
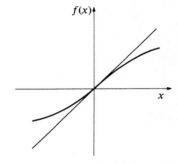
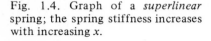

Fig. 1.4. Graph of a *superlinear* spring; the spring stiffness increases with increasing x.

Fig. 1.5. Graph of a *sublinear* spring; the spring stiffness decreases with increasing x.

In particular—as for the pendulum—$f(x)$ may be a trigonometric function; but it may also represent the non-linear load-displacement curve of a spring, where one distinguishes between 'superlinear' and 'sublinear' springs; or, it may be a non-linear element in a network, such as a non-linear capacitor (Figs. 1.4 and

1.5). A multiplication of (54) by $\dot{x}$ and a subsequent integration over t yields

$$\frac{1}{2} m\dot{x}^2 + \int f(x) \, dx = \text{const.} = E_0 \,. \tag{55}$$

If m has the dimension of mass and x that of length, then the kinetic energy is given by $T = \frac{1}{2}m\dot{x}^2$, while the potential energy is given by $U(x) = \int f(x)dx$ ($U(x)$ is defined up to an arbitrary constant.† One thus obtains

$$\dot{x} = \pm \sqrt{\left\{ \frac{2}{m}(E_0 - U(x)) \right\}}, \tag{56}$$

and one may immediately draw the phase diagram for a given energy level E_0 (Fig. 1.6). It is easy to deduce that the phase trajectories must be orthogonal to the x-axis at points where they cross, if one ignores the critical points ('equilibrium positions').

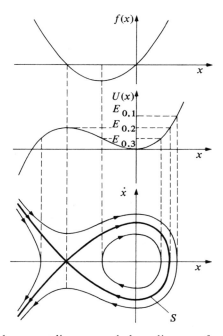

Fig. 1.6. Spring graph, energy diagram, and phase diagram of a non-linear oscillator.

---

† As is generally done, the symbol T is used for both the kinetic energy and for the period. This should cause no confusion, since the meaning will be clear from the context.

One generally obtains closed phase trajectories, corresponding to periodic solutions, aperiodic solutions, as well as the *separatrix S*. In the phase plane, the separatrix separates regions containing periodic solutions from those which contain aperiodic solutions or periodic solutions of another type. The type of motion thus may readily be deduced from the phase diagram.

Finally, to determine the oscillation as a function of time, a further integration must be performed:

$$t = t_0 + \int_{x_0}^{x} \frac{\mathrm{d}\bar{x}}{\dot{x}(\bar{x})} = t_0 \pm \int_{x_0}^{x} \frac{\mathrm{d}\bar{x}}{\sqrt{\left\{\frac{2}{m}(E_0 - U(\bar{x}))\right\}}} \tag{57}$$

Naturally, it is not always possible to give a simple closed form solution for (57), but at least the solution of the differential equation (54) has been reduced to *quadratures*, that is, to integrations. If U is a polynomial of at most fourth degree, then (57) leads to an elliptic integral.

The mathematical pendulum of equation (1) now becomes

$$\frac{1}{2} ml^2 \dot{x}^2 + \int_{0}^{x} mgl \sin \bar{x}\, \mathrm{d}\bar{x} = E_0, \tag{58}$$

where the factor l was introduced so that E_0 will have the dimension of an energy. In (58), the limits of integration were chosen in such a way that the potential energy is zero for the equilibrium position $x = 0$. From (58) one obtains

$$\dot{x} = \pm \sqrt{\left[\frac{2}{ml^2}\left\{E_0 - ml^2\omega_0^2(1 - \cos x)\right\}\right]} \tag{59}$$

If $E_0/(ml^2\omega_0^2)$ is denoted by E^*, then this becomes

$$\dot{x} = \pm \omega_0 \sqrt{\{2(\cos x - 1 + E^*)\}}, \tag{60}$$

where $0 < E^* < 2$ corresponds to the actual periodic solutions and $E^* > 2$ to the rotating pendulum. For $0 < E^* < 2$ the amplitude of the oscillation, C, is obtained from $\cos C = 1 - E^*$. The phase diagram may now be drawn without difficulty (Fig. 1.7).

Because of the periodicity of the system, it is advantageous here to introduce a cylindrical phase space. For this purpose, a strip of width $0 \leqslant x \leqslant 2\pi$ is cut out of the phase diagram in Fig. 1.7 and the two edges parallel to the $\dot{x}$-axis are joined. The periodic solutions circle the stable equilibrium position on the surface of the cylinder, without circumventing the cylinder, whereas the motions

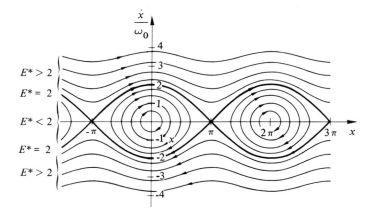

Fig. 1.7. Phase diagram of the mathematical pendulum.

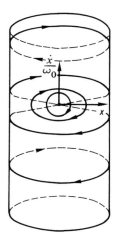

Fig. 1.8. Cylindrical phase diagram for the mathematical pendulum.

of the rotating pendulum correspond to the curves which circumvent the cylinder (Fig. 1.8).

The computation of the integral

$$t = t_0 \pm \frac{1}{\omega_0} \int_0^x \frac{d\bar{x}}{\sqrt{\{2 (\cos \bar{x} - \cos C)\}}} \tag{61}$$

yields the time dependence of the periodic motions with amplitude C and with initial conditions $t_0 = 0, x(0) = 0$. The use of $\cos x = 1 - 2 \sin^2 x/2$ yields

$$\frac{d\bar{x}}{\sqrt{\{2(\cos \bar{x} - \cos C)\}}} = \frac{d\bar{x}}{2\sqrt{\left(\sin^2 \dfrac{C}{2} - \sin^2 \dfrac{\bar{x}}{2}\right)}}$$

and the substitution of $\sin(\bar{x}/2) = \sin(C/2) \sin z$ then results in

$$d\bar{x} = 2 \sin \frac{C}{2} \cos z \frac{dz}{\cos \dfrac{\bar{x}}{2}} = 2 \sin \frac{C}{2} \cos z \frac{dz}{\sqrt{\left(1 - \sin^2 \dfrac{C}{2} \sin^2 z\right)}},$$

which may be used to transform (61) into

$$t = \pm \frac{1}{\omega_0} \int_0^\alpha \frac{dz}{\sqrt{(1 - k^2 \sin^2 z)}},$$

$$k = \sin \frac{C}{2}, \quad \alpha = \arcsin \frac{\sin \dfrac{x}{2}}{\sin \dfrac{C}{2}} \tag{62}$$

The integral in (62), however, is the elliptic integral of the first kind, $F(k, \alpha)$, which may be found tabulated in handbooks as a function of the variable α and of the *modulus* $k = \sin C/2$. One thus has

$$t = \pm \frac{1}{\omega_0} F\left(\sin \frac{C}{2}, \arcsin \frac{\sin \dfrac{x}{2}}{\sin \dfrac{C}{2}}\right) \tag{63}$$

In order to express x as an explicit function of t, the inverse function of $F(k, \alpha)$, the Jacobi elliptic function $\mathrm{sn}(k, \omega_0 t)$, is needed. The period may then be calculated as

$$T = \frac{4}{\omega_0} \int_0^{\pi/2} \frac{dz}{\sqrt{(1 - k^2 \sin^2 z)}} = \frac{4}{\omega_0} F\left(k, \frac{\pi}{2}\right) = \frac{4}{\omega_0} K(k) =$$

$$= \frac{4}{\omega_0} K\left(\sin \frac{C}{2}\right) \tag{64}$$

where K is the complete elliptic integral

$$K(k) = \frac{\pi}{2}\left[1 + \left(\frac{1}{2}\right)^2 k^2 + \left(\frac{1 \cdot 3}{2 \cdot 4}\right)^2 k^4 + \dots \right].$$

For small amplitudes, $\sin(C/2) \approx C/2$ may be used and one obtains

$$T \approx \frac{2\pi}{\omega_0}\left(1 + \frac{1}{16}\, C^2\right) \tag{65}$$

for the period, and

$$\omega \approx \omega_0 \left(1 - \frac{C^2}{16}\right), \tag{66}$$

for the corresponding circular frequency, thus substantiating the results previously obtained from the use of the approximation methods.

In this section, it has been shown how differential equations of the type (54) may be solved. Since they always have a first integral of the form (55) (the energy integral), such systems are also called conservative systems.

1.2. Damped free oscillations

1.2.1. The influence of small damping terms

Hitherto, it was assumed that no damping forces of any kind were acting on the mathematical pendulum, with the result that the mechanical energy was conserved. This assumption naturally is not satisfied in practice: it is known that damping results in a steady decrease of the amplitude of oscillation. The kind of damping terms included in the mathematical model depends on the physical modelling of the pendulum. Two types of damping laws will be investigated here: damping which consists of a term proportional to the velocity and damping due to Coulomb friction (dry friction). Both 'damping laws' occur not only in applications from mechanics but also play an important role in other fields. The equation of motion of the pendulum is taken to be given by

$$ml\ddot{x} + ml\, h(\dot{x}) + mg \sin x = 0 \tag{67}$$

where

$$h(\dot{x}) = 2\,\delta\dot{x}, \quad 2\,\delta > 0 \tag{68}$$

for linear damping, and

$$h(\dot{x}) = \rho \, \text{sgn}\,(\dot{x}), \quad \rho > 0 \tag{69}$$

for Coulomb damping (in this chapter, the coefficient of static friction and that of dynamic friction are taken to be equal). Some other commonly hypothesized damping laws are, for example, quadratic damping with corresponding damping term $\dot{x}^2\,\text{sgn}(\dot{x})$ or a term of the form $x^2\dot{x}$ for 'mechanical hysteresis'. The effort here will not be directed toward a justification of these assumptions for physical systems, but rather toward the determination of the influence of these terms on the free oscillation.

For the x-linearized differential equation, where $\sin x$ has been replaced by x in (67), the solution for the damping laws (68) and (69) is familiar from the theory of linear oscillations. For the velocity-proportional damping according to (68), one has the usual linear damped oscillations, and when (69) is assumed, one obtains a piecewise linear problem whose solution is assumed to be known also. Here, the treatment will be restricted to the application of approximation methods to the non-linear problem. In this context, it will be assumed that the damping forces are sufficiently small, so that the motion observed during a short time interval is of the same type as in the undamped case. This assumption is justifiable for most physical systems.

It is futhermore assumed that the amplitude is small enough to allow the use of $\sin x \approx x - x^3/6$ in (67), with the result

$$\ddot{x} + h(\dot{x}) + \omega_0^2\left(x - \frac{x^3}{6}\right) = 0. \tag{70}$$

The multiplication of this equation by $ml^2\dot{x}$ and the subsequent integration over time from t to $t + \Delta t$ yield

$$(T + U)_{t+\Delta t} = (T + U)_t + \Delta E \tag{71}$$

along with

$$T = \frac{1}{2}ml^2\dot{x}^2, \quad U = ml^2\omega_0^2\,\frac{1}{2}\left(x^2 - \frac{x^4}{12}\right), \quad \Delta E = -\int_t^{t+\Delta t} ml^2 h(\dot{x})\dot{x}\,\mathrm{d}t.$$

The term ΔE in (71) corresponds to the change in mechanical energy (a loss) during the motion over the time interval $[t, t + \Delta t]$. The value of this integral cannot be computed directly since the solution, $x(t)$, of (70) is not known. However, if one assumes an approximate solution of the form

$$x(t) = C\sin(\omega t + \varphi)$$

valid over a time interval of length $T = 2\pi/\omega$, where the relationship between C and ω is that of the small undamped oscillation, that is,

$$\omega = \omega_0 \left(1 - \frac{C^2}{16} \right),$$

and where C and φ are taken to be constant during that interval, then

$$\Delta E = - \int_0^T ml^2 h(\dot{x}) \dot{x} \, dt \tag{72}$$

may be computed. For the case of linear damping, one obtains

$$\Delta E = - 2 ml^2 \delta C^2 \omega^2 \int_0^T \cos^2(\omega t + \varphi) \, dt = - 2 ml^2 \delta \pi \omega C^2. \tag{73}$$

However, an amplitude C subject to the assumptions above yields

$$E = \frac{1}{2} ml^2 C^2 \omega^2 \tag{74}$$

for the total energy, $E = T + U$ (this is the value of kinetic energy as the system passes through $x = 0$). A first approximation thus is given by

$$\Delta E = ml^2 \omega^2 C \Delta C \tag{75}$$

from which follows

$$\frac{\Delta C}{C} = - T\delta \tag{76}$$

as a consequence of (73) (T is the period of oscillation!). An approximate solution of (67) and (68) now may be obtained by assuming that the solution is given by

$$x(t) = C_0 \sin (\omega(C_0)t + \varphi_0),$$

over the time interval $\{0, 2\pi/\omega(C_0)\}$, and by

$$x(t) = C_1 \sin (\omega(C_1)t + \varphi_1)$$

over the time interval $\{2\pi/\omega(C_0), 2\pi/\omega(C_0) + 2\pi/\omega(C_1)\}$, where

$$C_1 = C_0 \left(1 - \frac{2\pi\delta}{\omega(C_0)} \right),$$

and so on. Since the duration of oscillation, T, is approximately constant for sufficiently small amplitudes, it may also be said that the difference quotient $\Delta C/C$ is approximately constant and, consequently, that the amplitude decreases exponentially in time. In reality, the changes in amplitude naturally are continuous, and by writing

$$\frac{dC}{dt} \approx \frac{\Delta C}{T} = -C\delta \tag{77}$$

one obtains

$$C = C_0 e^{-\delta t}. \tag{78}$$

An analagous procedure may be followed in the case of Coulomb damping; from (72), one obtains

$$\Delta E = -ml^2 \rho C\omega \int_0^T |\cos(\omega t + \varphi)| \, dt = -4\,ml^2 \rho C \tag{79}$$

along with

$$\Delta C = -\frac{2\rho}{\pi\omega} T \tag{80}$$

or

$$\frac{dC}{dt} \approx -\frac{2\rho}{\pi\omega}. \tag{81}$$

Coulomb damping thus results in an amplitude which decreases almost linearly with increasing time as long as the circular frequency ω remains essentially constant. However, if one takes the dependence of the circular frequency on the amplitude into account, then an integration of (81) together with

$$\omega = \omega_0 \left(1 - \frac{C^2}{16}\right)$$

yields

$$\omega_0 C \left(1 - \frac{C^2}{48}\right) = \omega_0 C_0 \left(1 - \frac{C_0^2}{48}\right) - \frac{2\rho}{\pi} t, \tag{82}$$

where C_0 is the amplitude corresponding to $t = 0$. In order to have any motion at all in the presence of Coulomb damping, it must furthermore be assumed that the 'restoring force' is greater than the 'adhesive force' (maximum static friction force), that is, one must have

$$c_0 \omega_0^2 \left(1 - \frac{c_0^2}{6} \right) > \rho$$

since the pendulum would otherwise remain at rest in an equilibrium position.

1.2.2. The method of slowly changing phase and amplitude

The results (77) and (81) also may be obtained by a possibly less clear but more generally applicable approach. Consider the equation

$$\ddot{x} + \omega_0^2 x = f(x, \dot{x}) , \tag{83}$$

where $f(x, \dot{x})$ now may be an arbitrary integrable function, and introduce the coordinate transformation from x, $\dot{x}$ to a, ψ as defined by

$$\left. \begin{array}{l} x(t) = a(t) \sin (\omega_0 t + \psi(t)), \\[2mm] \dot{x}(t) = a(t) \omega_0 \cos (\omega_0 t + \psi(t)) . \end{array} \right\} \tag{84}$$

The differentiation of the first of eqns (84) with respect to time and a comparison of the result with the second yield

$$\dot{a}(t) \sin (\omega_0 t + \psi(t)) + a(t) \dot{\psi}(t) \cos (\omega_0 t + \psi(t)) = 0. \tag{85}$$

Equation (83) now is written in terms of the new variables $a(t)$ and $\psi(t)$. For this purpose, $\ddot{x}$ is calculated from the second of eqns (84) and then substituted in eqn (83), together with x from the first of eqns (84), to obtain the result

$$\dot{a} \omega_0 \cos (\omega_0 t + \psi) - a \dot{\psi} \omega_0 \sin (\omega_0 t + \psi) =$$

$$= f(x(a, \psi), \dot{x}(a, \psi)) . \tag{86}$$

The alternate multiplications of (85) and (86) by $\sin(\omega_0 t + \psi)$ and $\cos(\omega_0 t + \psi)$, respectively, eventually yield

$$\left. \begin{array}{l} \dot{a} = \dfrac{1}{\omega_0} f(a \sin (\omega_0 t + \psi), a \omega_0 \cos (\omega_0 t + \psi)) \cos (\omega_0 t + \psi) , \\[4mm] \dot{\psi} = -\dfrac{1}{\omega_0 a} f(a \sin (\omega_0 t + \psi), a \omega_0 \cos (\omega_0 t + \psi)) \sin (\omega_0 t + \psi) . \end{array} \right\} \tag{87}$$

Up to this point, no more than a coordinate transformation has been carried out, and the differential eqns (87) are still exactly equivalent to (83). If $f(x, \dot{x})$ is 'small', then $\dot{a}$ and $\dot{\psi}$ are also small, that is, the amplitude a and the phase ψ change only slowly. 'Slowly' here means that the value of ψ in the argument $(\omega_0 t + \psi)$ as well as the value of $a(t)$ remain nearly constant during a time interval of duration $T_0 = 2\pi/\omega_0$. Since it generally is not possible to obtain an exact solution to (87), the differential equation is simplified by replacing the right-hand sides by their temporal mean over the interval $[t, t + T_0]$. In forming this mean value, a and ψ will be kept constant on the right-hand side of (87). Eqns (87) thus are replaced by

$$\left.\begin{aligned}
\dot{a} &= \frac{1}{\omega_0 2\pi} \int_0^{2\pi} f(a \sin(\Theta + \psi), a\omega_0 \cos(\Theta + \psi)) \cos(\Theta + \psi)\, d\Theta, \\[2mm]
\dot{\psi} &= \frac{-1}{a\omega_0 2\pi} \int_0^{2\pi} f(a \sin(\Theta + \psi), a\omega_0 \cos(\Theta + \psi)) \sin(\Theta + \psi)\, d\Theta.
\end{aligned}\right\} \quad (88)$$

The result is an autonomous (that is, time-independent) system of equations providing a first approximation to the time dependence of the amplitude and phase. For this reason the method is often called the method of slowly changing phase and amplitude. At the same time, it is equivalent to the first approximation in accordance with the asymptotic method by Bogoliubov and Mitropolsky (1965).

Eqns (88) now are used in the case of linear damping, as described by eqns (70) and (68); with

$$\begin{aligned}
f(x, \dot{x}) &= \omega_0^2 \frac{x^3}{6} - 2\delta\dot{x} \\[2mm]
&= \frac{\omega_0^2}{6} a^3 \sin^3(\omega_0 t + \psi) - 2\delta a\omega_0 \cos(\omega_0 t + \psi) \\[2mm]
&= \frac{\omega_0^2}{24} a^3 [3\sin(\omega_0 t + \psi) - \sin(3\omega_0 t + 3\psi)] - \\[2mm]
&\quad - 2\delta a\omega_0 \cos(\omega_0 t + \psi) \qquad\qquad\qquad\qquad\qquad (89)
\end{aligned}$$

equations (88) result in

$$\left.\begin{aligned}
\dot{a} &= -\delta a, \\[2mm]
\dot{\psi} &= -\omega_0 \frac{a^2}{16}.
\end{aligned}\right\} \quad (90)$$

An integration of the first differential equation, a substitution of the result into the second, and a use of the initial conditions $a(0) = C_0$, $\psi(0) = 0$ eventually yield

$$a(t) = C_0\, e^{-\delta t},$$

$$\psi(t) = C_0^2\, \frac{\omega_0}{32\,\delta}\,(e^{-2\delta t} - 1).$$

In accordance with the first of eqns (84), one thus obtains the approximate solution

$$x(t) = C_0\, e^{-\delta t} \sin\, [\,\omega_0 t + C_0^2\, \frac{\omega_0}{32\,\delta}\,(e^{-2\delta t} - 1)\,]. \tag{91}$$

With $\delta = 0$, eqn (90) yields the analogous result

$$x(t) = C_0 \sin \left[\omega_0 t \left(1 - \frac{C_0^2}{16} \right) \right]$$

corresponding to the approximate solution for the undamped case.

For the Coulomb damping, as given by eqn (69), $f(x, \dot{x})$ is given by

$$f(x, \dot{x}) = \omega_0^2 \frac{x^3}{6} - \rho\, \mathrm{sgn}\,(\dot{x})$$

$$= \frac{\omega_0^2}{24}\, a^3\, \{3 \sin(\omega_0 t + \psi) - \sin(3\,\omega_0 t + 3\,\psi)\} -$$

$$- \rho\, \mathrm{sgn}\,\{\cos(\omega_0 t + \psi)\}. \tag{92}$$

The use of eqns (88) then results in

$$\left. \begin{aligned} \dot{a} &= -\frac{2\rho}{\pi\omega_0}, \\[2mm] \dot{\psi} &= -\omega_0 \frac{a^2}{16}. \end{aligned} \right\} \tag{93}$$

Integration yields

$$a(t) = C_0 - \frac{2\rho}{\pi\omega_0} t,$$

$$\psi(t) = -C_0^2 \frac{\omega_0}{16} t + C_0 \frac{\rho}{8\pi} t^2 - \frac{\rho}{12\,\pi^2\omega_0} t^3$$

so that

$$x(t) = C_0 \left(1 - \frac{2\rho}{\pi\omega_0 C_0} t \right) \sin\left\{ \omega_0 \left(1 - \frac{C_0^2}{16} \right) t + \right.$$

$$\left. + C_0 \frac{\rho}{8\pi} t^2 - \frac{\rho}{12\,\pi^2\omega_0} t^3 \right\} \tag{94}$$

is the approximate solution for eqn (70) with Coulomb damping.

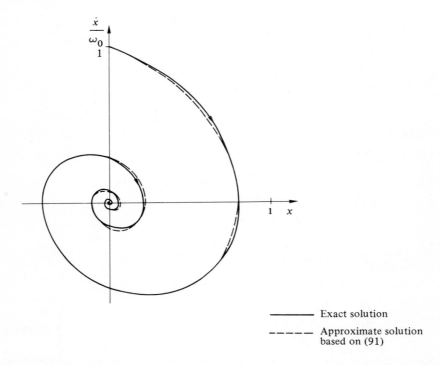

——— Exact solution

- - - - - Approximate solution
based on (91)

Fig. 1.9. Phase diagram of damped linear free oscillations of the mathematical pendulum with $C_0 = 1, \omega_0 = 1, \delta = 0.2$.

This easy and intuitive method will still be used for a number of other problems. The quality of the results which one may obtain under the appropriate circumstances may be deduced, for example, from the phase diagrams in Figs. 1.9 and 1.10, where the 'exact' curves—as determined with computer methods —are compared to the approximate curves as obtained here.

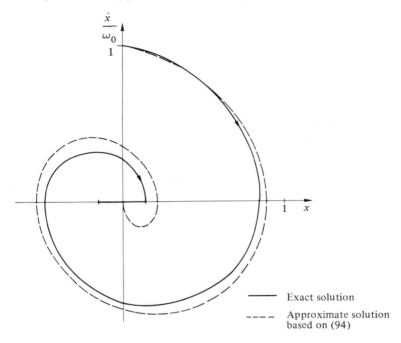

Exact solution

Approximate solution based on (94)

Fig. 1.10. Phase diagram of the free oscillation of the mathematical pendulum with Coulomb damping and with $C_0 = 1, \omega_0 = 1, \rho = 0.16$.

1.3. Forced oscillations

1.3.1. The existence of periodic solutions

Consider now the differential equation for the damped forced oscillation of the pendulum. It is assumed that the excitation is harmonic with circular frequency Ω and with period $T = 2\pi/\Omega$, so that the differential equation takes on the form

$$ml\ddot{x} + ml h(\dot{x}) + mg \sin x = F \sin \Omega t \tag{95}$$

where the constant F represents the amplitude of the exciting force. Similar differential equations also arise in the investigation of certain electrical circuits as well as in a number of other problems. The differential eqn (95) can no longer be solved exactly and it is therefore necessary to rely on approximation schemes in any quantitative investigations.

In general, it is not even known beforehand whether differential equations of the type

$$\ddot{x} = g(x, \dot{x}, t), \quad g(x, \dot{x}, t + T) = g(x, \dot{x}, t) \tag{96}$$

and of the type (95), in particular, have periodic solutions with period T. All that is generally assured from theorems in the theory of differential equations are the existence and uniqueness of the solution for a given set of initial conditions. That eqn (96) may have periodic solutions with periods other than T, and even incommensurable with T, is shown by an example due to Forbat (1966): $\ddot{x} + x = (x^2 + \dot{x}^2 - 1) \sin(\sqrt{2}t)$. This differential equation has the periodic solutions $x = \sin t$ and $x = \cos t$, in spite of the fact that the exciting frequency is $\Omega = \sqrt{2}$. In practice, however, one is generally interested mainly in those cases where response and excitation have the same period, T. At the end of section 1.3 a brief treatment of subharmonic oscillations is included, where the excitation frequency is an integral multiple of the oscillation frequency; also included are ultraharmonic oscillations and combination oscillations where the exciting frequency and the response frequency differ from one another.

Often the existence of periodic solutions with the same frequency as that of the excitation is simply assumed. However, in certain cases it can also be proven rigorously, for example, by making use of Brouwer's fixed point theorem.

A well known theorem from analysis states that a function, continuous on $[a, b]$, with opposing signs at the end-points, has at least one zero in the interval $[a, b]$. Brouwer's fixed point theorem may be viewed as a generalization of this perceptive result. The fixed point theorem no longer refers to scalar real-valued functions of a real variable on an interval but to mappings (or transformations) A of an m-dimensional (simply connected) region S_m of m-dimensional Euclidean space into itself. If x is an element of S_m then one also has $A(x) \in S_m$ or $A(S_m) \subset S_m$. One calls y a 'fixed point' of A if and only if $A(y) = y$. The Brouwer fixed point theorem expresses the fact that a continuous transformation A from S_m into S_m has at least one fixed point.† Just how one may use the fixed point theorem to prove the existence of periodic solutions is the subject of the following discussion.

---

†Fixed point theorems are applied in many areas of mathematics; often they are used to construct iterative solution methods. A theorem for somewhat more general spaces may be formulated as follows:

Let S be a closed, non-empty subset of a Banach-space B (a complete, normed linear space). Let the operator A be defined on S such that A maps S into itself, $A(S) \subset S$. Furthermore, assume that A satisfies a Lipschitz-condition with constant $k < 1$:

$\| Ax - Ay \| \leqslant k \| x - y \|, x, y \in S.$

Toward this purpose, it is advantageous to write the system (96) as a first-order system:

$$\left. \begin{array}{l} \dot{x} = X(x, y, t), \\[2ex] \dot{y} = Y(x, y, t), \end{array} \right\} \quad (97)$$

where X and Y are periodic in t with period T. The system (97) need not have any equilibrium positions.

If S is a simply connected closed region in the *generalized phase plane* (the xy-plane), then a consequence of the Brouwer fixed point theorem is that every continuous transformation from S into itself has at least one fixed point. Consider now the solutions of (97),

$$\left. \begin{array}{l} x = x(x_0, y_0, t_0; t), \\[2ex] y = y(x_0, y_0, t_0; t), \end{array} \right\} \quad (98)$$

which pass through (x_0, y_0) at the time $t = t_0$, that is, it is agreed that $x(x_0, y_0, t_0; t_0) = x_0$ and $y(x_0, y_0, t_0; t_0) = y_0$. From (98) one may deduce the transformation

$$\left. \begin{array}{l} x_T = x(x_0, y_0, t_0; t_0 + T), \\[2ex] y_T = y(x_0, y_0, t_0; t_0 + T) \end{array} \right\} \quad (99)$$

which maps every point (x_0, y_0) onto a point (x_T, y_T) in the phase plane. The transformation is continuous at (x_0, y_0) insofar as the usual theorems from analysis concerning the continuous dependence of the solution of a differential equation on the initial conditions are applicable. It is assumed that the corresponding hypotheses (say, a Lipschitz-condition for the right-hand sides of (97))

Then the equation $Ax = x$ has exactly one solution $x = \bar{x}$ in S. If one forms the 'successive approximations' x_n in accordance with

$$x_1 = Ax_0, x_2 = Ax_1, \ldots, x_{n+1} = Ax_n, \ldots,$$

beginning with an arbitrary element $x_0 \in S$, then one has the estimate

$$\| \bar{x} - x_n \| \leqslant \frac{k^n}{1-k} \| x_1 - x_0 \|$$

and the sequence $\{x_n\}$ converges to $\bar{x}$ (in the sense of the norm). In this form, the theorem may be found in Walter (1972), for example. Instead of the continuity requirement, as in Brouwer's theorem, the requirement on the transformation here is that it be a *contraction* ($k < 1$). This guarantees the uniqueness of the solution and also yields an approximation procedure.

are satisfied. A fixed point of the transformation (99) obviously corresponds to a T-periodic solution of (97). If one thus is able to find a region S in the xy-plane such that the transformation (99) maps the region S into itself, then it follows that there exists at least one fixed point in S, that is, a periodic solution with period T (or an equilibrium position). For a given system (97), the objective thus is to find such a region S in the xy-plane. However, a sufficient condition assuring that S is mapped into itself by (99) is obviously given by the require-ment that for all points of the boundary ∂S of S the solution curves (98) penetrate the boundary from the outside to the inside, that is, one must have

$$(X(x, y, t), \ Y(x, y, t)) \cdot \mathbf{n} < 0 \qquad (100)$$

for all points (x, y) of the boundary ∂S and for all values of $t \geqslant t_0$ (Fig. 1.11).

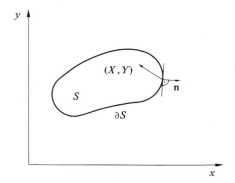

Fig. 1.11. An aspect of the Brouwer fixed point theorem.

Here, $\mathbf{n}$ is taken to be the outward normal for ∂S at (x, y). If the curve ∂S is specified by an expression of the form $D(x, y) = c$, in such a way that the curve $D(x, y) = c$ lies within the curve $D(x, y) = c'$ for $c' > c$, then

$$\mathbf{n} = \frac{1}{\sqrt{(D_x^2 + D_y^2)}} (D_x, D_y)$$

is the outward normal, and, in accordance with Brouwer's theorem,

$$\dot{D} = D_x X(x, y, t) + D_y Y(x, y, t) < 0, \ \mathcal{V}(x, y) \in \partial S, \ \mathcal{V}t \qquad (101)$$

is a sufficient condition for the existence of a periodic solution entirely in S.†

---

†The expression $\mathcal{V}(x, y) \in \partial S$ means: 'for every (x, y) on the boundary of S'.

The curve ∂S which must be constructed for a given system (97) need not be everywhere differentiable, by any means; it suffices to be dealing with a Jordan curve (a curve is a Jordan curve if and only if it may be represented in the parametric form $\mathbf{r}(s)$, where $\mathbf{r}(s)$ is continuous and has no self-intersections). At the edge-points of ∂S, where the normal is not uniquely defined, eqn (101) obviously may not be used; eqn (100) then must be fulfilled for *all* $\mathbf{n}$.

The application of the Brouwer theorem to differential equations is closely related to Liapounov's second method as it will be treated in Chapter 2. With its aid, one may prove the existence of periodic solutions for quite general differential equations, say for

$$\ddot{x} + h(x)\dot{x} + f(x) = p(t) \tag{102}$$

subject to the following assumptions:

(a) $h(x), f(x)$, and $p(t)$ are continuous functions on their domains of definition,

(b) for $H(x) = \int_0^x h(\bar{x})\mathrm{d}\bar{x}$ one has

$$\lim_{x \to -\infty} H(x) = -\infty \text{ as well as } \lim_{x \to +\infty} H(x) = +\infty,$$

(c) $f(x)\dfrac{x}{|x|} > 0$ for $|x| > q$ $(q = \text{const.} \geqslant 0)$,

(d) $p(t + T) = p(t)$ $(T > 0)$, $\displaystyle\int_0^T p(t)\mathrm{d}t = 0$,

which assure the existence of at least one periodic solution of (102) with period T. The proof here is that of Mizohata and Yamaguti, as given in Forbat (1966). For this purpose, eqn (102) is replaced by the equivalent system

$$\begin{aligned} \dot{x} &= y - H(x) + P(t), \\ \dot{y} &= -f(x) \end{aligned} \tag{103}$$

with $P(t) = \displaystyle\int_0^t p(\bar{t})\mathrm{d}\bar{t}$. A sufficiently large positive number $L > q$ is chosen such that

$$H(x) > \max_t P(t) \quad \text{for } x \geqslant L$$

and

$$H(x) < \min_t P(t) \quad \text{for } x \leqslant -L$$

are satisfied. Furthermore, a linear function $y = \psi(x)$ is chosen which passes through the point $(-L, 0)$ and which satisfies the conditions $\psi' = \text{const.} > 0$ and $0 < \psi(L) \leqslant H(x) - \max_t P(t)$, $\forall x \geqslant L$. With the function

$$F(x) = \int_0^x f(\bar{x}) \, d\bar{x}$$

and with an arbitrary constant $c > 0$, one then defines the arcs

$$
\begin{aligned}
D_1(x, y) &= \frac{1}{2}\{y - \psi(x)\}^2 = c \quad \text{for } -L \leqslant x \leqslant L, \\[2mm]
D_2(x, y) &= \frac{y^2}{2} + F(x) - F(-L) = c \quad \text{for } x \leqslant -L, \\[2mm]
D_3(x, y) &= \frac{1}{2}\{y - \psi(L)\}^2 + F(x) - F(L) = c \quad \text{for } x \geqslant L,
\end{aligned}
\tag{104}
$$

which, as one may easily check, define the boundary of a region S in such a way that $c' > c$ implies $S' \supset S$. Furthermore, the arcs have coincident terminal points at $(-L, -\sqrt{(2c)})$ and $(-L, \sqrt{(2c)})$ as well as at $(L, \psi(L) + \sqrt{(2c)})$ and $(L, \psi(L) - \sqrt{(2c)})$ (Fig. 1.12). It now is a simple matter to compute the expression (101). After a routine transformation, one obtains

$$
\begin{aligned}
\dot{D}_1 &= -\psi'(x)\{y - \psi(x)\}^2 + \{y - \psi(x)\}\{-f(x) - \\[1mm]
&\quad - \psi'(x)P(t) - \psi(x)\psi'(x) + H(x)\psi'(x)\}, \\[2mm]
\dot{D}_2 &= -f(x)\{H(x) - P(t)\}, \\[2mm]
\dot{D}_3 &= -f(x)\{H(x) - \psi(L) - P(t)\}.
\end{aligned}
\tag{105}
$$

Clearly, $\dot{D}_2$ and $\dot{D}_3$ are negative on the coresponding parts of ∂S. By setting $y - \psi(x) = \sqrt{(2c)}$ for the upper arc $D_1 = c$ and $y - \psi(x) = -\sqrt{(2c)}$ for the lower part in the expression for $\dot{D}_1$, it follows that $\dot{D}_1 < 0$ also, as long as c is chosen sufficiently large. This proves the existence of at least one periodic solution occurring entirely within S, as long as c and L are chosen sufficiently large.

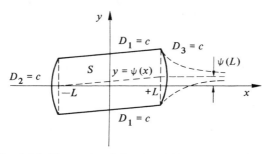

Fig. 1.12. The region S for the differential eqn (102).

It has been assumed here that the region S of Fig. 1.12 is everywhere finite. It is feasible, however, that a curve $D_3 = c$ may have the form of the dashed line in Fig. 1.12 so that x tends to infinity as $y \to \psi(L)$. This case may be excluded by insisting on the additional hypotheses

$$\lim_{x \to +\infty} F(x) = +\infty, \quad \lim_{x \to -\infty} F(x) = -\infty . \tag{106}$$

There may still be other periodic solutions; however, the given proof no longer suffices to guarantee their existence.

Forbat (1966), for example, gives proofs of the existence of periodic solutions for various other differential equations. Besides Brouwer's theorem, there are a variety of other fixed point theorems which often yield important results in the theory of non-linear oscillations (e.g., see Sansone and Conti 1964).

In conclusion, the reader is reminded that a proof of the existence of periodic solutions was not necessary for the free motion of the undamped pendulum since it was possible there to obtain a closed form solution of the differential equation.

1.3.2. Undamped forced oscillations

Here, the undamped forced oscillations of the pendulum with harmonic excitation are to be investigated. Again, the approximation $\sin x \approx x - (x^3/6)$ is used, which transforms eqn (95) into the differential equation

$$\ddot{x} + \omega_0^2 x + \mu x^3 = P \sin \Omega t \tag{107}$$

where $\omega_0^2 = g/l$, $\mu = -g/(6l)$, and $P = F/(ml)$. Now, no closed form solution exists. For the time being, the discussion will be restricted to periodic solutions with circular frequency Ω. The existence of such periodic motions can be proven rigorously.

In order to obtain a survey of the most important phenomena in as simple a manner as possible, the method of Duffing (1918) will be used, in spite of the fact that the convergence of the method remains largely unresolved. Some of the results will be checked further on with other methods. Eqn (107) now is written in the form

$$\ddot{x} = -\omega_0^2 x - \mu x^3 + P \sin \Omega t \tag{108}$$

and a first approximation to the solution thereof is taken to be given by $x_1 = C \sin \Omega t, C = \text{const.}$

This expression is substituted in the right-hand side of equation (108), the computed sum is designated as $\ddot{x}_2$, and the expression is integrated twice to obtain x_2. The use of

$$\sin^3 \Omega t = \frac{1}{4}(3 \sin \Omega t - \sin 3 \Omega t)$$

yields

$$\ddot{x}_2 = \left(P - \omega_0^2 C - \frac{3}{4}\mu C^3\right) \sin \Omega t + \frac{\mu C^3}{4} \sin 3 \Omega t. \tag{109}$$

Two integrations and the assumption of periodicity for x_2 and for the higher approximations (necessitating a vanishing of the constants of integration) result in:

$$x_2 = \frac{1}{\Omega^2}\left\{\omega_0^2 + \frac{3}{4}\mu C^2 - \frac{P}{C}\right\}C \sin \Omega t - \frac{1}{36}\frac{\mu}{\Omega^2}C^3 \sin 3 \Omega t. \tag{110}$$

The iterative procedure may then be continued by the renewed introduction of x_2 into the right-hand side of (108) along with further integrations. This will not be done here; instead, the process will be terminated, since the first iteration step already supplies a quite satisfactory approximation. As of yet, the constant C in eqn (110) is undetermined. Duffing (1918) determined it by equating the contributions with frequency Ω in $x_1(t)$ and $x_2(t)$; that is,

$$C = \frac{1}{\Omega^2}\left\{\omega_0^2 + \frac{3}{4}\mu C^2 - \frac{P}{C}\right\}C.$$

which results in the frequency–amplitude relation

$$\frac{\Omega^2}{\omega_0^2} = 1 - \frac{P}{C\omega_0^2} + \frac{3}{4}\frac{\mu}{\omega_0^2}C^2. \tag{111}$$

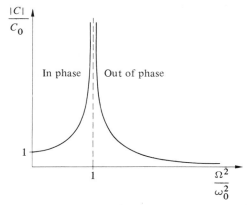

Fig. 1.13. Resonance curve for the linear oscillator ($\mu = 0$).

In the framework of linear oscillations (that is, for $\mu = 0$), this relationship is known to be exact. For $\mu \neq 0$, some other methods will still be used to provide a check on (111). The second approximation then is

$$x_2(t) = C \sin \Omega t - \frac{1}{36} \frac{\mu}{\omega_0^2 - \dfrac{P}{C} + \dfrac{3}{4}\mu C^2} C^3 \sin 3\Omega t$$

$$= C \sin \Omega t - \frac{1}{36} \frac{\mu}{\omega_0^2 - \dfrac{P}{C}} C^3 \sin 3\Omega t + o(\mu), \qquad (112)$$

where $C(\Omega^2, \omega_0^2, P)$ is given by (111). The resonance diagram for the linear case ($\mu = 0$, Fig. 1.13) now is replaced by a more complicated diagram. For the non-linear case, the resonance curve may easily be drawn by making use of the auxiliary diagrams in Fig. 1.14. This results in the resonance curve of Fig. 1.15. The magnitude C—not exactly the oscillation amplitude, as may be seen from (112)—has been plotted with respect to the 'static deflection' $C_0 = P/\omega_0^2$ of the linearized problem.

As opposed to only *one* possible amplitude for the forced oscillation in the linear problem, one now has as many as three values for C corresponding to certain values of Ω! A further difference is the fact that C here remains finite for all values of Ω, whereas the amplitude is indeterminate for resonance in the linear case. Thus, non-linear terms must be taken into account to determine the amplitude of the forced oscillation in any investigation of undamped oscillating systems in a neighbourhood of resonance. A comparison of Figs. 1.13 and 1.15 indicates that Fig. 1.15 may be obtained by a bending of the dash-dotted *backbone curve*. Because of $\mu = -\omega_0^2/6$, Fig. 1.15(b) is the one which applies for the pendulum.

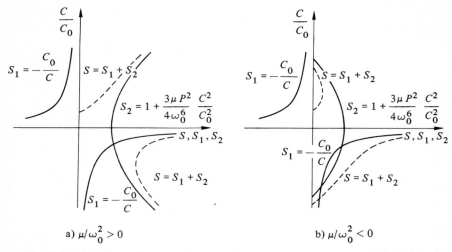

Fig. 1.14. Auxiliary diagrams for the determination of the resonance curves.

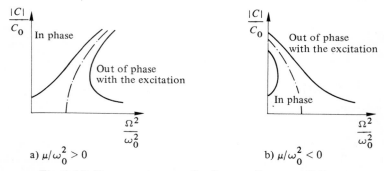

Fig. 1.15. Resonance curves for the non-linear oscillator.

Another method for the computation of forced oscillations is Rauscher's method (e.g., see Stoker 1950). Here, the free non-linear oscillations are used as a basis for the first approximation rather than the linear forced ones. In contrast to other methods, however, P and C are taken as given and the corresponding exciting frequency Ω is determined iteratively. Consider

$$\ddot{x} + f(x) = P \sin \Omega t, \tag{113}$$

where $f(x) = -f(-x)$ is an odd function. This latter assumption is not essential but it simplifies the following calculations. It is advantageous to introduce the dimensionless time $\tau = \Omega t$; eqn (113) then takes on the form

$$\Omega^2 x'' + f(x) = P \sin \tau \tag{114}$$

with $x'' = d^2x/d\tau^2$. The iteration is initiated with the free undamped oscillation, more specifically with the solution of

$$\Omega_1^2 x'' + f(x) = 0, \tag{115}$$

where Ω_1^2 is chosen in such a way as to render $x(\tau)$ periodic with period 2π. With the initial conditions $x(0) = C, x'(0) = 0$, and with

$$F(x) = \int_0^x f(\bar{x}) \, d\bar{x}$$

the first approximation on $0 \leqslant \tau \leqslant \pi$ is given by

$$\tau = \tau_1(x) = \Omega_1 \int_C^x \frac{-d\bar{x}}{\sqrt{[2\{F(C) - F(\bar{x})\}]}} \tag{116}$$

and

$$\frac{1}{\Omega_1} = \frac{2}{\pi} \int_0^C \frac{d\bar{x}}{\sqrt{[2\{F(C) - F(\bar{x})\}]}} \tag{117}$$

follows. The now known function $\tau_1(x)$ is substituted into the right side of (114) to obtain

$$\Omega_2^2 x'' + f(x) - P \sin \tau_1(x) = 0,$$

where Ω_2^2 still needs to be determined. This differential equation again is of the type (115) and may be integrated. As a result, one obtains the second estimates $\tau_2(x)$ and Ω_2. The iteration process may be continued as long as desired in accordance with the prescription

$$\Omega_n^2 x'' + f(x) - P \sin \tau_{n-1}(x) = 0, \tag{118}$$

subject to $x(\tau) = x(\tau + 2\pi), x(0) = C, x'(0) = 0$. The procedure is repeated until the difference $\Omega_{n+1}^2 - \Omega_n^2$ is smaller than some given number. Naturally, in a slightly altered form, the process may also be used for problems where $f(x)$ is no longer an odd function or even when damping is present. Generally, convergence is quite good as long as P is not too large.

1.3.3. The influence of damping and the jump phenomenon

For the undamped forced oscillations in eqn (107), the phase angle between the excitation and the periodic response $x(t)$ is always 0 or π. If a linear damping term $2\delta\dot{x}$ with $\delta > 0$ is added, then one may expect intermediate phase angles just as for the linear oscillator. Instead of writing $P \sin \Omega t$ for the excitation and $x_1 = C \sin(\Omega t - \gamma)$ for the periodic solution, it is preferable to write

$$\ddot{x} + 2\delta\dot{x} + \omega_0^2 x + \mu x^3 = P_1 \sin \Omega t + P_2 \cos \Omega t \qquad (119)$$

with $P^2 = P_1^2 + P_2^2$ and $x_1 = C \sin \Omega t$. The use of this formulation, togther with the method of harmonic balance, and the neglect of the term containing $\sin 3\Omega t$ in eqn (119) result in

$$(\omega_0^2 - \Omega^2)C + \frac{3}{4}\mu C^3 = P_1, \qquad 2\delta C\Omega = P_2,$$

from which follow

$$P^2 = P_1^2 + P_2^2 = \left\{(\omega_0^2 - \Omega^2)C + \frac{3}{4}\mu C^3\right\}^2 + 4\delta^2\Omega^2 C^2 \qquad (120a)$$

and

$$\frac{\Omega^2}{\omega_0^2} = 1 - 2\frac{\delta^2}{\omega_0^2} + \frac{3}{4}\frac{\mu}{\omega_0^2}C^2$$

$$\pm \frac{1}{\omega_0^2}\sqrt{\left\{\frac{P^2}{C^2} + 4\delta^2\left(\delta^2 - \omega_0^2 - \frac{3}{4}\mu C^2\right)\right\}} \qquad (120b)$$

respectively, along with

$$\tan \gamma = \frac{P_2}{P_1} = \frac{2\delta C\Omega}{(\omega_0^2 - \Omega^2)C + \frac{3}{4}\mu C^3}. \qquad (121)$$

For different values of δ and for a fixed P, Fig. 1.16 depicts the *resonance curves*, whereas Fig. 1.17 shows the corresponding curves for a fixed $\delta > 0$, but for different values of P. Here, C in Fig. 1.16 is again normalized with respect to $C_0 = P/\omega_0^2$. The dash-dotted *backbone curves* in Fig. 1.17 are given by the sum of terms prior to the square root in eqn (120b).

What, then, is the behaviour of a periodic solution for a fixed P with slowly changing excitation frequency Ω? For this investigation, it is assumed that the frequency is changing 'quasi-statically' so that the solution becomes a sequence of stationary oscillations with different values for Ω. Beginning with Ω_A

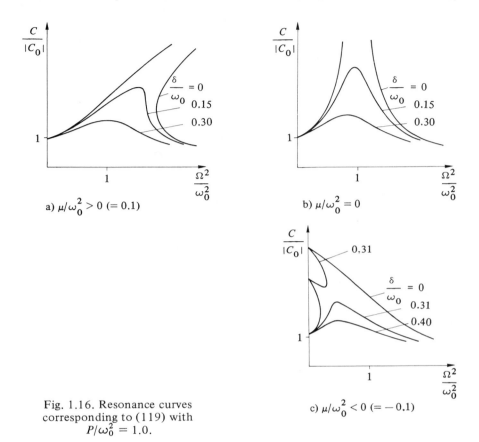

Fig. 1.16. Resonance curves corresponding to (119) with $P/\omega_0^2 = 1.0$.

c) $\mu/\omega_0^2 < 0 \ (= -0.1)$

(Fig. 1.18(a)), if one slowly decreases the excitation frequency Ω, then the corresponding point on the resonance curve moves from A to B_1. If Ω is reduced still further from Ω_B, then one suddenly encounters strong non-stationary oscillations which eventually again reduce to a stationary oscillation corresponding to the point B_2. For any further decrease in Ω the representative point on the resonance curve travels from B_2 in the direction of D. Conversely, for an increase of the excitation frequency Ω from zero, the point on the resonance curve jumps from C_2 to C_1, as soon as Ω_C is exceeded. Although the part of the resonance curve between B_1 and C_2 corresponds to a stationary solution, it is unstable and thus cannot be realized because of the ever present small disturbances. In the case $\mu < 0$ the jumps in the resonance curve occur in a similar manner (Fig. 1.18(b)). Such jump phenomena may be observed during run-up of machines, for example, where the torque generally is a non-linear function of the rotational frequency. It is known that for certain combinations of drive and load, some operational states cannot be attained because they correspond to unstable solutions.

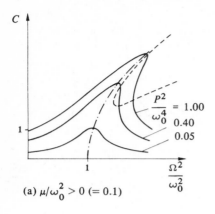

(a) $\mu/\omega_0^2 > 0 (= 0.1)$

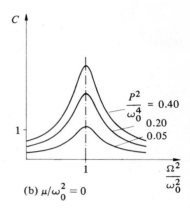

(b) $\mu/\omega_0^2 = 0$

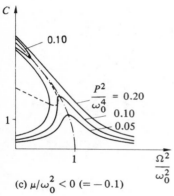

(c) $\mu/\omega_0^2 < 0 (= -0.1)$

Fig. 1.17. The resonance curves corresponding to (119) with $\delta/\omega_0 = 0.1$.

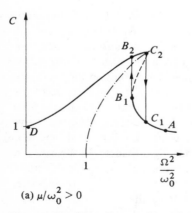

(a) $\mu/\omega_0^2 > 0$

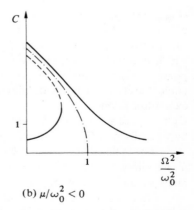

(b) $\mu/\omega_0^2 < 0$

Fig. 1.18. The 'jump-phenomenon' for forced oscillations in the Duffing equation with damping.

As will be shown in Chapter 2 (Exercise 2.5), the boundary points of the unstable region occur where the resonance curve has a vertical tangent. These points may easily be determined by differentiating the relationship (120a) with respect to C and equating $d\Omega/dC$ to zero. The result is the equation

$$(\omega_0^2 - \Omega^2 + \frac{3}{4} \mu C^2)(\omega_0^2 - \Omega^2 + \frac{9}{4} \mu C^2) + 4\delta^2\Omega^2 = 0, \quad (122)$$

whose solutions corresponding to $\delta = 0$ are given by

$$\frac{\Omega^2}{\omega_0^2} = 1 + \frac{3}{4} \frac{\mu}{\omega_0^2} C^2, \qquad (123)$$

$$\frac{\Omega^2}{\omega_0^2} = 1 + \frac{9}{4} \frac{\mu}{\omega_0^2} C^2. \qquad (124)$$

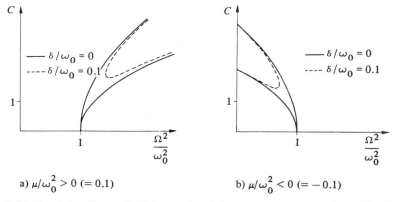

a) $\mu/\omega_0^2 > 0 \ (= 0.1)$ b) $\mu/\omega_0^2 < 0 \ (= -0.1)$

Fig. 1.19. Loci for the vertical tangents of the resonance curves from Fig. 1.17.

For small values of δ the solutions certainly lie near the curves defined by (123) and (124). In Fig. 1.19, the solutions of (122) for the undamped case are indicated by the solidly drawn curve, whereas the solutions for a fixed $\delta/\omega_0 > 0$ are represented by the dashed lines. These dashed lines also have been indicated already in the resonance diagrams of Fig. 1.17. The fact that the dashed curves $C(\Omega)$ of Figs. 1.19(a) and (b) exhibit a relative minimum shows that for sufficiently small P/ω_0^2 the resonance curves have no vertical tangent and consequently no unstable regions.

Naturally, the results obtained here by Duffing's method may also be obtained by other means. For example, the method of slowly changing phase and amplitude may be used to investigate the equation

$$\ddot{x} + 2\delta\dot{x} + \omega_0^2 x + \mu x^3 = P \sin \Omega t. \tag{125}$$

The coordinate transformation

$$\left.\begin{aligned} x &= a \sin (\Omega t + \psi), \\ \dot{x} &= a\Omega \cos (\Omega t + \psi) \end{aligned}\right\} \tag{126}$$

yields

$$\left.\begin{aligned} \dot{a} &= \frac{P}{\Omega} c \sin \Omega t + \frac{a}{\Omega} (\Omega^2 - \omega_0^2) sc - 2\delta ac^2 - \frac{\mu}{\Omega} a^3 s^3 c, \\ \dot{\psi} &= -\frac{P}{\Omega} \frac{s}{a} \sin \Omega t - \frac{1}{\Omega} (\Omega^2 - \omega_0^2) s^2 + 2\delta sc + \frac{\mu}{\Omega} a^2 s^4, \end{aligned}\right\} \tag{127}$$

where the abbreviatons

$$s = \sin (\Omega t + \psi), \quad c = \cos (\Omega t + \psi)$$

were used. Taking the mean of the right-hand sides results in the autonomous equations

$$\left.\begin{aligned} \dot{a} &= -\frac{P}{2\Omega} \sin \psi - \delta a, \\ \dot{\psi} &= -\frac{P}{2\Omega a} \cos \psi - \frac{1}{2\Omega} (\Omega^2 - \omega_0^2) + \frac{3}{8} \frac{\mu}{\Omega} a^2. \end{aligned}\right\} \tag{128}$$

The stationary solutions are obtained with $\dot{a} = 0$ or $a = a_s = C$; the first of equations (128) then yields $\psi = \psi_s$, or $\dot{\psi} = 0$. For the computation of C and ψ_s one thus has

$$0 = -\frac{P}{2\Omega} \sin \psi_s - \delta C,$$

$$0 = -\frac{P}{2\Omega C} \cos \psi_s - \frac{1}{2\Omega} (\Omega^2 - \omega_0^2) + \frac{3}{8} \frac{\mu}{\Omega} C^2$$

and, eventually,

$$P^2 = C^2 \left\{ 4\delta^2\Omega^2 + \left(\omega_0^2 - \Omega^2 + \frac{3}{4} \mu C^2 \right)^2 \right\}, \tag{129}$$

which is identical to (120a).

The approximation eqns (128) not only allow the computation of the stationary solution but also make an investigation of the non-stationary motion possible (see Exercise 2.5). A clear picture of the 'transient motions' approximated in this manner is obtained if one plots the solutions of (128) in a cartesian coordinate system with $a \cos \psi$ and $a \sin \psi$ as coordinates. The result is a phase diagram of (128) in these new coordinates (a phase diagram for (125) does not make sense, since this differential equation contains the time explicitly). The result is especially simple in the undamped case (with $\delta = 0$), since (128) then has the first integral

$$\frac{P}{\Omega} a \cos \psi + \frac{a^2 (\Omega^2 - \omega_0^2)}{2\Omega} - \frac{3}{16} \frac{\mu}{\Omega} a^4 = K. \tag{130}$$

One obtains (130) by using (128) to form

$$\frac{d\psi}{da} = - \frac{\dfrac{P}{2\Omega a} \cos \psi + \dfrac{\Omega^2 - \omega_0^2}{2\Omega} - \dfrac{3}{8} \dfrac{\mu}{\Omega} a^2}{\dfrac{P}{2\Omega} \sin \psi}$$

and by then writing this expression as

$$\frac{Pa}{2\Omega} \sin \psi d\psi - \left\{ \frac{P}{2\Omega} \cos \psi + \frac{a}{2\Omega} (\Omega^2 - \omega_0^2) - \frac{3}{8} \frac{\mu}{\Omega} a^3 \right\} da = 0. \tag{131}$$

Clearly, the expression (131) is an exact differential of the function on the left-hand side of (130). The constant K is determined from the initial values of a and ψ.

In Figs. 1.20(a) and (b), the corresponding curves have been drawn in the 'Van der Pol plane' for $\mu < 0$. This plane is rotating clockwise about the origin with angular velocity Ω, with respect to the $x(\dot{x}/\Omega)$-plane. Depending upon the choice of the parameters μ, ω_0^2, Ω, and P, one then has one or three stationary solutions. Note that there exists a multitude of periodic solutions around the 'critical points' E and F: the stationary solutions E and F are stable, that is, small disturbances in the initial conditions result in motions which remain in a neighbourhood of E and F for all time. In every arbitrarily small neighbourhood of the point G, however, there exist initial conditions leading to solutions which move away from G; the point G is unstable. A rigorous definition of the stability of motion will not be given until Chapter 2.

Figs. 1.20(a) and (b) are related to the resonance curve of the undamped Duffing oscillator. The points E, F, and G of Figs. 1.20(a) and (b) are located

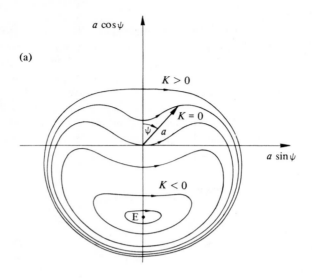

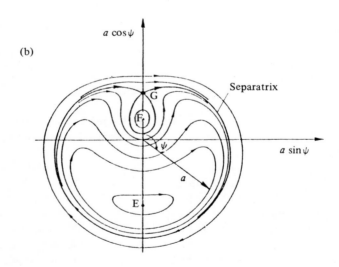

Fig. 1.20. Phase diagram of the forced oscillations involving the Duffing equation in the Van der Pol plane ($\mu/\omega_0^2 < 0$). (a) Only one stationary solution; (b) three stationary solutions.

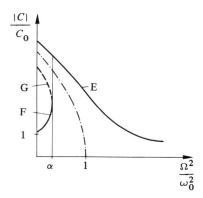

Fig. 21. Resonance curve of the undamped Duffing oscillator.

on the correspondingly designated branches of Fig. 1.21. Here, Figure 1.20(b) corresponds to $\Omega^2/\omega_0^2 < \alpha$ and Fig. 1.20(a) corresponds to $\Omega^2/\omega_0^2 > \alpha$.

Consider now the manner in which one might obtain a periodic solution of eqn (125) by using the method of the harmonic balance. For this purpose, the approximation

$$x(t) \approx \frac{1}{2} B_0 + \sum_{n=1}^{m} (A_n \sin n\Omega t + B_n \cos n\Omega t) , \tag{132}$$

is introduced, where A_n and B_n are constants, still to be determined, in the desired periodic solution. This approximation is substituted into the left side of the equation

$$\ddot{x} + 2\delta\dot{x} + \omega_0^2 x + \mu x^3 - P \sin \Omega t = 0 \tag{133}$$

with resulting error

$$e = -\Omega^2 \sum_{n=1}^{m} n^2 (A_n \sin n\Omega t + B_n \cos n\Omega t) +$$

$$+ 2\delta\Omega \sum_{n=1}^{m} n (A_n \cos n\Omega t - B_n \sin n\Omega t) +$$

$$+ \frac{\omega_0^2}{2} B_0 + \omega_0^2 \sum_{n=1}^{m} (A_n \sin n\Omega t + B_n \cos n\Omega t) +$$

$$+ \mu \left\{ \frac{1}{2} B_0 + \sum_{n=1}^{m} (A_n \sin n\Omega t + B_n \cos n\Omega t) \right\}^3 -$$

$$- P \sin \Omega t , \tag{134}$$

which naturally does not vanish identically. With the use of some elementary trigonometric formulas, e may be written in the form

$$e = E_0 + \sum_{i=1}^{p} (D_i \sin i\Omega t + E_i \cos i\Omega t) \tag{135}$$

with $p > m$, where the $D_i, i \geqslant 1$, and the $E_i, i \geqslant 0$, depend only on A_n, B_n along with δ, ω_0^2, μ, and P. The A_n and the B_n may be chosen in such a manner that the E_i, $i = 0, 1, \ldots, m$ and the D_i, $i = 1, 2, \ldots, m$ become zero, although e itself will not vanish. It is difficult to implement this, since the E_i and D_i depend on the A_n and B_n in a complicated non-linear manner. However, a restriction to the first approximation

$$x(t) = \frac{1}{2} B_0 + A \sin \Omega t + B \cos \Omega t \tag{136}$$

still allows a solution of the problem. The result is

$$\begin{aligned}
e = {}& \{(\omega_0^2 - \Omega^2)A - 2\delta\Omega B - P\} \sin \Omega t + \\
& + \{(\omega_0^2 - \Omega^2)B + 2\delta\Omega A\} \cos \Omega t + \\
& + \frac{\omega_0^2}{2} B_0 + \mu \left\{ \frac{1}{2} B_0 + A \sin \Omega t + B \cos \Omega t \right\}^3,
\end{aligned} \tag{137}$$

where it is apparent that $E_0 = 0$ also implies $B_0 = 0$. With

$$\begin{aligned}
\{A \sin \Omega t + B \cos \Omega t\}^3 = {}& \frac{3}{4} A (A^2 + B^2) \sin \Omega t + \\
& + \frac{3}{4} B (A^2 + B^2) \cos \Omega t + \frac{1}{4} A (- A^2 + 3 B^2) \sin 3\Omega t + \\
& + \frac{1}{4} B (- 3 A^2 + B^2) \cos 3\Omega t
\end{aligned}$$

$E_1 = 0$ and $D_1 = 0$ then yield the equations

$$\left. \begin{aligned}
\left(\omega_0^2 - \Omega^2 + \frac{3}{4} \mu C^2 \right) A - 2\delta\Omega B &= P, \\
\left(\omega_0^2 - \Omega^2 + \frac{3}{4} \mu C^2 \right) B + 2\delta\Omega A &= 0
\end{aligned} \right\} \tag{138}$$

with $C^2 = A^2 + B^2$. Their simultaneous solution results in

$$A = \frac{P(\omega_0^2 - \Omega^2 + \frac{3}{4}\mu C^2)}{4\delta^2\Omega^2 + (\omega_0^2 - \Omega^2 + \frac{3}{4}\mu C^2)^2},$$

$$B = -\frac{2\delta P\Omega}{4\delta^2\Omega^2 + (\omega_0^2 - \Omega^2 + \frac{3}{4}\mu C^2)^2}$$

and, eventually,

$$C^2 \left\{ 4\delta^2\Omega^2 + (\omega_0^2 - \Omega^2 + \frac{3}{4}\mu C^2)^2 \right\} = P^2,$$

corresponding to the result (129) as obtained before. In a similar manner, the phase shift between excitation and response may be computed.

The method of Rauscher (1938) and perturbation theory may be used equally well in the investigation of damped forced oscillations. Higher order approximations only result in small changes in the resonance curves obtained from the first approximation, as long as μ does not get too large (e.g., see Kauderer 1958).

1.3.4. Subharmonic oscillations

An essential difference between linear and non-linear systems is the fact that the latter present not only periodic oscillations with the excitation frequency Ω but also periodic oscillations with other circular frequencies. Other than the oscillations with the frequency Ω, those with circular frequencies $\Omega/2, \Omega/3, \ldots, \Omega/n$ are observed most often; these are called *subharmonic* oscillations. The most important subharmonic oscillation of the Duffing equation is that with circular frequency $\Omega/3$. It may be approximately computed with any of the previously introduced methods. Here, only a short discussion using the method of harmonic balance will be given (see Stoker 1950), and that only for the undamped case.

A periodic solution of

$$\ddot{x} + \omega_0^2 x + \mu x^3 = P \sin \Omega t \tag{139}$$

with circular frequency $\Omega/3$ is desired. Such a solution may be written in the form

$$x = \sum_{n=1}^{\infty} \left(A_n \sin \frac{n\Omega t}{3} + B_n \cos \frac{n\Omega t}{3} \right).$$

It is easy to show that only those terms with odd n are different from zero. Consequently, one has

$$x = C_{1/3} \sin \frac{\Omega t}{3} + C_1 \sin \Omega t + C_{5/3} \sin \frac{5\Omega t}{3} + \ldots . \tag{140}$$

The substitution of

$$x = C_{1/3} \sin\frac{\Omega t}{3} + C_1 \sin \Omega t \tag{141}$$

in eqn (139) and a comparison of coefficients provide

$$\left.\begin{aligned}
\left(\omega_0^2 - \frac{\Omega^2}{9}\right) C_{1/3} + \frac{3}{4}\mu \left(C_{1/3}^3 - C_{1/3}^2 C_1 + 2 C_{1/3}C_1^2\right) &= 0, \\[2mm]
(\omega_0^2 - \Omega^2) C_1 + \frac{1}{4}\mu \left(- C_{1/3}^3 + 6 C_{1/3}^2 C_1 + 3 C_1^3\right) &= P.
\end{aligned}\right\} \tag{142}$$

For $C_{1/3} \neq 0$, the first of eqns (142) results in

$$\Omega^2 = 9\,\omega_0^2 + \frac{27}{4}\,\mu(C_{1/3}^2 - C_{1/3} C_1 + 2 C_1^2). \tag{143}$$

The elimination of Ω^2 yields

$$-8\,\omega_0^2 C_1 = P - \frac{1}{4}\mu \left(- C_{1/3}^3 - 21 C_{1/3}^2 C_1 + 27 C_{1/3} C_1^2 - 51 C_1^3\right). \tag{144}$$

These equations are to be solved iteratively for small values of μ. For $\mu = 0$ with an arbitrarily given $C_{1/3}$ one obtains the first approximation

$$\Omega_{(1)} = 3\,\omega_0, \quad C_{1,(1)} = -\frac{P}{8\,\omega_0^2}$$

whose use in (143) and (144) yields the second approximation

$$\left.\begin{aligned}
\Omega_{(2)}^2 &= 9\,\omega_0^2 + \frac{27}{4}\mu \left(C_{1/3}^2 + C_{1/3}\frac{P}{8\,\omega_0^2} + \frac{P^2}{32\,\omega_0^4}\right), \\[2mm]
C_{1,(2)} &= -\frac{P}{8\,\omega_0^2} + \frac{1}{32}\frac{\mu}{\omega_0^2}\left(- C_{1/3}^3 + 21 C_{1/3}^2\frac{P}{8\,\omega_0^2} + \right. \\[2mm]
&\qquad\qquad \left. + 27 C_{1/3}\frac{P^2}{8^2\,\omega_0^4} + 51\frac{P^3}{8^3\,\omega_0^6}\right).
\end{aligned}\right\} \tag{145}$$

Depending upon the sign of μ, the first of these equations represents either an ellipse or a hyperbola in the $C_{1/3}$ Ω-plane.

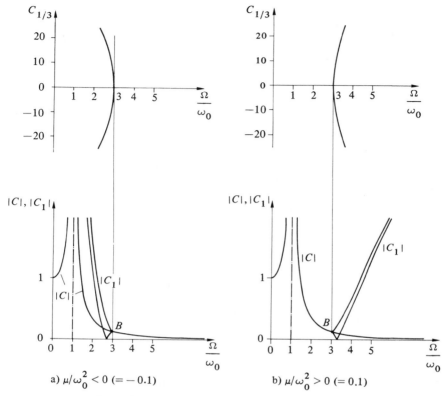

Fig. 1.22. Resonance curves for C_1, $C_{1/3}$, and C.

For any assumed value of $C_{1/3}$ the first of these equations may be used to calculate the corresponding value of Ω, whereas the second equation supplies the appropriate value of C_1. It is apparent from the upper diagrams in Fig. 1.22 and from the first of eqns (145) that the subharmonic resonance, that is, $C_{1/3} \neq 0$, is not possible for all frequencies Ω but only for those values of Ω which lie above (below) a certain critical value for $\mu > 0$ ($\mu < 0$). This 'critical' frequency Ω corresponds to the apex of the curve for $C_{1/3}$ in Fig. 1.22, and it is given by

$$\Omega^2 = 9 \left(\omega_0^2 + \mu \, \frac{21}{16} \, \frac{P^2}{8^2 \, \omega_0^4} \right).$$

The corresponding value of $C_{1/3}$ is

$$C_{1/3} = \frac{-P}{16 \, \omega_0^2}.$$

For small values of $|\mu|$ and of P/ω_0^2 the apex in the upper diagrams of Fig. 1.22 is located practically (but not exactly!) on the abscissa. For $C_{1/3} = 0$, the second of eqns (142) again yields (111), that is, the subharmonic occurs as a branching of the 'harmonic' oscillation at the point B in Fig. 1.22 determined by

$$C_1 = C = \frac{P}{8\,\omega_0^2}\left(\frac{51}{32}\,\mu\,\frac{P^2}{8^2\,\omega_0^6} - 1\right).$$

Fig. 1.22 shows the resonance curves for C_1 and $C_{1/3}$ for subharmonic resonance as well as the resonance curves for the 'ordinary' forced oscillations, $C(\Omega/\omega_0)$. Of course, the backbone curves are not vertical as they appear to be here due to the choice of scale (see Fig. 1.18 for comparison).

1.3.5. Combination frequencies

Until this point, only forced oscillations due to a single harmonic force have been investigated. For linear systems, it was possible to solve the case of the simultaneous excitation by two or more harmonic forcing terms by means of superposition. This is no longer possible in the non-linear case and completely new types of oscillations may result. Consider the undamped Duffing equation when the simultaneous excitation by means of two terms with different frequencies is included:

$$\ddot{x} + \omega_0^2 x + \mu x^3 = P_1 \cos \Omega_1 t + P_2 \cos \Omega_2 t. \tag{146}$$

This equation may again be treated with the various approximation schemes previously used. Only a brief treatment of some of the results is given here. Duffing used the initial formulation

$$x_1 = A \cos \Omega_1 t + B \cos \Omega_2 t \tag{147}$$

and used his procedure (see section 1.3.2) to obtain

$$x_2 = A \cos \Omega_1 t + B \cos \Omega_2 t - \frac{\mu A^3}{36} \cos 3\,\Omega_1 t - \frac{\mu A^3}{36} \cos 3\,\Omega_2 t -$$

$$- \frac{3}{4}\mu A^2 B \left\{ \frac{1}{(\Omega_2 + 2\,\Omega_1)^2} \cos(\Omega_2 + 2\,\Omega_1)t + \right.$$

$$\left. + \frac{1}{(\Omega_2 - 2\,\Omega_1)^2} \cos(\Omega_2 - 2\,\Omega_1)t \right\} -$$

$$- \frac{3}{4}\mu A B^2 \left\{ \frac{1}{(\Omega_1 + 2\,\Omega_2)^2} \cos(\Omega_1 + 2\,\Omega_2)t + \right.$$

$$+ \frac{1}{(\Omega_1 - 2\,\Omega_2)^2} \cos{(\Omega_1 - 2\,\Omega_2)\,t} \Bigg\}, \tag{148}$$

as his second approximation, where A and B satisfy the algebraic equations

$$(\omega_0^2 - \Omega_1^2)\,A + \frac{3}{4}\,\mu A\,(A^2 + 2\,B^2) = P_1,$$

$$(\omega_0^2 - \Omega_2^2)\,B + \frac{3}{4}\,\mu B\,(B^2 + 2\,A^2) = P_2. \tag{149}$$

It is essential to note that the forced oscillations now contain terms with the circular frequencies $\Omega_2 \pm 2\Omega_1$ and $\Omega_1 \pm 2\Omega_2$ which are designated as *combination frequencies*. In a quite analogous manner, Helmholtz used the non-linear character of the human ear to explain the fact that one also hears tones with the frequencies $\omega_1 \pm \omega_2$ for two given tones with the circular frequencies ω_1 and ω_2, especially when these tones are very loud.

An in-depth discussion of the results would lead too far here even though they are quite important in connection with celestial mechanics, for example; instead, the reader is referred to Stoker (1950) and other authors.

1.4. General comments

The results used here about ordinary differential equations may be found, for example, in the classical books by Levinson (1955), Cesari (1959), Pontryagin (1965), Hale (1963), and Struble (1962). Of the more recent German works, the two excellent books by Walter (1972) and by Knobloch and Kappel (1974) are recommended. An understanding of the physical connections in oscillation problems is emphasized by Klotter (1960) and Magnus (1955, 1961). A certain intermediate position between the purely mathematical writings and these more technically oriented books is occupied by Forbat's (1966) *Analytische Mechanik der Schwingungen* (*Analytical mechanics of oscillations*), the classical work of Andronov, Witt, and Chaikin (1965), Blaquière's *Non-linear system analysis* (1966) and Kauderer's *Nichtlineare Mechanik* (*Non-linear mechanics*) (1958).

Perturbation theory in the form as presented in this chapter was developed in the context of celestial mechanics by Poincaré (1957), Lindstedt (1883), and Newcomb during the last century. Since then it has been used extensively in practically all fields of mathematical physics: in fluid mechanics (see Cole 1968 and Van Dyke 1964), in the theory of elasticity, and also in the modern problems of quantum mechanics. Malkin (1959) has made extensive use of perturbation theory in the investigation of non-linear oscillations. A systematic collection of the many variants of perturbation theory with numerous modern applications from all areas is contained in the excellent book by Nayfeh (1973).

It is noteworthy that even today there are new and important discoveries for such well-known differential equations as the Duffing equation. Recently, for example, Hale and Rodrigues (1976) used perturbation theory with independent parameters and discovered new branches of the periodic solutions.

In the investigation of non-linear oscillations by perturbation methods, two difficulties arise: the avoidance of secular terms which was mentioned in section 1.1.1 and the appearance of small denominators. This second point has not yet been touched upon since its characteristic form arises only in systems with more than a single degree of freedom. When perturbation methods are used for the free oscillation problem, then linear combinations of the eigen-frequencies of the linearized system occur in the denominators of the series expansion. Some of these may get very small or even vanish ('inner resonance'). These difficulties were already treated by Poincaré (1957) and they will be discussed further here in Chapter 4. Even today, the 'small denominators' still are a very active problem area in which intensive work is being done (see, for example, Eminhizer, Hellemann, and Montroll 1976; Giacaglia 1972; Moser 1968).

The method of harmonic balance is used especially by Hayashi (1964), who uses it to treat numerous oscillation problems, especially those including sub-harmonic resonances. The method of Ritz has the advantages such that it is often possible to prove convergence (in the sense of a norm) and to provide error estimates (see Mikhlin 1962). The method of equivalent linearization was discussed in detail by Magnus (1955) and is also used, for example, in control theory (see Graham and McRuer 1971); equivalent linearization is also known under the name 'K-transformation'. In the examples treated here, it leads to the same results as the method of slowly changing phase and amplitude, which coincides with the first approximation obtained with the asymptotic method by Bogoliubov and Mitropolsky (1965). The latter, however, is more general: not only can it be used without further difficulty in systems with several degrees of freedom, but the higher order approximations may also be used for the systematic construction of an asymptotic approximate solution. Tondl (1975), for example, has used equivalent linearization to obtain new and interesting results.

References

Andronov, A. A., Witt, A. A., and Chaikin, S. E. (1965). *Theorie der Schwin-gungen* [*Theory of oscillations*], Vols. 1 and 2. Akademie-Verlag, Berlin.

Blaquière, A. (1966). *Nonlinear system analysis*. Academic Press, New York.

Bogoliubov, N. N. and Mitropolsky, J. A. (1965). *Asymptotische Methoden in der Theorie der nichtlinearen Schwingungen* [*Asymptotic methods in the theory of non-linear oscillations*]. Akademie-Verlag, Berlin.

Cesari, L. (1959). *Asymptotic behavior and stability problems in ordinary differential equations.* Springer, Berlin.

Cole, J. D. (1968). *Perturbation methods in applied mathematics*. Blaisdell, Waltham, Massachusetts.

Duffing, G. (1918). *Erzwungene Schwingungen bei veränderlicher Eigenfrequenz* [*Forced oscillations in the presence of variable eigenfrequencies*]. Vieweg, Braunschweig.

Eminhizer, C. R., Hellemann, R. H. G., and Montroll, E. W. (1976). On a convergent nonlinear perturbation theory without small denominators or secular terms. *J. math. Phys.* **17** (1), 121–40.

Forbat, N. (1966). *Analytische Mechanik der Schwingungen* [*Analytical mechanics of oscillations*]. VEB Deutscher Verlag der Wissenschaften, Berlin.

Giacaglia, G. E. O. (1972). *Perturbation methods in non-linear systems*. Springer, Berlin.

Graham, D. and McRuer, D. (1971). *Analysis of nonlinear control systems*. Dover, New York.

Hale, J. K. (1963). *Oscillations in nonlinear systems*. McGraw-Hill, New York.

—— and Rodrigues, H. M. (1976). *Bifurcation in the Duffing equation with independent paradmeters I*. Research Note of the Lefschetz Center for Dynamical Systems, Division of Applied Mathematics, Brown University, Providence, Rhode Island.

Hayashi, Ch. (1964). *Nonlinear oscillations in Physical systems*. McGraw-Hill, New York.

Kauderer, H. (1958). *Nichtlineare Mechanik* [*Nonlinear mechanics*]. Springer, Berlin.

Klotter, K. (1951). *Technische Schwingungslehre* [*Applied oscillation theory*], Vol. 1. Springer, Berlin.

—— (1960). *Technische Schwingungslehre* [*Applied oscillation theory*], Vol. 2. Springer, Berlin.

Knobloch, H. W. and Kappel, F. (1974). *Gewöhnliche Differentialgleichungen* [*Ordinary differential equations*]. Teubner, Stuttgart.

Levinson, N. (1955). *Theory of ordinary differential equations*. McGraw-Hill, New York.

Lindstedt, A. (1883). *Mem. Acad. Imp. St. Petersburg* **31**.

Magnus, K. (1961). *Schwingungen* [*Oscillations*]. Teubner, Stuttgart.

—— (1955). *Über ein Verfahren zur Untersuchung nichtlinearer Schwingungs- und Regelunssysteme* [*A method for the investigation of non-linear oscillation- and control-systems*]. VDI-Forschungsheft 451, VDI-Verlag, Düsseldorf.

Malkin, I. G. (1959). *Some problems in the theory of nonlinear oscillations*, 2 Volumes. United States Atomic Energy Commission, AEC-tr-3766, Washington, DC.

Mikhlin, S. G.. (1962). *Variationsmethoden der mathematischen Physik* [*Variational methods of mathematical physics*]. Akademie-Verlag, Berlin.

Minorsky, N. (1962). *Nonlinear oscillations*. Princeton University Press, Princeton, Pennsylvania.

Moser, J. (1968). *Lectures on Hamiltonian systems*. American Mathematical Society.

Nayfeh, A. H. (1973). *Perturbation methods*. John Wiley, New York.

Poincaré, H. (1957). *Les méthodes nouvelles de la mécanique céleste* [*New methods in celestial mechanics*], Vols. 1–3. Dover, New York. [First edn 1892].

Pontryagin, L. S. (1965). *Gewöhnliche Differentialgleichungen* [*Ordinary differential equations*.] VEB Deutscher Verlag der Wissenschaften, Berlin.

Rauscher, M. (1938). Steady oscillations of systems with nonlinear and unsymmetrical elasticity. *J. appl. Mech.* **5**.

Sansone, G. and Conti, R. (1964). *Non-linear differential equations*. Pergamon Press, Oxford.

Stoker, J. J. (1950). *Nonlinear vibrations*. Interscience, New York.

Struble, R. A. (1962). *Nonlinear differential equations*. McGraw-Hill, New York.

Tondl, A. (1975). The application of skeleton curves and limit envelopes to the analysis of nonlinear systems. *The Shock and Vibration Digest* **7**, 3–20.

Van Dyke, M. (1964). *Perturbation methods in fluid mechanics, applied mathematics and mechanics*. Academic Press, New York.

Walter, W. (1972). *Gewöhnliche Differentialgleichungen [Ordinary differential equations]*. Springer, Berlin.

Exercises

1.1. The system in Fig. 1.23 consists of two non-linear springs and of two particles with masses m_1 and m_2. Let q_1, q_2 be the stretching of the springs 1 and 2 from their unstressed positions; then one may take the restoring forces to be given by

$$f_1(q_1) = c_1 q_1 (1 + \alpha_1^2 q_1^2),$$

$$f_2(q_2) = c_2 q_2 (1 + \alpha_2^2 q_2^2),$$

where $c_1, c_2, \alpha_1, \alpha_2$ are constant (take $\alpha_1/\alpha_2 = 8, c_1/c_2 = 2, m_1/m_2 = 1/4$, $\alpha_1 g = 2c_1/m_1$, with $g =$ gravitational acceleration).

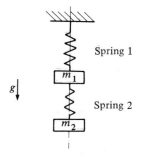

Fig. 1.23. Exercise 1.1.

Obtain the equations of motion of the system and use linearization about the equilibrium position to determine an approximate solution for small amplitude oscillation.

1.2. Two massless linear springs with stiffness c are hinged at A and B, separated by a distance $2l$ (see Fig. 1.24). In their unstressed position, they have a length

$s_0 = l(1 + \alpha)$ and they are connected to one another by means of a hinge support-ing a mass m and moving without friction along the straight line EF. The weight is to be neglected (the motion occurs on a horizontal, smooth plane).

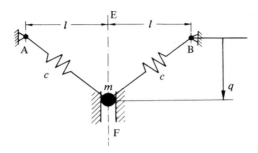

Fig. 1.24. Exercise 1.2.

(a) Obtain the differential equation of motion and normalize it in a suitable manner, say, with $x = q/l$.

(b) Draw the restoring force (in the direction EF) as a function of x when the parameter values are given by $\alpha = -0.5; 0; +0.5$. For what parameter values does a linearization about the equilibrium position $q = 0$ not make sense?

(c) Draw the phase diagram for $\alpha = -0.5; 0; +0.5$.

1.3. The oscillator in Fig. 1.25 has a mass m and is supported by a linear mass-less spring (spring constant c) and a string (which cannot sustain compressive forces). Draw the phase diagram and determine the period of oscillation for abitrary amplitudes.

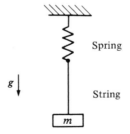

Fig. 1.25. Exercise 1.3.

1.4. The non-linear differential equation

$$\ddot{x} + x + x^2 = 0$$

has an exact solution in terms of elliptic functions.

(a) Consider small amplitudes of oscillation; transform the equation in such a way that the perturbation methods of Lindstedt may be used.

(b) Compute the first three approximations.

(c) Determine the circular frequency ω as a function of the amplitude.

1.5. Use the method of slowly changing amplitude and phase to obtain an approximate solution of the equation $\ddot{x} + g(x) = 0$ for the restoring forces (a) and (b) as sketched in Fig. 1.26. Compare the period obtained in this manner with that of the exact solution. Draw the phase diagrams.

(a)

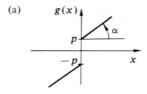

(b)

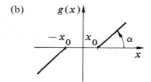

Fig. 1.26. Exercise 1.5.

1.6. A non-linear system is described by the differential equation

$$\ddot{x} + \rho \operatorname{sgn} \dot{x} + g \operatorname{sgn} x = 0, \quad \rho < g.$$

(a) Determine the exact amplitude decay per 'complete oscillation' and the 'period' (the time between two maximum deflections).

(b) Obtain an approximate solution by using the method of slowly changing amplitude and phase.

1.7. Assume small β and use perturbation theory to obtain periodic solutions for the differential equation

$$\ddot{q} + \omega_0^2 (q + \beta q^2) = P \cos \Omega t$$

(a) Transform the equation to the form

$$x'' + x = \cos \eta \tau - \mu x^2$$

and perform a perturbation calculation for the non-resonance case, $\Omega \neq \omega_0$.

(b) Transform the equation into the form

$$\eta^2 x'' + x = \mu (p_0 \cos \tau - x^2)$$

and construct a periodic solution for the resonance case $\Omega \approx \omega_0$.

1.8. Obtain periodic solutions for the differential equation

$$\ddot{x} + \omega_0^2 (x - \mu^2 x^3 + \nu^4 x^5) = P \sin \Omega t.$$

(a) Use the method of Duffing and the initial formulation $x(t) = C \sin \Omega t$ to determine an approximate solution.

(b) Draw the resonance curves $C(\eta^2)$ for $\eta = \Omega/\omega_0$ and for the parameter values $\mu^2 = 0.6$; $\nu^4 = 1.2$; $P/\omega_0^2 = 0.015$ as well as $P/\omega_0^2 = 0.05$ in the interval $0.5 < \eta^2 < 1.7$.

(c) What are the amplitude jumps for changes of η^2 in a neighbourhood of $\eta^2 = 1$?

1.9. Determine a subharmonic solution with period $4\pi/\Omega$ for the differential equation in Exercise 1.7.

2

LIAPOUNOV STABILITY THEORY

2.1. The concept of Liapounov stability

The concept of the stability of an equilibrium is somewhat familiar from elementary mechanics. It is known, for example, that in a system whose mechanical energy is conserved—that is, in a 'conservative system'—an equilibrium position corresponding to a minimum of the potential energy is a stable equilibrium position. This is schematically represented in Fig. 2.1, where the 'frictionless' motion of a particle under the influence of gravity on a given curve $y(x)$ in the vertical xy-plane is depicted.

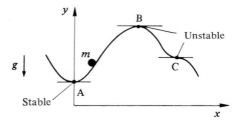

Fig. 2.1. The concept of stability of an equilibrium position.

Equilibrium positions are located at all points where the curve has a horizontal tangent, that is where dy/dx is equal to zero. The point A (a relative minimum of the potential energy) corresponds to a *stable* equilibrium position; the points B (a relative maximum of the potential energy) and C (a point of inflection with horizontal tangent) correspond to *unstable* equilibrium positions. These considerations intuitively make good sense in spite of the fact that no definition of stability (and of instability) has been given yet.

The theorem implying the stability of an equilibrium for a minimum of the potential energy may already be found in Lagrange's *Mécanique analytique* (1788); a rigorous proof was given later by Dirichlet. The stability definition on which the theorem was based was quite similar to the modern definition as it will shortly be given here. In fact, the Lagrange–Dirichlet stability theorem is often used as the definition of stability in elastomechanics: there, an equilibrium position is called stable when it corresponds to a relative minimum of the potential energy; otherwise, it is called unstable. This approach is unsatisfactory for several reasons which will be discussed in more detail later. Dirichlet's proof of the instability theorem then provided the inspiration for the Russian engineer A. M. Liapounov to develop his stability theory (especially his 'direct method') toward the end of the last century. Today, the stability concept which he introduced plays an important role in the theory of ordinary differential equations. In the following, this concept will be used unless specifically stated otherwise.

In order to give a clear presentation of general results, it is advisable to use matrix notation in this chapter and to write all differential equations as first-order systems in the form

$$\dot{\mathbf{x}} = \mathbf{f}(\mathbf{x}, t) \tag{1}$$

where $\dot{\mathbf{x}}^T = (\dot{x}_1, \dot{x}_2, \ldots, \dot{x}_n)$, $\mathbf{f}^T = (f_1, f_2, \ldots, f_n)$. It is assumed that conditions sufficient to guarantee the existence and uniqueness of the solutions of (1) on their domain of definition are satisfied for $t \in [t_0, \infty)$.† A solution of (1) thus is uniquely determined by its initial conditions; one generally denotes this by $\mathbf{x} = \mathbf{x}(\mathbf{x}_0, t_0; t)$ with $\mathbf{x}(\mathbf{x}_0, t_0; t_0) = \mathbf{x}_0$.

Consider now a specific solution $\mathbf{x}(\mathbf{a}, t_0; t)$. Then $\mathbf{x}(\mathbf{a}, t_0; t)$ is said to be stable, if the difference $|\mathbf{x}(\mathbf{x}_0, t_0; t) - \mathbf{x}(\mathbf{a}, t_0; t)|$ remains smaller than an arbitrarily given small ϵ, for all time, as long as $\mathbf{x}_0$ is chosen sufficiently close to $\mathbf{a}$. More precisely: $\mathbf{x}(\mathbf{a}, t_0; t)$ *is stable, if for every (arbitrarily small)* $\epsilon > 0$ *there exists a* $\delta(\epsilon) > 0$ *such that* ‡

$$|\mathbf{x}_0 - \mathbf{a}| < \delta(\epsilon) \Rightarrow |\mathbf{x}(\mathbf{x}_0, t_0; t) - \mathbf{x}(\mathbf{a}, t_0; t)| < \epsilon, \quad \forall t \geq t_0. \tag{2}$$

The solution $\mathbf{x}(\mathbf{x}_0, t_0; t)$ thus remains in an arbitrarily thin 'tube' about $\mathbf{x}(\mathbf{a}, t_0; t)$ in the 'augmented state space' ($\mathbb{R}^{n+1}$ corresponding to $x_1, x_2, \ldots, x_n, t$) for all time, as long as $\mathbf{x}_0$ is chosen sufficiently close to $\mathbf{a}$ (Fig. 2.2). The vertical lines here, for example, may refer to the Euclidean norm $|\mathbf{x}| = \sqrt{(x_1^2 + x_2^2 + \ldots + x_n^2)}$ or to any other norm, such as $|\mathbf{x}| = |x_1| + |x_2| + \ldots + |x_n|$ (in *finite*-dimensional spaces all norms are equivalent in the sense that 'smallness' with respect to any of them implies 'smallness' with respect to all others).

Within this definition it thus makes no sense to use terms such as 'stable system' or 'stable differential equation', since one and the same differential equation may have stable as well as unstable solutions (linear differential equations are an exception). *A solution of* $\mathbf{x}(\mathbf{a}, t_0; t)$ *of (1) is called unstable whenever it is not stable*; in the case of instability, there always exists some $\epsilon > 0$, and some $\mathbf{x}_0$ in an arbitrarily small neighbourhood of $\mathbf{a}$ such that $\mathbf{x}(\mathbf{x}_0, t_0; t)$ will leave the ϵ-tube for some $t > t_0$ (by now it is apparent that stability is nothing more than *uniformly* continuous dependence on the initial conditions).

† $t \in [t_1, t_2)$ corresponds to $t_1 \leq t < t_2$.
‡ $a \Rightarrow b$ means that the statement a implies the statement b; $\forall t \geq t_0$ means 'for *all* values of t greater than or equal to t_0'.

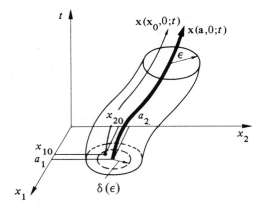

Fig. 2.2. The Liapounov stability definition.

As an example, consider a brief investigation of the stability of various solutions of the governing differential equation for the mathematical pendulum

$$\ddot{x} + \omega_0^2 \sin x = 0 \tag{3}$$

which may also be written in the form

$$\left. \begin{aligned} \dot{x}_1 &= \omega_0 x_2, \\ \dot{x}_2 &= -\omega_0 \sin x_1. \end{aligned} \right\} \tag{4}$$

A brief scrutiny of the phase diagram, Fig. 2.3, indicates that $\mathbf{x} \equiv \mathbf{0}$ (the lower equilibrium position) is a stable solution. For this example, the function $\delta(\epsilon)$ may be constructed in accordance with Fig. 2.3. For a given $\epsilon > 0$ a phase trajectory contained entirely within the circle $|\mathbf{x}| = \epsilon$ is chosen; a possible choice for δ then is the radius of any circle contained entirely within this phase trajectory.

The instablility of the solution $\mathbf{x}^T \equiv (\pi, 0)$ is equally obvious: in every arbitrarily small neighbourhood of this point in the phase plane, there always exist initial conditions leading to solutions which may 'move far away from this point'. Now, what about the stability of any of the periodic solutions which correspond to the closed phase trajectories? All of the periodic solutions of (4) are unstable! This is apparent from Fig. 2.4. Consider, for example, the stability of the solution which passes through the point A for $t = 0$. A small change in the initial conditions from A to B, obviously produces a slight change not only in the amplitude of oscillation but also in the period of oscillation—as is known from Chapter 1.

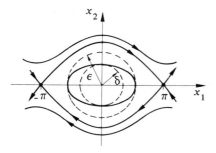

Fig. 2.3. Stability of the static equilibrium of the pendulum.

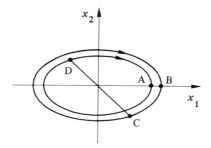

Fig. 2.4. The stability of the periodic solutions of (4).

The point on the phase trajectory which passes through B moves around more slowly, that is, for some time $t > 0$ it will happen that the points of the two motions occupy positions which are diametrically opposed to one another with respect to **0**; then the distance between these two points is $|CD|$. It is *not* possible to make this distance arbitrarily small by choosing B sufficiently close to A! From this, one concludes instability. For similar reasons, the motion of an artificial satellite about the earth is unstable since the square of the time of revolution is proportional to the third power of the length of the semi-major axis, in accordance with Kepler's third law. A small change in the initial conditions may result in only a small change in the time of revolution; however, every change in the time of revolution, no matter how small, means that the 'disturbed' and 'undisturbed' motion will eventually be a large distance from one another in a sufficiently large time interval.

In contrast hereto, all of the solutions of the linearized system (4),

$$\begin{rcases} \dot{x}_1 = \omega_0 x_2, \\ \dot{x}_2 = -\omega_0 x_1, \end{rcases} \quad (5)$$

are stable.

Thus, in spite of the fact that the new (disturbed) phase trajectory corresponding to a small change in the initial conditions remained everywhere close to the original phase trajectory (Fig. 2.4) it turned out that the periodic solutions of (4) were unstable. This phenomenon is present in many of the applications from mathematical physics. Thus, although a motion may be unstable in the Liapounov sense, it is useful to further distinguish that case for which the phase trajectories remain close to each other. This is the purpose of the concept of a *stable trajectory* or of *orbital stability*:

The solution $\mathbf{x}(\mathbf{a}, t_0 ; t)$ *has a stable trajectory or is orbitally stable iff for every (arbitrarily small)* $\epsilon > 0$ *there exist a* $\delta(\epsilon) > 0$ *and a function* $t_1(t)$ *such that*

$$|\mathbf{x}_0 - \mathbf{a}| < \delta \;\Rightarrow\; |\mathbf{x}\,(\mathbf{x}_0, t_0; t) - \mathbf{x}(\mathbf{a}, t_0; t_1(t))| < \epsilon, \; \forall t \geqslant t_0 \,. \qquad (6)$$

Expressed differently, the 'ϵ-tube' about $\mathbf{x}(\mathbf{a}, t_0; t)$ is now introduced in the phase space (in $\mathbb{R}^n$ as implied by $x_1, x_2, \ldots, x_n$) not in the augmented state space as before. If for every $\epsilon > 0$ there exists a δ-sphere about $\mathbf{a}$ such that all solutions which begin in this sphere at $t = t_0$, never leave this tube, then $\mathbf{x}(\mathbf{a}, t_0; t)$ is orbitally stable.† Obviously, the periodic oscillations of the pendulum are orbitally stable.

A solution $\mathbf{x}(\mathbf{a}, t_0; t)$ is attractive iff there exists an $\epsilon > 0$ such that

$$|\mathbf{x}_0 - \mathbf{a}| < \epsilon \;\Rightarrow\; \lim_{t \to \infty} |\mathbf{x}\,(\mathbf{x}_0, t_0; t) - \mathbf{x}(\mathbf{a}, t_0; t)| = 0 \,. \qquad (7)$$

A solution which is both stable and attractive is called asymptotically stable. It may very well be that a solution $\mathbf{x}(\mathbf{a}, t_0; t)$ is attractive without being stable (see Hahn 1967, p. 191 ff).

For the investigation of the stability of $\mathbf{x}(\mathbf{a}, t_0; t)$, it is often useful to introduce the coordinate transformation

$$\mathbf{y} = \mathbf{x} - \mathbf{x}(\mathbf{a}, t_0; t) \,. \qquad (8)$$

The differential equation (1) then takes on the form

$$\dot{\mathbf{y}} = \dot{\mathbf{x}} - \dot{\mathbf{x}}(\mathbf{a}, t_0; t) = \mathbf{f}\,(\mathbf{x}) - \mathbf{f}\,(\mathbf{x}(\mathbf{a}, t_0; t)) =$$
$$= \mathbf{f}\,(\mathbf{y} + \mathbf{x}(\mathbf{a}, t_0; t)) - \mathbf{f}\,(\mathbf{x}(\mathbf{a}, t_0; t)), \qquad (9)$$

that is,

$$\dot{\mathbf{y}} = \mathbf{g}\,(\mathbf{y}, t) \qquad (10)$$

since $\mathbf{x}(\mathbf{a}, t_0; t)$ is assumed known. The solution $\mathbf{x}(\mathbf{a}, t_0; t)$ of (1) now corresponds to the trivial solution $\mathbf{y} = \mathbf{0}$ of (10) and the stability of this solution corresponds exactly to that of $\mathbf{x}(\mathbf{a}, t_0; t)$.

As an example, consider again the stability of a periodic solution $\mathbf{x}^*(t) = \mathbf{x}(\mathbf{a}, t_0; t)$ of (4). With $\mathbf{y} = \mathbf{x} - \mathbf{x}^*$ eqn (4) becomes

$$\left. \begin{aligned} \dot{y}_1 &= \omega_0 y_2, \\ \dot{y}_2 &= -\omega_0 \sin\,(x_1^* + y_1) + \omega_0 \sin x_1^* \,; \end{aligned} \right\} \qquad (11)$$

† In analytical mechanics, there also are other definitions of 'orbital' stability which turn out to be useful (see Schräpel 1969).

the system (11), however, is no longer autonomous but contains the time t explicitly! For the investigation of the motions in a neighbourhood of the trivial solution $\mathbf{y} = \mathbf{0}$ of (10), it is often useful to develop the right-hand side in a Taylor series with respect to $\mathbf{y}$, where the coefficients corresponding to the solution $\mathbf{x}^*(t)$ are periodic in t. The periodic pendulum oscillations from (11) then become

$$\left. \begin{aligned} \dot{y}_1 &= \omega_0 y_2, \\ \dot{y}_2 &= -\omega_0 y_1 \cos x_1^* + \frac{\omega_0}{2} y_1^2 \sin x_1^* + \ldots \quad . \end{aligned} \right\} \tag{12}$$

Another example which will be used a number of times concerns the free rotation of a rigid body supported by a frictionless ball-joint at its centre of gravity. Let A, B, and C be the three principal moments of inertia and let p, q, and r be the projections of the angular velocity ω onto the corresponding principal axes; then the Euler equations (see Gantmacher (1958, 1970), for example) yield the system

$$\left. \begin{aligned} A\dot{p} &= (B - C)qr, \\ B\dot{q} &= (C - A)rp, \\ C\dot{r} &= (A - B)pq \end{aligned} \right\} \tag{13}$$

with the particular solutions $p = \omega, q = r = 0; p = 0, q = \omega, r = 0; p = q = 0$, $r = \omega$, where ω is an arbitrary constant in each case. Each of these solutions corresponds to the rotation of the rigid body about one of the three principal axes with angular velocity ω. To investigate the stability of the first solution, it it useful to introduce the transformation $y_1 = p - \omega, y_2 = q, y_3 = r$, and to write (13) in the form

$$\left. \begin{aligned} \dot{y}_1 &= \frac{B-C}{A} y_2 y_3, \\ \dot{y}_2 &= \frac{C-A}{B} (y_1 + \omega) y_3, \\ \dot{y}_3 &= \frac{A-B}{C} (y_1 + \omega) y_2. \end{aligned} \right\} \tag{14}$$

The trivial solution $y_1 = 0, y_2 = 0, y_3 = 0$ of (14) then corresponds to the solution $p = \omega, q = r = 0$ of (13).

The transformation which was carried out in the first example always makes it possible to reduce the concept of the stability of a motion to a treatment of the special case of the stability of an equilibrium position (or of a 'critical point'). Although the definition of the stability of a motion naturally includes that of the stability of an equilibrium position, the latter will be repeated here. Assume that the differential equation

$$\dot{\mathbf{y}} = \mathbf{g}(\mathbf{y}, t) \tag{15}$$

has the trivial solution $\mathbf{y} = \mathbf{0}$, that is $\mathbf{g}(\mathbf{0}, t) \equiv \mathbf{0}$.

This trivial solution is stable iff for every $\epsilon > 0$ there exists a $\delta(\epsilon) > 0$ such that

$$|\mathbf{y}_0| < \delta(\epsilon) \;\Rightarrow\; |\mathbf{y}(\mathbf{y}_0, t_0; t)| < \epsilon, \quad \forall t \geqslant t_0. \tag{16}$$

Fig. 2.2 now is replaced by Fig. 2.5.

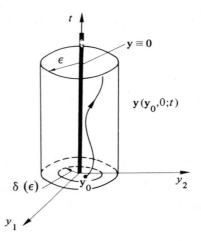

Fig. 2.5. The stability of the trivial solution of (15).

Other than the Liapounov stability definition there are a number of sometimes related concepts which—as was seen in the case of orbital stability—often play a significant role in applications. For example, an important question concerns the influence of additional 'small' terms on the right-hand side of (1) on the behaviour of the solutions. The Liapounov definition allows only for disturbances in the initial conditions without producing any change in the differential equation itself. Although extensive investigations thereof are available, nothing more about this topic will be discussed here (see Hahn 1952, for example).

In applications, it is sometimes a disadvantage that Liapounov theory deals with *infinitesimal* disturbances. Thus, it may happen that a solution is L-unstable ('unstable in the sense of Liapounov') but that it may be considered to be 'stable' for all practical purposes. In this context, consider the differential equation

$$\dot{x} = x\,(a^2 - x^2),\tag{17}$$

where a is a constant. It has the trivial solution $x \equiv 0$ and two further critical points $x = a$ and $x = -a$. All other solutions $x(x_0, t_0; t)$ are given by

$$a^2\,(t - t_0) = \ln\left\{ \frac{x}{x_0} \sqrt{\left(\frac{a^2 - x_0^2}{a^2 - x^2} \right)} \right\}\tag{18}$$

(Fig. 2.6). The solution $x = 0$ is unstable whereas the solutions $x = +|a|$, $x = -|a|$ are stable (even asymptotically stable). If a is a very small number, however, then $x = 0$ may still be called *practically stable* for certain applications.

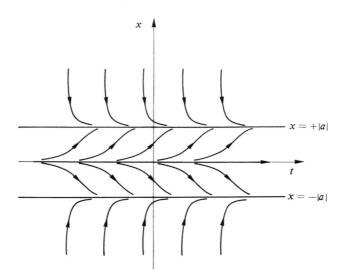

Fig. 2.6. The stability of the solutions of (17)

Outside of the fact that a solution is stable, it thus is also important to know how far the 'disturbed' solutions will separate from the motion being investigated. Naturally, one may similarly have *practical instability* simultaneous with Liapounov stability. In Fig. 2.7, the example of a particle is again used to illustrate this possibility. Just what constitutes practical stability or practical instability in an actual situation naturally depends on the orders of magnitude involved in the technical or physical problem under investigation.

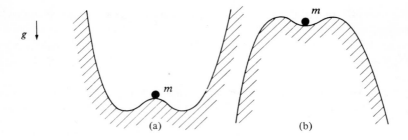

Fig. 2.7. The concept of practical stability. (a) L-unstable, eventually 'practically stable'; (b) L-stable, eventually 'practically unstable'.

The stability behaviour of any given solution of (1) may be determined without difficulty, if the general solution is known. However, for non-linear differential equations this is almost never the case; with few exceptions, one generally knows only certain particular, usually stationary or periodic solutions whose stability then is of interest.† It thus becomes necessary to search for means to clarify the stability behaviour without solving the differential equations. Generally, the transformation (8) is introduced and one then has available at least two different methods for attacking the problem, both of which were developed by Liapounov. The right-hand side of eqn (10) may be developed in a Taylor series with respect to $\mathbf{y}$,

$$\dot{\mathbf{y}} = \mathbf{A}(t)\,\mathbf{y} + \mathbf{n}(\mathbf{y}, t),\qquad\qquad(19)$$

where $\mathbf{n}(\mathbf{y}, t)$ stands for all terms of higher than first order, that is, for all of the non-linear terms in eqn (10). Since a general solution of (19) is usually not available, one is led to try to deduce results from the linearized differential equation

$$\dot{\mathbf{y}} = \mathbf{A}(t)\,\mathbf{y}.\qquad\qquad(20)$$

It is a good deal easier to investigate the stability of the trivial solution of (20) rather than the stability of the solutions $\mathbf{y} = \mathbf{0}$ of (10) since the theory of linear differential equations is more complete. Liapounov was the first to obtain conditions subject to which the stability results obtained for (20) are also valid for eqn (10); this result is also called the method of first approximation.

---

†Such stationary or periodic solutions often provide the basis for extensive investigations about the general character of the solutions. As noted by Poincaré, they are thus of great importance: 'Ce qui nous rend ces solutions périodiques si précieuses, c'est qu'elles sont, pour ainsi dire, la seule brèche par où nous puissons essayer de pénétrer dans une place jusqu'ici réputée inabordable.'

More generally, *Liapounov's first method* consists of the direct investigation of the solutions of (19). Usually, such a solution must be sought in series form. Another approach is given by what is now called *Liapounov's second* or *direct method*. It is based on a direct estimate of the solutions of eqn (10). Consider the example:

$$\left.\begin{array}{l} \dot{y}_1 = -y_2 + a\,y_1^3, \\[2mm] \dot{y}_2 = y_1 + a\,y_2^3, \end{array}\right\} \tag{21}$$

where a is a constant. The stability of the trivial solution $\mathbf{y} = \mathbf{0}$ may be investigated, even though the general solution of equations (21) is not immediately available. Toward this purpose, the time derivative of $\frac{1}{2}|\mathbf{y}(t)|^2$ for an (unknown) solution $\mathbf{y}(t)$ of (21) is computed. The result is

$$\frac{1}{2}\frac{d}{dt}(y_1^2(t) + y_2^2(t)) = y_1(t)\,\dot{y}_1(t) + y_2(t)\dot{y}_2(t)$$

$$= y_1(t)\{-y_2(t) + a\,y_1^3(t)\} + y_2(t)\{y_1(t) + a\,y_2^3(t)\}$$

$$= a\,(y_1^4(t) + y_2^4(t)). \tag{22}$$

For $a > 0$ the norm of all of the (non-trivial) solutions grows beyond all bounds so that the solution $\mathbf{y} = \mathbf{0}$ is unstable; for $a < 0$, however, it is asymptotically stable. For $a = 0$, $\mathbf{y} = \mathbf{0}$ is stable but not asymptotically stable (this is also called *weakly stable*).

If one considers the linearized problem

$$\left.\begin{array}{l} \dot{y}_1 = -y_2, \\[2mm] \dot{y}_2 = y_1 \end{array}\right\} \tag{23}$$

with the general solution

$$\left.\begin{array}{l} y_1(t) = y_{10}\cos t - y_{20}\sin t, \\[2mm] y_2(t) = y_{10}\sin t + y_{20}\cos t, \end{array}\right\} \tag{24}$$

then it is apparent that the corresponding trivial solution is always weakly stable (eqns (23) are those of the linear oscillator). Thus, the linearized equations here yield no valid information concerning the stability of the non-linear system. In many other cases, however, the deductions for the linear system are equally valid for the complete non-linear system. Some criteria for such an equivalence will be given in sections 2.4 and 2.5.

2.2. The direct method of Liapounov

The direct method may be used to investigate the stability of the trivial solution of

$$\dot{\mathbf{x}} = \mathbf{f}(\mathbf{x}, t) \tag{25}$$

without knowing the general solution or even an approximation thereof. For this purpose, one needs functions $V(\mathbf{x}, t): \mathbb{R}^{n+1} \to \mathbb{R}$, $V(\mathbf{x}, t) \in C^1$ (in other words: V is a mapping from the $(n + 1)$-dimensional real Euclidean space into the reals; V has continuous first partial derivatives with respect to all of its variables), with the property $V(\mathbf{0}, t) \equiv 0$, defined in a neighbourhood of the point $\mathbf{x} = \mathbf{0}$ in phase space for all $t \geqslant t_0$.

First, *time-independent* functions of this type will be considered. In the following, some properties of $V(\mathbf{x})$ will be used frequently and it is convenient to list the corresponding definitions.

The function $V(\mathbf{x})$ is positive definite iff there exists an $h > 0$ such that $V(\mathbf{x}) > 0$ for $0 < |\mathbf{x}| \leqslant h$.

The function $V(\mathbf{x})$ is positive semi-definite iff there exists an $h > 0$ such that $V(\mathbf{x}) \geqslant 0$ for $0 < |\mathbf{x}| \leqslant h$ (in every arbitrarily small neighbourhood of $\mathbf{x} = \mathbf{0}$ there may be points such that $V = 0$).

Negative definiteness is analogously defined.

The function $V(\mathbf{x})$ is indefinite iff it is neither definite nor semi-definite. In that case, every arbitrarily small neighbourhood of $\mathbf{x} = \mathbf{0}$ contains points for which V takes on positive values, as well as points for which V takes on negative values.

Consider some *examples* for $n = 3$:

$V(\mathbf{x}) = x_1^2 + x_2^2 + x_3^4$ is positive definite (h is arbitrary);

$V(\mathbf{x}) = x_1^2 + 2x_1 x_2 + 3x_2^2 + x_3^2$ is positive definite (h is arbitrary);

$V(\mathbf{x}) = x_1^2 + x_2^2 + x_3^2 - x_3^3$ is positive definite (for sufficiently small h);

$V(\mathbf{x}) = x_1^2 + x_2^2 + 2x_1 x_2 + x_3^2$ is positive semi-definite;

$V(\mathbf{x}) = x_1^2 + x_2^2$ is positive semi-definite;

$V(\mathbf{x}) = x_1$ is indefinite; and

$$V(\mathbf{x}) = x_1^2 + x_2^2 - x_3^4 \qquad \text{is indefinite.}$$

To check the definiteness or indefiniteness of a function, one would like to have as general criteria as possible. Unfortunately, criteria exist for only fairly simple functions $V(\mathbf{x})$.

If one has

$$V(\lambda\mathbf{x}) = \lambda^m V(\mathbf{x}) \qquad (26)$$

for arbitrary λ and $\mathbf{x}$, then $V(\mathbf{x})$ is called a 'form of order m'. It is immediately clear that a form is definite or indefinite on all of $\mathbb{R}^n$ as long as the same is valid in only a neighbourhood of $\mathbf{x} = \mathbf{0}$. Furthermore, a form with odd order certainly is always indefinite, whereas a form of even order may be definite, indefinite, or semi-definite. A simple criterion exists only for quadratic forms which are, of course, given by

$$V(\mathbf{x}) = \frac{1}{2} \mathbf{x}^T \mathbf{A}\,\mathbf{x}, \qquad \mathbf{A}^T = \mathbf{A} = (a_{ij}). \qquad (27)$$

Here, a theorem due to Sylvester applies: *A necessary and sufficient condition for the positive definiteness of the form (27) is*

$$a_{11} > 0, \quad \begin{vmatrix} a_{11} & a_{12} \\ a_{21} & a_{22} \end{vmatrix} > 0, \ldots, \quad \begin{vmatrix} a_{11} & a_{12} & \cdots & a_{1n} \\ a_{21} & a_{22} & \cdots & a_{2n} \\ \cdot & & & \cdot \\ \cdot & & & \cdot \\ a_{n1} & a_{n2} & \cdots & a_{nn} \end{vmatrix} > 0.$$

This theorem is proven in Bellman (1969), for example.

Now, let $V(\mathbf{x})$ be a positive definite (indefinite) form of order m. Then it is easy to prove the following theorem:

There exists a number $a > 0$, depending only on $V(\mathbf{x})$, such that

$$V(\mathbf{x}) + W(\mathbf{x}) \qquad (28)$$

is also positive definite (indefinite), where $W(\mathbf{x})$ is an arbitrary function $\mathbb{R}^n \to \mathbb{R}$, which satisfies the inequality

$$|W(\mathbf{x})| < a|\mathbf{x}|^m \qquad in \ 0 < |\mathbf{x}| \leqslant h \qquad (29)$$

and for which $W(\mathbf{0}) = 0$.

The proof will be given only for the definite case. For this purpose, introduce $U = V + W$ and note that

$$U(\mathbf{x}) = |\mathbf{x}|^m \, V\left(\frac{\mathbf{x}}{|\mathbf{x}|}\right) + W(\mathbf{x}) \geqslant a|\mathbf{x}|^m + W(\mathbf{x}) \tag{30}$$

where $a = \min\limits_{|\mathbf{x}|=1} V(\mathbf{x})$; from condition (29) it then follows that $U = V + W$ is also definite.

This theorem has the immediate corollary: *If $V(\mathbf{x})$ is a definite (indefinite) form, then the same is true for*

$$U(\mathbf{x}) = V(\mathbf{x}) + W(\mathbf{x}),$$

provided $W(\mathbf{x})$ is a form of the same order with sufficiently small coefficients.

Finally, consider an arbitrary function $V(\mathbf{x})$ which has a Taylor series expansion about $\mathbf{x} = \mathbf{0}$. Write this expansion as the sum

$$V(\mathbf{x}) = V_m(\mathbf{x}) + V^*(\mathbf{x}), \tag{31}$$

where $V_m(\mathbf{x})$ is a form of order m representing the non-vanishing terms of lowest order in the expansion of V, whereas all of the terms of higher order are contained in $V^*(\mathbf{x})$. Then one may consider $V^*(\mathbf{x})$ itself as an mth order form whose coefficients are themselves continuous functions of $\mathbf{x}$ vanishing for $\mathbf{x} = \mathbf{0}$. From this then follows the theorem:

If V_m is definite (indefinite), then $V = V_m + V^*$ is also definite (indefinite).

The definiteness or indefiniteness of V thus depends on the terms of lowest order in the expansion of V, *if these do not consist of a semi-definite form.*

Consider some *examples* for $n = 2$:

$V(\mathbf{x}) = x_1^2 + x_2^2 + x_1 x_2^2 + x_2^3$ is obviously positive definite;

$V(\mathbf{x}) = x_1^2 - x_2^2 + x_1 x_2^2 + x_2^3$ is indefinite;

$V(\mathbf{x}) = x_1^2$ is positive semi-definite;

$V(\mathbf{x}) = x_1^2 - 2x_1 x_2^2$ is indefinite;

$V(\mathbf{x}) = x_1^2 - 2x_1 x_2^2 + x_2^4 + x_1^4$

$\quad\quad = (x_1 - x_2^2)^2 + x_1^4$ is positive definite;

$V(\mathbf{x}) = x_1^2 - 2x_1 x_2^2 + x_2^4 + x_1^4 + x_1 x_2^5$ is indefinite.

On the parabola $x_1 = x_2^2$ the last of the functions $V(\mathbf{x})$ above takes on values which are given by $V = x_2^7 + x_2^8$ and it changes sign on this curve at the origin of coordinates. It thus is apparent that the addition of terms of higher order may eliminate the definiteness or indefiniteness of a function $V(\mathbf{x})$, if $V(\mathbf{x})$ is not a form.

The theorem about the definiteness of $V = V_m + V^*$ still is valid even if one does not assume that V^* begins with the terms of order $m + 1$, but instead demands that there exist numbers $a > 0$, $\alpha > 0$ such that

$$|V^*(\mathbf{x})| < a \, |\mathbf{x}|^{m+\alpha}$$

holds in a neighbourhood $|\mathbf{x}| \leqslant h$ of $\mathbf{x} = \mathbf{0}$.

If $V(\mathbf{x})$ is positive definite, then, for sufficiently small c, $V(\mathbf{x}) = c$ corresponds to a one-parameter family of hypersurfaces which contain the point $\mathbf{x} = \mathbf{0}$ in their interior (see Fig. 2.8).

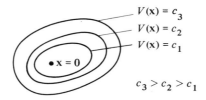

Fig. 2.8. The geometric interpretation of the positive definite function $V(\mathbf{x})$.

Until now, just functions depending only on $\mathbf{x}$ and not on t have been considered. Now, a dependence on t is also admitted.†

The function $V(\mathbf{x}, t)$ is positive definite iff there exists a positive definite function $W(\mathbf{x})$, independent of t, such that the inequality $V(\mathbf{x}, t) \geqslant W(\mathbf{x})$, $\forall t \geqslant t_0$ is satisfied for $|\mathbf{x}| < h$.

The function $V(\mathbf{x}, t) = e^{-t} |\mathbf{x}|^2$ is not positive definite, since it tends to zero for $t \to \infty$; the function $V(\mathbf{x}, t) = (2 + \sin t) |\mathbf{x}|^2$, however, is definite. The geometric interpretation of a positive definite function $V(\mathbf{x}, t)$ is obvious.

The function $V(\mathbf{x}, t)$ is positive semi-definite iff it takes on no negative values in the neighbourhood $|\mathbf{x}| < h$, for sufficiently small h, and for $t \geqslant t_0$. Thus, semi-definiteness here is defined in the same manner as in the time-independent case; the same holds for indefiniteness. The definitions for negative definiteness and of negative semi-definiteness are analogous.

†With this it then is possible to cite the theorems for the general case where the time appears explicitly on the right-hand side of (25). The examples, however, will generally be restricted to the treatment of autonomous (that is, time-independent) problems. Simple, non-autonomous problems are treated in the exercises.

A further definition which was unnecessary in the time-independent case now is needed:

The function $V(\mathbf{x}, t)$ is uniformly small iff there exists a positive definite function $W(\mathbf{x})$ such that the inequality $|V(\mathbf{x}, t)| \leqslant W(\mathbf{x})$, $\forall t \geqslant t_0$ is satisfied for $|\mathbf{x}| \leqslant h$.

Thus, the function $V(\mathbf{x}, t) = |\mathbf{x}| \sin t$ is uniformly small; the function $V(\mathbf{x}, t) = \sin\{t(x_1 + \ldots + x_n)\}$, however, is not.

These functions, previously discussed, may now be used to formulate the Liapounov stability and instability theorems for the stability of the trivial solution of (25).

First stability theorem. *If there is a positive definite function $V(\mathbf{x}, t)$ for (25) such that*

$$\dot{V}(\mathbf{x}, t) = \frac{\partial V}{\partial t} + \text{grad } V \cdot \mathbf{f}(\mathbf{x}, t)$$

is negative semi-definite or vanishes identically, then the trivial solution of (25) is stable.

Second stability theorem. *If there is a positive definite and uniformly small function $V(\mathbf{x}, t)$ for (25) such that $V(\mathbf{x}, t)$ is negative definite, then the trivial solution of (25) is asymptotically stable.*

Liapounov's instability theorem. *If there is a uniformly small function $V(\mathbf{x}, t)$ for (25) such that $\dot{V}(\mathbf{x}, t)$ is positive definite, whereas $V(\mathbf{x}, t)$ may take on positive values for arbitrarily small $\mathbf{x}$ and arbitrarily large $t > t_0$, then the trivial solution is unstable.*

All three of these theorems can be proven by simple geometric means (for example, see Malkin 1959). In particular, in the autonomous case the second theorem is based on the fact that the trivial solution certainly is asymptotically stable if all of the solution trajectories $\mathbf{x}(t)$ penetrate the trajectories $V(\mathbf{x}) = c$ of Fig. 2.8 from outside to inside. Functions which satisfy the theorems above are called Liapounov functions.

Some applications

(1) Lagrange's theorem concerning the stability of equilibrium. Consider a conservative holonomic mechanical system with kinetic energy $T(\mathbf{q}, \dot{\mathbf{q}}) = \frac{1}{2}\dot{\mathbf{q}}^T A(\mathbf{q})\dot{\mathbf{q}}$ and with potential energy $U(\mathbf{q})$ and assume that the system has an equilibrium position for $\mathbf{q} = 0$. With the *Lagrangian* $L = T - U$ the equations of motion follow from Lagrange's equations

$$\frac{d}{dt}\frac{\partial L}{\partial \dot{q}_i} - \frac{\partial L}{\partial q_i} = 0, \quad i = 1, 2, \ldots, n \tag{32}$$

and may always be written in the normal form

$$\ddot{\mathbf{q}} = \mathbf{f}(\mathbf{q}, \dot{\mathbf{q}}) \tag{33}$$

since $\mathbf{A}(\mathbf{q})$ is assumed to be a symmetric positive definite matrix for all $\mathbf{q}$. The system (33) may now be written as a first-order system. Prior thereto, it is advantageous to introduce different coordinates. Instead of the column matrix $\dot{\mathbf{q}}$ of the generalized velocities, the generalized momenta

$$\mathbf{p} = \frac{\partial T}{\partial \dot{\mathbf{q}}} = \mathbf{A}(\mathbf{q})\dot{\mathbf{q}} \qquad (34)$$

are introduced. The kinetic energy is expressed in terms of $\mathbf{p}$ rather than $\mathbf{q}$ and the *Hamiltonian* $H(\mathbf{q}, \mathbf{p})$ is defined as the sum of the kinetic and of the potential energy:

$$H(\mathbf{q},\mathbf{p}) = \frac{1}{2}\,\mathbf{p}^{\mathrm{T}}\mathbf{A}^{-1}(\mathbf{q})\mathbf{p} + U(\mathbf{q}). \qquad (35)$$

The equations of motion now are given by

$$\left.\begin{aligned}\dot{\mathbf{q}} &= \frac{\partial H}{\partial \mathbf{p}}\,, \\[2mm]\dot{\mathbf{p}} &= -\frac{\partial H}{\partial \mathbf{q}}\,.\end{aligned}\right\} \qquad (36)$$

Obviously, the function $H(\mathbf{q}, \mathbf{p})$ is positive definite if the potential energy, given to within an arbitrary additive constant, is set equal to zero for $\mathbf{q} = 0$ and if it has a minimum there. Furthermore, one has

$$\dot{H} = \left(\frac{\partial H}{\partial \mathbf{q}}\right)^{\mathrm{T}}\dot{\mathbf{q}} + \left(\frac{\partial H}{\partial \mathbf{p}}\right)^{\mathrm{T}}\dot{\mathbf{p}} = 0 \qquad (37)$$

along the solutions of eqns (36) so that $H(\mathbf{q}, \mathbf{p})$ is a *first integral* of the system (36). The function H satisfies all of the hypotheses of the first stability theorem of Liapounov and from this it follows that the static equilibrium position $(\mathbf{q}, \mathbf{p}) = (0, 0)$ is stable. In stability theory this result is known as the Lagrange–Dirichlet Theorem.

Consider briefly two extensions of this theorem: the case of dissipative systems and the case of conservative systems with gyroscopic forces. If the system is dissipative, eqns (32) are replaced by

$$\frac{\mathrm{d}}{\mathrm{d}t}\frac{\partial L}{\partial \dot{q}_i} - \frac{\partial L}{\partial q_i} = Q_i(\mathbf{q},\dot{\mathbf{q}})\,, \qquad i = 1, 2, \ldots, n \qquad (38)$$

where one has $\sum_{i=1}^{n} Q_i(\mathbf{q}, \dot{\mathbf{q}})\dot{q}_i \leqslant 0$. In fact, if $\sum_{i=1}^{n} Q_i(\mathbf{q}, \dot{\mathbf{q}})\dot{q}_i$ is negative definite with respect to $\dot{\mathbf{q}}$, then one has *complete dissipation (complete damping)*. All motions of the system then experience damping (complete dissipation implies the *pervasive damping* defined in section 5.1; not every system with pervasive damping, however, has complete dissipation!). If one again chooses $V = T + U$, then it is apparent that the second stability theorem is not applicable, since $\dot{V}$ is negative definite only with respect to $\dot{\mathbf{q}}$ but not with respect to $\mathbf{q}, \dot{\mathbf{q}}$. However, asymptotic stability of the equilibrium position still follows from Krasovskii's (1963) theorem (p. 82).

Other than terms quadratic in $\dot{\mathbf{q}}$ the Lagrangian occasionally also contains terms which are linear in $\dot{\mathbf{q}}$. The corresponding terms in the equations of motion (32) are called *gyroscopic terms*. These always occur, for example, when a cyclic coordinate is being eliminated (see Gantmacher 1970). It may easily be checked that even then a minimum of the potential energy still provides a sufficient condition for stability—in the case of complete dissipation, even for asymptotic stability.

In elastomechanics the Lagrange–Dirichlet stability theorem often is used as the definition of stability. There, an equilibrium position is stable iff the corresponding potential energy takes on a relative minimum, and it is unstable otherwise. This approach is unsatisfactory for various reasons. On the one hand, the concept of stability is best visualized in terms of motion: an equilibrium position is called stable iff all *motions* whose initial conditions are sufficiently close to the equilibrium position occur in a sufficiently small given neighbourhood of the equilibrium (for this purpose, some concept of distance must be introduced). On the other hand, however, the stability of equilibrium positions for *non-conservative* systems for which it may not even be possible to define a potential energy, and that of periodic and other motions is to be investigated also.

The main reason for this approach in elastomechanics is due to the considerable difficulties which may be encountered in the use of a Liapounov stability theory extended to include applications involving partial differential equations.

(2) The instability of equilibrium for a maximum of $U(\mathbf{q})$. Consider again the system described by eqns (36) and choose

$$V = \mathbf{p}^{\mathrm{T}} \mathbf{q} \qquad (39)$$

as a Liapounov function. Write

$$\mathbf{A}^{-1}(\mathbf{q}) = \mathbf{A}^{-1}(0) + \mathbf{B}(\mathbf{q}), \qquad (40)$$

where $\mathbf{B}(0) = 0$ and $\mathbf{B}(\mathbf{q})$ is continuous. From (35), (36), (39), and (40) one then obtains

$$\dot{V} = \mathbf{p}^{\mathrm{T}} \mathbf{A}^{-1}(0)\mathbf{p} + \mathbf{p}^{\mathrm{T}}\left(b_{ij}(\mathbf{q}) - \frac{1}{2}\sum_{k=1}^{n} q_k \frac{\partial b_{ij}}{\partial q_k} \right)\mathbf{p} - \mathbf{q}^{\mathrm{T}}\frac{\partial U}{\partial \mathbf{q}}. \qquad (41)$$

The coefficients of the second quadratic form in $\mathbf{p}$ tend to zero as $|\mathbf{q}| \to 0$, so that $\dot{V}$ is at least positive definite with respect to $\mathbf{p}$, since $A^{-1}(0)$ is a positive definite matrix. $U(\mathbf{q})$ now is written in the form

$$U(\mathbf{q}) = U_m(\mathbf{q}) + U_{m+1}(\mathbf{q}) + \ldots, \qquad (42)$$

where U_k stands for the kth-order terms in the power series expansion of U. Since $\mathbf{q} = 0$ is to be an equilibrium position, one has $\partial U/\partial \mathbf{q} = 0$ and $m \geqslant 2$ follows. By using Euler's theorem concerning homogeneous functions, eqn (41) may be replaced by

$$\dot{V} = \mathbf{p}^{\mathrm{T}} \mathbf{A}^{-1}(0)\,\mathbf{p} + \mathbf{p}^{\mathrm{T}}\left(b_{ij}(\mathbf{q}) - \frac{1}{2}\sum_{k=1}^{n} q_k \frac{\partial b_{ij}}{\partial q_k} \right)\mathbf{p} - mU_m - (m+1)\,U_{m+1} - \ldots . \qquad (43)$$

If U_m is negative definite with respect to $\mathbf{q}$, then $\dot{V}$ is positive definite in $\mathbf{p}, \mathbf{q}$ whereas $V = \mathbf{p}^{\mathrm{T}}\mathbf{q}$ takes on positive and negative values in every arbitrarily small neighbourhood of $(\mathbf{q}, \mathbf{p}) = (0, 0)$. This fulfills the hypotheses of the instability theorem; it has been shown that the equilibrium position is unstable if U_m is negative definite, that is, if $U(\mathbf{q})$ has a maximum, *and if the existence of this maximum follows from the terms of lowest order in the series expansion $U = U_m + U_{m+1} + \ldots$* .

Liapounov already proved this theorem. For an engineer, this theorem is extremely unsatisfactory since he believes that he knows from observation that the equilibrium position is unstable not only for a maximum of the potential energy but generally and without additional restrictions whenever there is no minimum. Furthermore, this Liapounov theorem may not even be used to show the instability of $q_1 = 0, q_2 = 0$, for

$$U = -q_1^2 - q_2^4,$$

since $U_2 = -q_1^2$ is not negative definite but only negative semi-definite. The hypothesis 'U_m negative definite' may not be omitted in the present theorem, even though this is occasionally done without comment (for example, see La Salle and Lefschetz 1967; Hahn 1952).†

Since the turn of the century, numerous mathematicians have concerned themselves with the question of the stability of an equilibrium position of a conservative system in the absence of a minimum of $U(q)$. Painlevé (1897) gave an example and showed that it is quite possible to have stability even in the absence of a minimum of $U(q)$! A general proof of instability for a maximum of $U(q)$ without any additional hypotheses on $U_m(q)$ was not available until given recently by Hagedorn (1971) (including a further, more detailed bibliography). In many practical applications, the stability problem is simplified considerably because of the often present dissipation of mechanical energy: then it is a great deal easier to prove instability!

(3) Stability of the rotational motion of a rocket. For nearly-level flight-trajectories of a projectile, it may be assumed that the centre of gravity experiences approximately linear and uniform motion. The same is approximately valid (at least during short time intervals) for the power-off motion of a rocket. Let β be the angle between the rocket axis and its projection onto the vertical plane of flight and let α be the angle between this projection and the velocity vector. The equations of motion then are given by

$$\left. \begin{array}{l} A\ddot{\beta} + A\dot{\alpha}^2\sin\beta\,\cos\beta - Cn\,\dot{\alpha}\cos\beta = eR\sin\beta\,\cos\alpha\,, \\[2mm] A\ddot{\alpha}\cos\beta - 2A\,\dot{\alpha}\dot{\beta}\sin\beta + Cn\,\dot{\beta} = eR\sin\alpha\,, \end{array} \right\} \qquad (44)$$

where C is the moment of inertia with respect to the longitudinal axis of symmetry and n is the constant projection of the angular velocity in the direction of this axis. The moment of inertia with respect to an arbitrary diameter through the centre of gravity is given by A and e denotes the distance between the centre of gravity and the centre of pressure (the point of action of the resultant R of the air resistance). For small angles α, β the resistance R may be taken to be constant. These equations of motion are derived, for example, in Gantmacher (1970; p. 186 ff.) and they are discussed in Lur'é (1968; p. 238 ff.). The eqns (44) have the particular solution $\alpha = \beta = 0, \dot{\alpha} = \beta = 0$. The stability of this trivial solution is to be investigated.

---

†Even for a system with $2T = p_1^2 + p_2^2$, $U = -(q_1 - q_2^2)^2 - \frac{3}{32}q_2^4$, $n = 2$, the function $V = \mathbf{p}^{\mathrm{T}}\mathbf{q}$ is not a Liapounov function. In fact, one has $\mathbf{q}^{\mathrm{T}}(\partial U/\partial\mathbf{q}) = -2(q_1 - \frac{3}{2}q_2^2)^2 + \frac{1}{8}q_2^4$, and this expression is indefinite, even though U has a maximum for $\mathbf{q} = 0$ (the expression is positive for $\frac{7}{4}q_2^2 > q_1 > \frac{5}{4}q_2^2$ and negative for $q_1 < \frac{5}{4}q_2^2$ and $q_1 > \frac{7}{4}q_2^2$). Thus $\dot{V}$ is also indefinite.

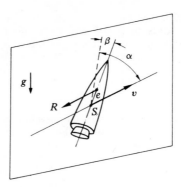

Fig. 2.9. Stability of a rocket.

From the theorems of mechanics, two first integrals of motion are immediate: the energy integral

$$F_1(\alpha,\dot{\alpha},\beta,\dot{\beta}) = \frac{1}{2}A(\dot{\beta}^2 + \dot{\alpha}^2\cos^2\beta) + eR(\cos\alpha\cos\beta - 1) \tag{45}$$

and the angular momentum integral

$$F_2(\alpha,\dot{\alpha},\beta,\dot{\beta}) = A(\dot{\beta}\sin\alpha - \dot{\alpha}\cos\beta\sin\beta\cos\alpha) + Cn(\cos\alpha\cos\beta - 1). \tag{46}$$

It is easy to convince oneself that F_1 and F_2 actually are first integrals of (44), that is, that one has $\dot{F}_1 = 0$ and $\dot{F}_2 = 0$ for all of the solutions of (44). For F_1, for example, one has

$$\dot{F}_1 = \frac{\partial F_1}{\partial\alpha}\dot{\alpha} + \frac{\partial F_1}{\partial\dot{\alpha}}\ddot{\alpha} + \frac{\partial F_1}{\partial\beta}\dot{\beta} + \frac{\partial F_1}{\partial\dot{\beta}}\ddot{\beta} =$$

$$= -eR\dot{\alpha}\sin\alpha\cos\beta + \cos\beta(eR\sin\alpha - Cn\dot{\beta} + 2A\dot{\alpha}\dot{\beta}\sin\beta)\dot{\alpha} -$$

$$- A\dot{\alpha}^2\dot{\beta}\cos\beta\sin\beta - eR\dot{\beta}\cos\alpha\sin\beta + \dot{\beta}(eR\sin\beta\cos\alpha -$$

$$- A\dot{\alpha}^2\sin\beta\cos\beta + Cn\dot{\alpha}\cos\beta) \equiv 0.$$

Unfortunately, neither of these first integrals F_1 and F_2 is definite. Consider, thus, a new integral

$$V = F_1 - \lambda F_2, \tag{47}$$

where λ is a constant which is to be chosen in such a way that V becomes positive definite. One has

$$V = \frac{1}{2}\{A\dot{\alpha}^2 + (Cn\lambda - eR)\beta^2 + 2A\lambda\dot{\alpha}\beta\} +$$

$$+ \frac{1}{2}\{A\dot{\beta}^2 + (Cn\lambda - eR)\alpha^2 - 2A\lambda\dot{\beta}\alpha\} + \dots, \tag{48}$$

where only the terms of second order in the expansion of V with respect to $\alpha, \dot{\alpha}, \beta, \dot{\beta}$ have been indicated. All additional terms are at least fourth order. Clearly, V_2 is positive definite precisely when the two quadratic forms

$$Ax_1^2 + (Cn\lambda - eR)x_2^2 \pm 2A\lambda x_1 x_2$$

are positive definite. However, V then is also positive definite and the trivial solution is stable. From Sylvester's theorem one obtains

$$A > 0, \qquad \begin{vmatrix} A & \pm A\lambda \\ \pm A\lambda & Cn\lambda - eR \end{vmatrix} > 0 \qquad (49)$$

as a necessary condition for the positive definiteness of V_2, that is,

$$A > 0, \qquad A(Cn\lambda - eR) - A^2\lambda^2 > 0$$

or

$$A > 0, \qquad Cn\lambda - eR - A\lambda^2 > 0. \qquad (50)$$

The first condition in (50) is always fulfilled. In order to be able to satisfy the second condition for at least one real value of λ, the two roots λ_1, λ_2 must be real and distinct from one another; this is the case only if one has

$$C^2 n^2 - 4A\,eR > 0. \qquad (51)$$

Whenever (51) holds, one may always choose λ in such a way that V_2 and hence V is definite with the consequent stability of the trivial solution. The inequality (51) provides a lower bound on n for which the stability of the trivial solution is assured. Later, it will be shown that the trivial solution is unstable for smaller values of n.

Note also that the trivial solution here is stable in spite of the fact that the potential energy, represented by the second term in (45), has a maximum for $\alpha = \beta = 0$. This is possible only because the equations of motion (44) contain terms which are linear in the generalized velocities. Under certain circumstances, such so-called *gyroscopic terms* may serve to stabilize the equilibrium position of a conservative mechanical system even for a maximum of the potential energy.

(4) Free rotation of a rigid body about a fixed point. Consider again Euler's equations (13) for the rotation of a rigid body. From mechanics it is known that both energy and angular momentum are conserved. The first integrals thus are known to be

$$\left. \begin{array}{l} T = \frac{1}{2}(Ap^2 + Bq^2 + Cr^2), \\[2mm] \mathbf{L} = Ap\,\mathbf{i} + Bq\,\mathbf{j} + Cr\,\mathbf{k}, \end{array} \right\} \qquad (52)$$

where $\mathbf{i}$, $\mathbf{j}$, $\mathbf{k}$ are the unit vectors in the directions of the principal axes of inertia (for example, $d\mathbf{i}/dt = \omega \times \mathbf{i} = r\mathbf{j} - q\mathbf{k}$). Naturally, the absolute value of the angular momentum is also a first integral, as is its square

$$L^2 = A^2 p^2 + B^2 q^2 + C^2 r^2. \qquad (53)$$

Eqns (14) now are used to investigate the stability of the particular solution $p = \omega, q = 0$, $r = 0$. In terms of these new coordinates the expressions (52) and (53) result in the two first integrals

$$
\left.
\begin{aligned}
F_1(y_1, y_2, y_3) &= Ay_1^2 + By_2^2 + Cy_3^2 + 2A\omega y_1, \\
F_2(y_1, y_2, y_3) &= A^2 y_1^2 + B^2 y_2^2 + C^2 y_3^2 + 2A^2 \omega y_1.
\end{aligned}
\right\} \tag{54}
$$

With $2A\omega y_1 = F_1 - Ay_1^2 - By_2^2 - Cy_3^2$ it follows that

$$
\begin{aligned}
F_3(y_1, y_2, y_3) &= A^2 y_1^2 + B^2 y_2^2 + C^2 y_3^2 - A^2 y_1^2 - ABy_2^2 - ACy_3^2 \\
&= B(B - A)y_2^2 + C(C - A)y_3^2
\end{aligned} \tag{55}
$$

is a first integral and, naturally, that

$$
\begin{aligned}
F(y_1, y_2, y_3) &= F_1^2 \pm F_3 \\
&= \{Ay_1^2 + By_2^2 + Cy_3^2 + 2A\omega y_1\}^2 \pm \\
&\quad \pm \{B(B - A)y_2^2 + C(C - A)y_3^2\}
\end{aligned} \tag{56}
$$

also is. However, the function F corresponding to the upper sign is positive definite for $A < B, C$; it is positive definite with the lower sign for $A > B, C$. Thus, the rotations about the axes corresponding to the least and to the largest principal moments of inertia are stable!

2.3. Supplementary remarks concerning the direct method of Liapounov

The Liapounov theorems considered in the previous section provide sufficient conditions for stability and instability. They contain no hint as to how a function $V(\mathbf{x}, t)$ may be found in a particular case. In problems from mechanics or, more generally, for differential equations which describe the behaviour of a physical system, it is often possible to deduce a suitable Liapounov function by using general physical principles. Thus, one often makes use of energy expressions, various first integrals, or the entropy in certain cases. It can be proven (see Krasovskii 1963, for example) that for every differential equation with the trivial solution $\mathbf{x} = \mathbf{0}$ there indeed exists a Liapounov function which satisfies the hypotheses of at least one of the three Liapounov theorems. In many cases, however, it just cannot be found. There are a multitude of procedures which have been proposed for the systematic construction of these functions (without solving the differential equation), but they are either too complicated or are suited only for special classes of differential equations. For this reason, much effort has gone into adjusting the Liapounov theorems in such a way that they may be more easily used and, consequently, there are a large number of related stability theorems. One of the most important is the following theorem due to Chetayev; a proof may be found in Malkin (1959), for example. For this instability theorem, the function $V(\mathbf{x}, t)$ need not be defined in a complete neighbourhood of $x = 0$ but only in a 'cone' whose apex is located at $x = 0$. For instability it suffices to establish the existence of a *single* solution which moves away from $x = 0$. In the case of Chetayev's theorem, this solution develops with the 'cone'. The theorem here is cited only for the autonomous case:

Consider the differential equation

$$\dot{x} = f(x) \quad , \quad f(0) = 0 \tag{57}$$

and assume that there is a function $V(x)$ *such that*
(1) in every arbitrarily small neighbourhood of $x = 0$ *there exists a region in which* $V > 0$ *holds and on whose boundary one has* $V = 0$, *and*
(2) at all points of the region defined by $V > 0$ *the derivative* $\dot{V}$ *takes on positive values,*
then, the solution $x = 0$ *of (57) is unstable.*

There is one essential disadvantage to the Liapounov theorems which have been considered. For example, if one tries to prove the asymptotic stability of the trivial solution of

$$\ddot{x} + c\dot{x} + \omega_0^2 x = 0 \tag{58}$$

by using the energy expression $E = \frac{1}{2}(\dot{x}^2 + \omega_0^2 x^2)$, then it turns out that this is not possible. In fact, one has

$$\dot{E} = \dot{x}\ddot{x} + \omega_0^2 x\dot{x} = -c\dot{x}^2 , \tag{59}$$

and it follows that $\dot{E}$ is only negative semi-definite in $x, \dot{x}$. Since $E(x, \dot{x})$ is positive-definite, Theorem 1 guarantees stability but Theorem 2, concerning asymptotic stability, is not applicable. Although (58) may be solved explicitly by analytical methods and one may of course also prove asymptotic stability by using some other function, it would clearly be desirable to change Theorem 2 in such a way that asymptotic stability may also be deduced by using the energy expression. One might expect that this new theorem then may also be used with more success for other more complicated differential equations. Such a generalization of the second Liapounov theorem will be given shortly; another generalization will be taken up in the process. Namely, it is evident from the geometric significance of the direct method that not only may the functions $V(x, t)$ be used to investigate stability, but one may also determine the 'domain of attraction' of $x = 0$ in the asymptotically stable case. The term 'domain of attraction' here is used to designate the region of those initial conditions x_0 which lead to motions $x(x_0, t_0; t)$ such that $x(x_0, t_0; t) \to 0$ for $t \to \infty$.

The following discussion will be restricted to the autonomous differential eqn (57) and to functions $V(x)$ which are independent of t. The set

$$G = \{\mathbf{x}_0 \mid \mathbf{x}(\mathbf{x}_0, t_0; t) \in G, \quad \forall t \geqslant t_0\}$$

(in words: G is the set of all points $\mathbf{x}_0$, such that if $\mathbf{x}$ is located in G then $\mathbf{x}(\mathbf{x}_0, t_0; t)$ is also in G for all $t \geqslant t_0$) is called an *invariant set* of (57). This term now is used to formulate *La Salle's theorem:*

   Let $V(\mathbf{x}) \in C^1$,

$$\Omega_l = \{\mathbf{x} \mid V(\mathbf{x}) < l\}, \quad \Omega_l \text{ bounded,}$$

$$V(\mathbf{x}) > 0 \quad for \quad \mathbf{0} \neq \mathbf{x} \in \Omega_l,$$

$$\dot{V}(\mathbf{x}) \leqslant 0 \quad for \quad \mathbf{x} \in \Omega_l,$$

$$L = \{\mathbf{x} \in \Omega_l \mid \dot{V}(\mathbf{x}) = 0\},$$

and let M be the largest invariant set in L. Then, every solution $\mathbf{x}(t)$ in Ω_l tends to M for $t \to \infty$. (For a proof, see La Salle and Lefschetz 1967).

This theorem may be used not only to investigate the stability of the trivial solution of (57) but also to investigate the stability of *limit cycles*, which will make their appearance later in connection with self-excited oscillations. For the determination of the domain of attraction of $\mathbf{x} = \mathbf{0}$ it is advantageous to write La Salle's theorem in a somewhat less general form, such as may be found, for example, in Krasovskii (1963).

   Krasovskii's theorem: Let $V(\mathbf{x}) \in C^1$, $V(\mathbf{0}) = 0$,

$$\Omega_l = \{\mathbf{x} \mid V(\mathbf{x}) \leqslant l\},$$

$$V(\mathbf{x}) > 0 \quad for \quad \mathbf{0} \neq \mathbf{x} \in \Omega_l,$$

$$\dot{V}(\mathbf{x}) \leqslant 0 \quad for \quad \mathbf{x} \in \Omega_l.$$

If there is no solution $\mathbf{x}^*(t)$ of (57), other than the trivial solution, for which $\dot{V}(\mathbf{x}^*(t)) \equiv 0$ and which lies completely in Ω_l, then every solution $\mathbf{x}(\mathbf{x}_0, t_0; t)$, $\mathbf{x}_0 \in \Omega_l$ tends to $\mathbf{x} = \mathbf{0}$ and $\mathbf{x} = \mathbf{0}$ is asymptotically stable.

This theorem now is used on (58) with $V(\mathbf{x}) = E(x, \dot{x})$; here, Ω_l is the interior of the ellipse $\frac{1}{2}(\dot{x}^2 + \omega_0^2 x^2) = l$. $\dot{V}$ vanishes on the x-axis, that is, for $\dot{x} = 0$. Other than the trivial solution, there is no further solution $\mathbf{x}^*(t)$ for which $\dot{V} = -c\dot{x}^2$ vanishes identically. Thus, the trivial solution also is asymptotically stable and for arbitrarily large l the ellipse is located in the domain of attraction of $\mathbf{x} = \mathbf{0}$ which here consists of the whole phase space.†

---

†The asymptotic stability of the equilibrium position may be proven for (38) in the completely damped case in the same manner as long as the equilibrium position is an 'isolated' one.

A second, less trivial example, which will also be discussed later in connection with self-excited oscillations, will now be treated. Consider the differential equation

$$\ddot{x} + \epsilon(x^2 - 1)\dot{x} + x = 0 \tag{60}$$

with $\epsilon < 0$ (for the case $\epsilon > 0$ the equation is known as the Van der Pol equation).

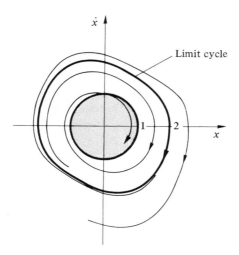

Fig. 2.10. Phase diagram for (60) with $\epsilon < 0$.

The trivial solution is asymptotically stable and its domain of attraction is to be estimated. The corresponding phase diagram is sketched in Fig. 2.10. It contains an isolated (unstable) periodic solution—a so-called *limit cycle*. Since (60) cannot be solved analytically, an estimate of the domain of attraction actually is of some importance here. The Liapounov function is chosen to be

$$V(x,\dot{x}) = \frac{1}{2}(\dot{x}^2 + x^2) \tag{61}$$

with the result

$$\dot{V}(x,\dot{x}) = \dot{x}\ddot{x} + x\dot{x} = -\epsilon(x^2 - 1)\dot{x}^2. \tag{62}$$

For $x^2 < 1$ the function $\dot{V}(x,\dot{x})$ is negative semi-definite since $\epsilon < 0$ was assumed. In order to enforce $x^2 < 1$, $l = \frac{1}{2}$ is chosen, so that Ω_l is the interior of the circle $\dot{x}^2 + x^2 = 1$. Since there are no non-trivial solutions in Ω_l for which

$\dot{V}$ vanishes identically, $x = 0$, $\dot{x} = 0$ is asymptotically stable and the region $\dot{x}^2 + x^2 \leqslant 1$ is located totally within the domain of attraction of the trivial solution, independent of the value of ϵ. This result may be considerably improved upon by introducing a 'suitable' coordinate transformation prior to the application of the theorem. This will be dealt with later in the case of self-excited oscillations (see Exercises 3.2, 3.3, and also La Salle and Lefschetz 1967; p. 60).

Together with this estimate of the domain of attraction, a simultaneous estimate of the limit cycle has been obtained: the limit cycle must definitely lie outside the shaded region in Fig. 2.10.

2.4. Stability by the first approximation (autonomous case)

A discussion of the 'method of the first approximation' will be given next. The method is used to obtain results concerning the stability of the trivial solution of

$$\dot{\mathbf{x}} = \mathbf{A}\mathbf{x} + \mathbf{h}(\mathbf{x},t) \tag{63}$$

by making use of the linearized differential equation

$$\dot{\mathbf{x}} = \mathbf{A}\mathbf{x}. \tag{64}$$

Here, $\mathbf{A}$ is a constant real-valued matrix and there exist numbers $\beta > 1$, $\alpha \geqslant 0$, such that

$$|\mathbf{h}(\mathbf{x},t)| \leqslant \alpha |\mathbf{x}|^\beta \tag{65}$$

holds in a neighbourhood of $\mathbf{x} = \mathbf{0}$.

In order to proceed in the indicated manner, the stability of the linear system (64) must be investigated first and it must then be determined when these results are also valid for the non-linear system (63).

The manner of obtaining a solution of (64) is known from the theory of linear differential equations or, equivalently, from the theory of linear oscillations. The substitution $\mathbf{x} = \mathbf{a}e^{\lambda t}$ in equation (64) results in the characteristic equation

$$\det (\mathbf{A} - \lambda \mathbf{E}) = 0 \tag{66}$$

from which one may then calculate the eigenvalues of $\mathbf{A}$. For the case $n = 2$, it is easy to draw the phase trajectories corresponding to the various combinations of eigenvalues. The following cases arise (Fig. 2.11):

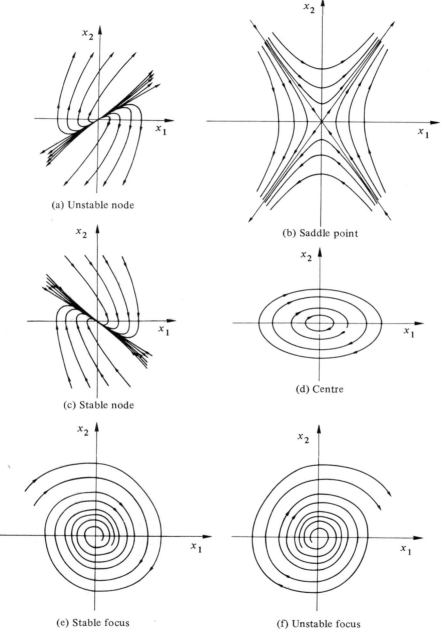

(a) Unstable node

(b) Saddle point

(c) Stable node

(d) Centre

(e) Stable focus

(f) Unstable focus

Fig. 2.11. Phase trajectories of an autonomous linear system with $n = 2$.

(a) λ_1, λ_2 real, $\lambda_1 > 0, \lambda_2 > 0$, 'unstable node';
(b) λ_1, λ_2 real, $\lambda_1 > 0, \lambda_2 < 0$, 'saddle point';
(c) λ_1, λ_2 real, $\lambda_1 < 0, \lambda_2 < 0$, 'stable node';
(d) λ_1, λ_2 imaginary ($\lambda_1 = -\lambda_2$, since $\mathbf{A}$ is real-valued), 'centre';
(e) λ_1, λ_2 complex (conjugates, since $\mathbf{A}$ is real), negative real part, 'stable focus';
(f) λ_1, λ_2 complex, positive real part, 'unstable focus'.

In addition, there may of course be vanishing and multiple eigenvalues; in each of these cases the general solution may be stated without difficulty.

It is known from linear algebra (for example, see Pontryagin 1965 or Gantmacher 1958) that for arbitrary real matrices $\mathbf{A}$ there always exists a coordinate transformation

$$\mathbf{y} = \mathbf{Sx} \tag{67}$$

which may be complex in general, such that

$$\dot{\mathbf{y}} = \mathbf{S}\dot{\mathbf{x}} = \mathbf{SAx} = \mathbf{SAS}^{-1}\mathbf{y} \tag{68}$$

and such that (64) may always be transformed to the form

$$\dot{\mathbf{y}} = \mathbf{Jy}, \tag{69}$$

where only the main diagonal and adjacent diagonal are non-zero in the *Jordan normal form* $\mathbf{J} = \mathbf{SAS}^{-1}$. Here, the matrix $\mathbf{J}$ consists of 'elementary blocks' whose main diagonal consists of one and the same eigenvalue, say λ_i, while all of the elements of the right-adjacent diagonal are unity; all of the remaining elements of the matrix are zero. Thus, an 'elementary block' has the form

$$\begin{pmatrix} \lambda_i & 1 & 0 & \cdots & 0 \\ 0 & \lambda_i & 1 & \cdots & 0 \\ 0 & 0 & \lambda_i & & \vdots \\ \vdots & \vdots & \vdots & & 1 \\ 0 & 0 & 0 & \cdots & \lambda_i \end{pmatrix} \tag{70}$$

Corresponding to every eigenvalue λ_i there exists at least one elementary block. For each distinct eigenvalue there always exists exactly one block of 1x1 form so that the adjacent diagonal vanishes. Such blocks may also occur for multiple eigenvalues. If all eigenvalues are distinct, then $\mathbf{J}$ reduces to the main diagonal form

$$J = \begin{pmatrix} \lambda_1 & 0 & \cdots & 0 \\ 0 & \lambda_2 & \cdots & 0 \\ \vdots & & & 0 \\ & & & \vdots \\ 0 & 0 & \cdots & \lambda_n \end{pmatrix} \quad ; \quad (71)$$

A more typical structure of J, however, is given by

$$J = \begin{pmatrix} & & & & & \\ & & & & & \\ & & & \cdots & & \\ & & & & & \\ & & & & & \end{pmatrix}, \quad (72)$$

where the squares represent elementary blocks of the type (70). The transformation S thus decouples the system (64) into as many single systems of differential equations as there exist elementary blocks. Consider, therefore, a system of order m of the form

$$\dot{z} = \begin{pmatrix} \lambda & 1 & 0 & \cdots & 0 \\ 0 & \lambda & 1 & \cdots & 0 \\ 0 & 0 & \lambda & & \vdots \\ \vdots & \vdots & \vdots & & 1 \\ 0 & 0 & 0 & \cdots & \lambda \end{pmatrix} z . \quad (73)$$

Define a corresponding function

$$V(\mathbf{z}) = -(\gamma - \epsilon)[z_1\bar{z}_1 + (\gamma - \epsilon)^2 z_2\bar{z}_2 + \ldots + (\gamma - \epsilon)^{2(m-1)} z_m\bar{z}_m], \quad (74)$$

where $\lambda = \gamma + i\delta$ (γ, δ real, i = unit imaginary), ϵ and γ are different real constants, and where $\bar{z}$ denotes the complex conjugate of z. From (73) and (74) one obtains

$$\dot{V}(\mathbf{z}) = 2(\gamma - \frac{1}{\gamma - \epsilon})V - [2z_1\bar{z}_1 + 2(\gamma - \epsilon)^2 z_2\bar{z}_2 + \ldots +$$

$$+ 2(\gamma - \epsilon)^{2(m-1)}z_m\bar{z}_m + (\gamma - \epsilon)(z_1\bar{z}_2 + \bar{z}_1 z_2) +$$

$$+ (\gamma - \epsilon)^3(z_2\bar{z}_3 + \bar{z}_2 z_3) + \ldots +$$

$$+ (\gamma - \epsilon)^{2m-3}(z_{m-1}\bar{z}_m + \bar{z}_{m-1} z_m)] .$$

$$(75)$$

It may easily be established that the expression in brackets is always positive definite by investigating the matrix

$$\begin{pmatrix} 2 & 1 & 0 & \ldots & 0 \\ 1 & 2 & 1 & \ldots & \cdot \\ 0 & 1 & 2 & \ldots & \cdot \\ \cdot & & & & \\ \cdot & & & 2 & 1 \\ 0 & \cdot & \cdot & 1 & 2 \end{pmatrix} \qquad (76)$$

of the corresponding quadratic form in the new variables $(\gamma - \epsilon)^k z_{k+1}$. If $\gamma < 0$, then ϵ may be chosen to satisfy $\epsilon > \gamma - (1/\gamma)$, resulting in a positive definite V and a negative definite $\dot{V}$. If one now adds the functions $V(\mathbf{z})$ defined for each block, one obtains a function $V(\mathbf{y})$. If all λ_i have a negative real part, then $V(\mathbf{y})$ also is positive definite and $\dot{V}(\mathbf{y})$ is negative definite. The functions V and $\dot{V}$ remain definite even when (67) is used to replace $\mathbf{y}$ by the real variable $\mathbf{x}$. It follows that the trivial solution is asymptotically stable. Instability may be proven in a similar manner if at least one eigenvalue has a positive real part.

In summary, the following statements are valid in connection with (64):

— *all EV (eigenvalues) have negative real part* ⇒ *asymptotic stability;*
— *at least one EV has positive real part* ⇒ *instability;*
— *there do not exist any EV with positive real part, but there are EV with vanishing real part of such a type that only 'singleton blocks' correspond to them in the Jordan normal form* ⇒ *stability (non-asymptotic);*

— there do not exist any EV with positive real part, but there are EV with vanishing real part of such a type that not only 'singleton blocks' correspond to them ⇒ instability.

Confidence in the last two assertions may easily be gained by means of the following two examples. Consider the differential equation

$$\ddot{x} + \omega^2 x = 0 . \tag{77}$$

If this is viewed as a first-order system, then

$$J = \begin{pmatrix} i\omega & 0 \\ 0 & -i\omega \end{pmatrix} \tag{78}$$

is the Jordan normal form of **A** and it follows from the previous comments that the equilibrium position is stable—but not asymptotically stable. Here, this may be verified by means of the available general solution. However, a consideration of the system

$$\left.\begin{array}{l} \dot{x}_1 = x_2 , \\[2ex] \dot{x}_2 = 0 \end{array}\right\} \tag{79}$$

with

$$J = \begin{pmatrix} 0 & 1 \\ 0 & 0 \end{pmatrix} , \tag{80}$$

indicates that a '2x2 block' corresponds to the multiple eigenvalue 'zero', and instability follows. Again this is easily verified by using the general solution

$$\left.\begin{array}{l} x_1 = x_{10} + x_{20}t, \\[2ex] x_2 = x_{20} . \end{array}\right\} \tag{81}$$

Thus, a necessary and sufficient condition for the asymptotic stability of (64) is given by the requirement that all of the roots of (66) have negative real parts. Generally, it is not a simple manner to determine all of the roots of (66). One thus makes use of criteria which provide assertions about the real parts of the roots of the characteristic equation

$$a_0\lambda^n + a_1\lambda^{n-1} + a_2\lambda^{n-2} + \ldots + a_{n-1}\lambda + a_n = 0, \ a_0 > 0 \tag{82}$$

without having to resort to an actual solution of the equation. The most important of these criteria is a *theorem due to Hurwitz*.

Use the coefficients of (82) to construct the minors

$$\Delta_1 = a_1, \quad \Delta_2 = \begin{vmatrix} a_1 & a_0 \\ a_3 & a_2 \end{vmatrix}, \quad \Delta_3 = \begin{vmatrix} a_1 & a_0 & 0 \\ a_3 & a_2 & a_1 \\ a_5 & a_4 & a_3 \end{vmatrix},$$

$$\Delta_n = \begin{vmatrix} a_1 & a_0 & 0 & 0 & \cdots & 0 \\ a_3 & a_2 & a_1 & a_0 & \cdots & 0 \\ \vdots & & & & & \vdots \\ \vdots & & & & & \vdots \\ a_{2n-1} & a_{2n-2} & a_{2n-3} & & \cdots & a_n \end{vmatrix} = a_n \Delta_{n-1};$$

$$\quad (83)$$

*then a necessary and sufficient condition assuring that all of the roots of (82)
have negative real parts is given by*

$$\Delta_1 > 0, \quad \Delta_2 > 0, \quad \ldots, \quad \Delta_{n-1} > 0, \quad a_n > 0 \qquad (84)$$

(For a proof, see Chetayev 1961, for example.)

An application of Hurwitz's theorem to the quadratic equation

$$a_0 x^2 + a_1 x + a_2 = 0, \quad a_0 > 0 \qquad (85)$$

yields

$$a_1 > 0, \quad \begin{vmatrix} a_1 & a_0 \\ 0 & a_2 \end{vmatrix} = a_1 a_2 > 0, \qquad (86)$$

which may be replaced by the conditions $a_0 > 0, a_1 > 0, a_2 > 0$.

For the cubic equation

$$a_0 x^3 + a_1 x^2 + a_2 x + a_3 = 0, \quad a_0 > 0 \qquad (87)$$

one obtains

$$a_1 > 0, \quad \begin{vmatrix} a_1 & a_0 \\ a_3 & a_2 \end{vmatrix} = a_1 a_2 - a_3 a_0 > 0, \quad a_3 > 0, \tag{88}$$

and for the quartic equation

$$a_0 x^4 + a_1 x^3 + a_2 x^2 + a_3 x + a_4 = 0, \quad a_0 > 0 \tag{89}$$

the criterion yields the conditions

$$a_1 > 0, \quad \begin{vmatrix} a_1 & a_0 \\ a_3 & a_2 \end{vmatrix} > 0, \quad \begin{vmatrix} a_1 & a_0 & 0 \\ a_3 & a_2 & a_1 \\ 0 & a_4 & a_3 \end{vmatrix} > 0, a_4 > 0 \tag{90}$$

or, equivalently,

$$\left. \begin{array}{l} a_1 > 0, \quad a_1 a_2 - a_0 a_3 > 0, \\ a_3 (a_1 a_2 - a_0 a_3) - a_4 a_1^2 > 0, \quad a_4 > 0. \end{array} \right\} \tag{91}$$

Some additional simplification is possible; namely, the third and the fourth of these conditions imply

$$a_3 (a_1 a_2 - a_0 a_3) > a_4 a_1^2 > 0$$

so that the second condition may be replaced by $a_3 > 0$. Thus, the conditions (91) may also be written in the form

$$\left. \begin{array}{l} a_1 > 0, \quad a_3 > 0, \\ a_3 (a_1 a_2 - a_0 a_3) - a_4 a_1^2 > 0, \quad a_4 > 0. \end{array} \right\} \tag{92}$$

For larger systems, the computation of the determinants Δ_i, $i = 1, 2, \ldots$, n in (84) is rather tedious. Hence, it becomes desirable to replace the conditions (84) by others which may be more easily evaluated. This is the case, for example, in the criterion of Liénard–Chipart, wherein the conditions (84) are replaced by

$$a_1 > 0, a_2 > 0, \ldots, a_n > 0,$$

$$\Delta_{n-1} > 0, \qquad \Delta_{n-3} > 0, \ldots.$$

$$\left. \right\} \qquad (93)$$

These also are necessary and sufficient conditions so that (93) is equivalent to (84) (for example, see Gantmacher 1970). For the example (89), one thus immediately obtains (92) in place of (91).

It will now be investigated in what manner the stability behaviour of (63) is determined by that of the linearized differential equation (64). If all of the real parts of the EV of $\mathbf{A}$ are negative, then an approach analogous to the one described in (74) may be used to construct a quadratic form which is itself positive definite and whose derivative is negative definite on the solutions of (64). This quadratic form then may also be used as a Liapounov function for (63). If one computes its time derivatives on the solutions of (63), then $\dot{V}$ is given by the negative definite quadratic form of the linear case with additional 'small terms of higher order', since $\mathbf{h}(\mathbf{x}, t)$ satisfies the inequality (65); thus, $\dot{V}$ also is negative definite on the solutions of (63)! Also, it follows that the trivial solution of the non-linear eqn (63) also is asymptotically stable if all of the EV of $\mathbf{A}$ have negative real parts! It may even be shown that one may choose an arbitrary negative definite quadratic form $W = \mathbf{x}^T \mathbf{C} \mathbf{x}$ in this case, so that $\dot{V} = W(\mathbf{x})$ on the solutions of (64), where the corresponding function $V(\mathbf{x}) = \mathbf{x}^T \mathbf{B} \mathbf{x}$ always exists and is positive definite. Because of

$$\dot{V} = \dot{\mathbf{x}}^T \mathbf{B} \mathbf{x} + \mathbf{x}^T \mathbf{B} \dot{\mathbf{x}} = \mathbf{x}^T \mathbf{A}^T \mathbf{B} \mathbf{x} + \mathbf{x}^T \mathbf{B} \mathbf{A} \mathbf{x} = \mathbf{x}^T \mathbf{C} \mathbf{x} \qquad (94)$$

the three matrices then are always related by the 'Liapounov' equation

$$\mathbf{A}^T \mathbf{B} + \mathbf{B} \mathbf{A} = \mathbf{C}. \qquad (95)$$

This means that the matrix equation (95) has a positive definite solution $\mathbf{B}$ for every negative definite $\mathbf{C}$ as long as all of the EV of $\mathbf{A}$ have negative real parts (for example, see Hahn 1967).

In a similar manner, one may construct a Liapounov function for (64) if at least one of the EV of $\mathbf{A}$ has a positive real part, and then use this function to prove the instability of the trivial solution of (63). A summary of these results is given by the statements:

— *if all of the EV of $\mathbf{A}$ have negative real parts, then the trivial solution of (63) is asymptotically stable;*
— *if at least one EV of $\mathbf{A}$ has a positive real part, then the trivial solution of (63) is unstable.*

These statements are valid independent of the higher order terms; $\mathbf{h}(\mathbf{x}, t)$ need only satisfy the inequality (65). The linear part of (63) then is also said to exhibit a *dominant* stability behaviour. However, one may also show:

— *if* **A** *has no EV with positive real part but at least one EV with vanishing real part, then the higher order terms in (63) may always be chosen in such a manner that one obtains either stability or instability, just as desired.*

In this case, the question of stability may not be decided on the basis of the linearized equation, but the effect of the non-linear terms must be taken into account; this is called the *critical case*. The solution of the stability problem in the critical case is often quite difficult and may be accomplished only in the special cases where one is able to find a Liapounov function. Systematic investi-ations of various types of critical cases may be found in Malkin (1959) for example.

Now, some *examples* appropriate to these stability and linearization theorems.

(1) Rotation of a rigid body about a fixed point. Consider once again the force free and moment free motion of a rigid body about a point (Example 4 in section 2.2). The equations of motion for 'disturbances' of the rotation with angular speed ω about an axis with corresponding moment of inertia A were given in section 2.1 as:

$$\left.\begin{aligned}
\dot{y}_1 &= \frac{B-C}{A} y_2 y_3, \\
\dot{y}_2 &= \frac{C-A}{B} (y_1 + \omega) y_3, \\
\dot{y}_3 &= \frac{A-B}{C} (y_1 + \omega) y_2;
\end{aligned}\right\} \tag{14}$$

with corresponding linearized differential equations

$$\left.\begin{aligned}
\dot{y}_1 &= 0, \\
\dot{y}_2 &= \frac{C-A}{B} \omega y_3, \\
\dot{y}_3 &= \frac{A-B}{C} \omega y_2
\end{aligned}\right\} \tag{96}$$

and with characteristic equation

$$\begin{vmatrix}
-\lambda & 0 & 0 \\
0 & -\lambda & \frac{C-A}{B} \omega \\
0 & \frac{A-B}{C} \omega & -\lambda
\end{vmatrix} = 0. \tag{97}$$

It has a root $\lambda_1 = 0$ along with

$$\lambda_{2,3} = \pm\omega \sqrt{\left\{\frac{(A - B)(C - A)}{BC}\right\}}. \tag{98}$$

For the case $A > B, C$ or for $A < B, C, \lambda_2$ and λ_3 are imaginary and all three EV have zero real parts: the case is a critical case, that is, the linearized differential equations yield no information concerning the stability of rotation about the principal axes corresponding to the largest and the smallest principal moment of inertia. In this case, stability has already been shown previously (Example 4 of section 2.2) by means of a suitable Liapounov function.

However, if $B > A > C$ or $C > A > B$, then λ_2 and λ_3 are real. Then there exists one EV with positive real part and it follows that the trivial solution of (96) as well as that of the non-linear eqn (14) are unstable. Thus, rotations about the principal axis corresponding to the intermediate principal moment of inertia are unstable!

   (2) The heavy symmetric top. The stability of rotation of a heavy symmetric top about its vertical axis of symmetry will now be investigated. First, the equations of motion are established. The usual manner of defining the Euler angles is illustrated in Fig. 2.12; the $Oxyz$ axis system is fixed in space. It is assumed that the axi-symmetric top rests in a frictionless ball-joint at 0 and that the ζ-axis coincides with the axis of symmetry passing through 0 and through the centre of gravity S, with C as the corresponding moment of inertia. In order to avoid any indeterminacy of the angles ϕ and ψ for the vertical position of the axis of the top, the positive y-direction is taken to be the same as that of the gravitational acceleration (the coordinates of the upright top are then given by $\phi = 0$, $\theta = \frac{\pi}{2}$, ψ arbitrary).

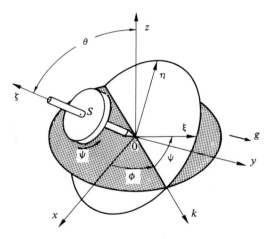

Fig. 2.12. Definition of the Euler angles.

   The potential energy thus may be written as

$$U = mg\,l\,\sin\theta\,\cos\phi \tag{99}$$

with $l = |OS|$, and the kinetic energy as

$$T = \frac{1}{2} A \, (\dot{\theta} \cos \psi \, + \, \dot{\phi} \sin \theta \sin \psi \,)^2 \, + \, \frac{1}{2} B \, (\dot{\theta} \sin \psi \, - \, \dot{\phi} \sin \theta \cos \psi \,)^2 \, +$$

$$+ \, \frac{1}{2} C \, (\dot{\psi} \, + \, \dot{\phi} \cos \theta)^2, \tag{100}$$

where A and B are the moment of inertia about the ξ and η axes, respectively. Because of symmetry, $A = B$ so that the Lagrangian has the form

$$L = T - U = \frac{1}{2} A \, (\dot{\theta}^2 \, + \, \dot{\phi}^2 \sin^2 \theta \,) \, + \, \frac{1}{2} C \, (\dot{\psi} \, + \, \dot{\phi} \cos \theta)^2 \, -$$

$$- \, mg \, l \sin \theta \, \cos \phi \, . \tag{101}$$

The Lagrangian equations for θ and ϕ are given by

$$A \, (\ddot{\theta} \, - \, \dot{\phi}^2 \sin \theta \cos \theta) \, + \, C \, (\dot{\psi} \, + \, \dot{\phi} \cos \theta) \dot{\phi} \sin \theta \, + \, mg \, l \cos \theta \cos \phi = 0 \, , \tag{102}$$

$$A \, (\ddot{\phi} \sin \theta \, + \, 2 \dot{\theta} \dot{\phi} \cos \theta) \sin \theta \, + \, C \frac{\mathrm{d}}{\mathrm{d}t} ((\dot{\psi} \, + \, \dot{\phi} \cos \theta) \cos \theta) \, -$$

$$- \, mg \, l \sin \theta \sin \phi = 0 \, . \tag{103}$$

The angle ψ is a cyclic coordinate from which it follows that

$$\frac{\partial L}{\partial \dot{\psi}} = C \, (\dot{\psi} \, + \, \dot{\phi} \cos \theta) = nC \tag{104}$$

is constant; that is, the 'eigenrotation' n (the component of the angular velocity in the direction of the axis of symmetry) is also constant. For $\sin \theta \neq 0$, eqns (102) and (103) then take on the form

$$\left. \begin{array}{l} A \, (\ddot{\theta} \, - \, \dot{\phi}^2 \cos \theta \sin \theta) \, + \, Cn \, \dot{\phi} \sin \theta \, + \, mg \, l \cos \theta \cos \phi = 0 \, , \\[2mm] A \, (\ddot{\phi} \sin \theta \, + \, 2 \dot{\theta} \dot{\phi} \cos \theta) \, - \, Cn \, \dot{\theta} \, - \, mg \, l \sin \phi = 0 \end{array} \right\} \tag{105}$$

with the particular solution $\theta = \frac{1}{2}\pi$, $\phi = 0$, corresponding to the rotation of the upright top about its axis of symmetry. Experience indicates that this axis position is stable as long as n is sufficiently large.

Use

$$\left. \begin{array}{l} \theta = \frac{\pi}{2} + \bar{\theta} \, , \\[2mm] \phi = \bar{\phi} \end{array} \right\} \tag{106}$$

and linearize (105) with respect to the 'disturbances' $\bar{\theta}$ and $\bar{\phi}$. This results in

$$\left. \begin{array}{l} A \ddot{\bar{\theta}} \, + \, Cn \dot{\bar{\phi}} \, - \, mgl\bar{\theta} = 0 \, , \\[2mm] A \ddot{\bar{\phi}} \, - \, Cn \dot{\bar{\theta}} \, - \, mgl\bar{\phi} = 0 \end{array} \right\} \tag{107}$$

with characteristic equation

$$\begin{vmatrix} A\lambda^2 - mgl & Cn\lambda \\ -Cn\lambda & A\lambda^2 - mgl \end{vmatrix} = 0 \tag{108}$$

or, equivalently,

$$A^2\lambda^4 + (-2A\,mgl + C^2n^2)\lambda^2 + (mgl)^2 = 0 \tag{109}$$

(it is superfluous here to write (107) as a first-order system). A necessary and sufficient condition to assure that there exist no roots with positive real part is given by

$$C^2n^2 > 4A\,mgl. \tag{110}$$

If this condition is violated, then the rotation of the upright top is unstable; if the condition is satisfied, then one has the critical case and the non-linear terms must be taken into consideration in order to draw any final conclusions about stability. It can be shown that the rotation about the upright axis of symmetry of the top is indeed stable as long as (110) is satisfied.

2.5. Stability by the first approximation (periodic case)

In the previous section it was assumed that linearization resulted in a linear differential equation with constant coefficients. It will now be assumed that

$$\dot{\mathbf{x}} = \mathbf{A}(t)\mathbf{x} + \mathbf{h}(\mathbf{x},t) \tag{111}$$

holds, where $\mathbf{h}(\mathbf{x}, t)$ is assumed small in the sense indicated in condition (65). Again, the linearized differential equation

$$\dot{\mathbf{x}} = \mathbf{A}(t)\mathbf{x} \tag{112}$$

is investigated first and any implications concerning the stability of the trivial solution of (111) are treated subsequently.

The square matrix $\mathbf{F}(t)$ which satisfies the differential equation

$$\dot{\mathbf{F}}(t) = \mathbf{A}(t)\,\mathbf{F}(t) \tag{113}$$

subject to the initial condition $\mathbf{F}(t_0) = \mathbf{E}$ (the unit matrix) is called the *fundamental matrix* of the system (112). The specific solution determined by the initial condition $\mathbf{x}(t_0) = \mathbf{x}_0$ then is given by $\mathbf{x}(t) = \mathbf{F}(t)\mathbf{x}_0$. The existence of the fundamental matrix of (112) follows from known existence theorems (e.g., see Pontryagin 1965).

For a constant $\mathbf{A}$ the form of the fundamental matrix of (112) is easily deduced, since the ith column of $\mathbf{F}(t)$ is given by the solution vector $\mathbf{x}(t)$

corresponding to the initial conditions $x_1 = x_2 = \ldots x_{i-1} = x_{i+1} \ldots = x_n = 0$, $x_i = 1$. With $t_0 = 0$ one often writes

$$\mathbf{F}(t) = e^{\mathbf{A}t} = \left(\mathbf{E} + \mathbf{A}t + \frac{1}{2!}\mathbf{A}^2 t^2 + \frac{1}{3!}\mathbf{A}^3 t^3 + \ldots \right); \qquad (114)$$

convergence may easily be proven for arbitrary values of t.

Next, the periodic case is discussed, where $\mathbf{A}(t)$ is periodic with period T so that one has $\mathbf{A}(t + T) = \mathbf{A}(t)$, $\forall t \geqslant 0$. Periodic differential equations of this type were investigated by Floquet. Liapounov later showed that corresponding to every periodic matrix $\mathbf{A}(t)$ there always exists a non-singular continuous matrix $\mathbf{P}(t)$ with the same period T and with $\mathbf{P}(t_0) = \mathbf{P}(t_0 + T) = \mathbf{E}$, such that the transformation

$$\mathbf{y} = \mathbf{P}(t)\mathbf{x} \qquad (115)$$

transforms the differential eqn (112) into the form

$$\dot{\mathbf{y}} = \mathbf{B}\mathbf{y} \qquad (116)$$

where $\mathbf{B} = (\dot{\mathbf{P}}(t) + \mathbf{P}(t)\mathbf{A}(t))\,\mathbf{P}^{-1}(t)$ is a constant matrix independent of t. The solutions of (116), however, have already been discussed in section 2.4. If the fundamental matrix of (116) for $t_0 = 0$ is written as $e^{\mathbf{B}t}$, then the fundamental matrix of (112) may be written as

$$\mathbf{F}(t) = \mathbf{P}^{-1}(t)\,e^{\mathbf{B}t} \qquad (117)$$

in view of the transformation (115). It follows that the solutions of (112) are products of periodic functions with $e^{\mathbf{B}t}$ and stability is determined by the eigenvalues of $\mathbf{B}$. Unfortunately, it is generally not possible to obtain the matrix $\mathbf{P}(t)$ explicitly. If it were, one could compute $\mathbf{B}$ and then use the Hurwitz criterion on $\mathbf{B}$, for example. In stability investigations of the linear periodic differential eqn (112), it thus is common to obtain an approximation to

$$\mathbf{F}(T) = \mathbf{P}^{-1}(T)\,e^{\mathbf{B}T} = e^{\mathbf{B}T} \qquad (118)$$

by numerical or analytical means. In view of

$$\mathbf{x}(T) = e^{\mathbf{B}T}\mathbf{x}(0) \qquad (119)$$

and because of the continuity of $\mathbf{P}(t)$, one has:

— *the trivial solution of (112) is asymptotically stable iff all of the EV of the matrix* $e^{\mathbf{B}T}$ *have absolute value less than one;*

— *if an EV of the matrix* $e^{\mathbf{B}T}$ *with absolute value greater than one exists, then the trivial solution of (112) is unstable;*

— *if the matrix* $e^{\mathbf{B}T}$ *has no EV with absolute value greater than one but has one or more EV with absolute value one, then the trivial solution of (112) may be stable or unstable, depending on the structure of the Jordan normal form corresponding to* $e^{\mathbf{B}T}$.

Note that an EV of the matrix $e^{\mathbf{B}T}$ with absolute value larger than one corresponds to an EV with positive real part for the matrix $\mathbf{B}$ (for example, see Knobloch and Kappel 1974). The eigenvalues of the matrix $\mathbf{B}$ are often designated as the *characteristic exponents* of the system (112).

Thus, if one wished to solve the stability problem of the linear system, one would first determine an approximate solution of the matrix equation (113) on the interval $[0, T]$ with initial conditions $\mathbf{F}(0) = \mathbf{E}$. Thereafter, one computes the EV of $e^{\mathbf{B}T} = \mathbf{F}(T)$ and checks their absolute values. Usually, this procedure would be applied in a form which is tailored to the particular type of differential eqn (112) under investigation (for example, see Malkin 1959).

Ultimately, one may prove linearization theorems which correspond exactly to those for systems with constant coefficients:

— *if all of the EV of* $e^{\mathbf{B}T}$ *have absolute values smaller than one, then the trivial solution of (111) is asymptotically stable, independent of the form of the higher order terms;*

— *if* $e^{\mathbf{B}T}$ *has at least one EV of absolute value greater than one, then the trivial solution of (111) is unstable, independent of the form of the higher order terms;*

— *if* $e^{\mathbf{B}T}$ *has no EV of absolute value greater than one but has at least one EV of absolute value equal to one, then the non-linear terms* $\mathbf{h}(\mathbf{x}, t)$ *may always be chosen in such a way that one obtains either stability or instability of the trivial solution in (111), just as desired.*

Because of the complicated calculations involved in the analytical determination of the fundamental matrix by means of peturbation or other methods, only a few simple *examples* will be considered here:

(1) The Hill and the Mathieu differential equations. One of the most important ordinary differential equations with periodic coefficients is Hill's differential equation

$$\ddot{x} + g(t)x = 0, \tag{120}$$

where $g(t)$ is a periodic function with period T. For example, such a differential equation describes the oscillations of a spring-mass-system with periodically changing spring stiffness, the small (linear) oscillations of a pendulum with periodically excited support, the transverse oscillations of a beam with pulsating axial load, as well as the oscillations of a loudspeaker signal coil. The most important special case arises when $g(t)$ has the form

$$g(t) = \omega_0^2 (1 + \epsilon \cos \Omega t) \tag{121}$$

in which case (120) becomes the Mathieu differential equation

$$\ddot{x} + \omega_0^2 (1 + \epsilon \cos \Omega t) x = 0. \tag{122}$$

Here, *parametrically excited oscillations* as described by (122) with $\epsilon \ll 1$ will be treated. This terminology is founded on the fact that one does not have a periodic excitation independent of x as is usual in the treatment of forced oscillations, that is, a term of the type $P \sin \Omega t$ 'on the right-hand side', but much rather that the system parameters such as the mass or the stiffness themselves are periodic functions of the time. Properly, this type of problem belongs in the realm of linear oscillations.

The stability of the trivial solution $x(t) \equiv 0$ of (120) and (122) is to be investigated. Consider, for the moment, the more general eqn (120) and write it in the form

$$\left.\begin{aligned} \dot{x}_1 &= x_2, \\ \dot{x}_2 &= -g(t) x_1 \end{aligned}\right\} \tag{123}$$

in which one now needs to compute the eigenvalues of the matrix $F(T) = e^{BT}$ (see (118)). One has

$$F(T) = \begin{pmatrix} \bar{x}_1(T) & \bar{\bar{x}}_1(T) \\ \bar{x}_2(T) & \bar{\bar{x}}_2(T) \end{pmatrix}, \tag{124}$$

where $\bar{x}(t)$ and $\bar{\bar{x}}(t)$ are the solutions of (123) corresponding to the initial conditions $\bar{x}_1(0) = 1$, $\bar{x}_2(0) = 0$, and $\bar{\bar{x}}_1(0) = 0$, $\bar{\bar{x}}_2(0) = 1$. The solutions may be determined approximately by numerical or analytical means. The characteristic equation is obtained in the form

$$\begin{vmatrix} \bar{x}_1(T) - \rho & \bar{\bar{x}}_1(T) \\ \bar{x}_2(T) & \bar{\bar{x}}_2(T) - \rho \end{vmatrix} = 0, \tag{125}$$

which may also be written as

$$\rho^2 - 2 a\rho + 1 = 0 \tag{126}$$

with $a = \frac{1}{2}(\bar{x}_1(T) + \bar{\bar{x}}_2(T))$.† The product of the two roots of (126) is always equal to one so that either both roots have absolute value one or one has absolute value greater than one and the other an absolute value less than one. From $\rho = a \pm \sqrt{(a^2 - 1)}$ it follows that for $a^2 < 1$ both

---

†If $F(t)$ is the fundamental matrix of $\dot{x} = A(t)x$, then the Wronskian determinant is given by

$$\Delta(t) = \det F(t) = \Delta(t_0) \exp \left[\int_{t_0}^{t_1} \sum_{i=1}^{n} a_{ii} \, dt \right],$$

and it then follows from (123) that the ρ-independent term in (126) is equal to unity.

roots are complex with absolute value one, whereas the roots are real, one with absolute value larger and one with absolute value smaller than one, for $a^2 > 1$. For the limiting case $a^2 = 1$, one has the double root $\rho = a$; that is, either $\rho = 1$ or $\rho = -1$ as roots of multiplicity 2. From the theorems cited, it now is apparent that the trivial solution of (120) is *unstable for $a^2 > 1$* and is *stable* (weakly stable) *for $a^2 < 1$*. The result for $a^2 > 1$ remains valid even when 'small' non-linear terms are added in (120).

Thus, stability results for (120) may be obtained in the following manner: the solutions $\bar{x}(t)$ and $\bar{\bar{x}}(t)$ on the interval $[0, T]$ are determined first; thereafter, with $a = \frac{1}{2}(\bar{x}_1 (T) + \bar{\bar{x}}_2 (T))$ instability may be deduced for $a^2 > 1$ and stability for $a^2 < 1$.

The stability of solutions of the Mathieu differential equation (122) obviously depends on the values of the parameters ω_0, Ω, and ϵ. The introduction of the dimensionless time τ, with $\Omega t = 2\tau$, in (122) results in

$$x'' + (\delta + \eta \cos 2\tau)x = 0. \tag{127}$$

where $x'' = d^2x/d\tau^2$, $\delta = (2\omega_0/\Omega)^2$, $\eta = \epsilon(2\omega_0/\Omega)^2$, so that the stability of the trivial solution depends only on δ and η or, equivalently, on Ω/ω_0 and ϵ. In the parameter plane of δ, η or Ω/ω_0, ϵ, respectively, there exist regions in which (127) is unstable and others in which (127) is stable (because of linearity, one may speak of the stability of a differential equation, since all of the solutions exhibit the same stability behaviour).

Approximate solutions for $\bar{x}(\tau)$ and $\bar{\bar{x}}(\tau)$ in the form $x(\tau) = x_0(\tau) + \eta x_1(\tau) + \eta^2 x_2(\tau) + \ldots$ may be obtained in the by now familiar manner; this is relatively easy, since only solutions on the interval $[0, \pi]$ are to be approximated so that the secular terms here do not introduce the difficulties which are encountered for approximations which are to be valid for 'secular times' (large values of τ) also.

The stability investigation is simplified still further if one realizes that the stability† and instability regions in the δ, η-plane are separated by curves whose corresponding parameter values result in periodic solutions. Thus, the boundaries of the stability regions in the parameter plane may be obtained by determining those parameters δ, η which result in periodic solutions. This will be done by using perturbation methods based on Lindstedt's procedure. The treatment will be limited to small values of δ and η. With

$$\left.\begin{aligned}
\delta &= n^2 + \eta\delta_1 + \eta^2\delta_2 + \ldots, \\
x(\tau) &= x_0 + \eta x_1 + \eta^2 x_2 + \ldots
\end{aligned}\right\} \tag{128}$$

eqn (127) may be used to deduce

$$\left.\begin{aligned}
x_0'' + n^2 x_0 &= 0, \\
x_1'' + n^2 x_1 &= -(\delta_1 + \cos 2\tau)x_0, \\
x_2'' + n^2 x_2 &= -(\delta_1 + \cos 2\tau)x_1 - \delta_2 x_0, \ldots.
\end{aligned}\right\} \tag{129}$$

It can be shown that periodic solutions are possible only for $n = 0, 1, 2 \ldots$ (with the assumption of another value for n it becomes apparent after a computation of the first approximation that the resulting solution cannot be periodic). Periodic solutions with

---

†More precisely: those regions in the parameter plane whose points correspond to parameter values for which the trivial solution of (122) is stable.

initial conditions $x(0) = 1$, $x'(0) = 0$, and $x(0) = 0$, $x'(0) = 1$ are to be determined, and a convenient way to satisfy these conditions is to impose them on x_0 in the calculations of the first approximation. Consequently, one has

$$x_0 = \cos n\tau \qquad (130a)$$

or, respectively,

$$x_0 = \frac{1}{n} \sin n\tau. \qquad (130b)$$

The first approximations corresponding to $n = 0, 1, 2$ are now computed.

For $n = 0$ with $x_0 \equiv 1$ the expression (130a) results in

$$x_1'' = -\delta_1 - \cos 2\tau \,; \qquad (131)$$

for periodic solutions, one must choose $\delta_1 = 0$ so that

$$x_1 = \frac{1}{4} \cos 2\tau + C. \qquad (132)$$

This yields

$$x_2'' = -\delta_2 - \frac{1}{8} - C \cos 2\tau - \frac{1}{8} \cos 4\tau, \qquad (133)$$

and $\delta_2 = -1/8$ is chosen. Based on (128), one now has

$$\delta = -\frac{1}{8} n^2 + O(n^3). \qquad (134)$$

For $n = 0$, the expression (130b) must be replaced by $x_0 \equiv \tau$, and it is impossible to construct a non-trivial periodic solution from this initial formulation!

For $n = 1$, the procedure is begun with $x_0(\tau) = \cos \tau$ which results in

$$x_1'' + x_1 = -\left(\delta_1 + \frac{1}{2}\right) \cos \tau - \frac{1}{2} \cos 3\tau, \qquad (135)$$

with $\delta_1 = -1/2$ and $x_1(\tau) = (1/16)(\cos 3\tau - \cos \tau)$ as a consequence. From

$$x_2'' + x_2 = -\left(\frac{1}{32} + \delta_2\right) \cos \tau + \frac{1}{16} \cos 3\tau - \frac{1}{32} \cos 5\tau \qquad (136)$$

one then concludes $\delta_2 = -1/32$ and obtains

$$\delta = 1 - \frac{1}{2} n - \frac{1}{32} n^2 + O(n^3). \qquad (137)$$

If the process had been begun with $x_0(\tau) = \sin \tau$, the result would have been

$$\delta = 1 + \frac{1}{2} n - \frac{1}{32} n^2 + O(n^3). \qquad (138)$$

For $n = 2$, the same approach yields the two equations

$$\delta \doteq 4 + \frac{5}{48} \eta^2 + O(\eta^3)$$

(139)

and

$$\delta = 4 - \frac{1}{48} \eta^2 + O(\eta^3).$$

(140)

A sketch of the curves $\delta(\eta)$ in terms of the variables Ω/ω_0 and ϵ in accordance with (137) through (140) yields the wedge-shaped, shaded regions emanating from the Ω/ω_0-axis as shown in Fig. 2.13; although not calculated above, the curves for $n = 3, 4$ have also been included.

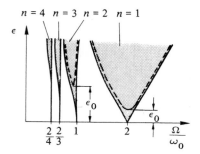

Fig. 2.13. The instability regions of the Mathieu differential equation.

Parameter combinations corresponding to points on these curves result in periodic solutions. For the shaded regions in between, one has $a^2 > 1$ resulting in an unstable trivial solution. For parameter combinations which are located outside the shaded regions, the trivial solution is stable. The instability regions emanate from the points $\Omega/\omega_0 = 2/n$ and they accumulate at $\Omega/\omega_0 = 0$. If one, futhermore, includes linear damping, (122) must be replaced by

$$\ddot{x} + \beta \dot{x} + \omega_0^2 (1 + \epsilon \cos \Omega t) x = 0.$$

(141)

The instability regions then are bounded by the dashed lines in Fig. 2.13. For sufficiently small values of the excitation (small values of ϵ), the trivial solution always remains asymptotically stable and corresponding to every instability region there exists a 'threshold' $\epsilon = \epsilon_0$ which must be exceeded before instability can occur. The linear differential eqn (141) has a dominant stability behaviour so that non-linear terms can no longer eliminate the stability or instability of the trivial solution.

(2) The Mathieu differential equation with additional non-linear terms. Consider again the Mathieu differential equation with additional linear and non-linear damping terms as well as a non-linear restoring force so that the equation now has the form

$$\ddot{x} + \omega_0^2 (1 + \epsilon \cos \Omega t) x + \beta \dot{x} + \delta \dot{x}^2 \operatorname{sgn} \dot{x} + \alpha x^3 = 0.$$

(142)

With α, β, and δ small and of the same order of magnitude as ϵ, eqn (142) may also be written as

$$\ddot{x} + \omega_0^2(1 + \epsilon \cos \Omega t)x + \epsilon(e\dot{x} + D\dot{x}^2 \operatorname{sgn} \dot{x} + f x^3) = 0. \tag{143}$$

From Fig. 2.13 it is apparent that the *first-order instability region*, emanating from $\Omega/\omega_0 = 2$ for the undamped case, is the most important region in any applications; thus, only this region will be investigated here. The method of slowly changing phase and amplitude will be used and special consideration will be given to the non-trivial stationary solutions and their stability.

The time is transformed with the substitution $\Omega t = \tau$; the derivative with respect to the transformed time is designated by a prime with $\dot{x} = \Omega x'$. The stability of the solutions in a neighbourhood of the critical frequency $\Omega_1 = 2\omega_0$ is of particular interest, and it is thus convenient to use $\Omega = \Omega_1 (1 - \lambda)$ where λ is a small factor of the order of magnitude of ϵ. The use of the abbreviations $K = \omega_0/\Omega_1$, $A = f/\omega_0^2$, and $E = e/\omega_0$ along with the omission of terms which are small and of second order in equation (143) result in

$$x'' + K^2(1 + 2\lambda)x + \epsilon(K^2 x \cos \tau + EKx' +$$
$$+ Dx'^2 \operatorname{sgn} x' + AK^2 x^3) = 0. \tag{144}$$

With the transformations

$$\left. \begin{array}{l} x = a(\tau) \sin\{K\tau + \psi(\tau)\}, \\[2mm] x' = Ka(\tau) \cos\{K\tau + \psi(\tau)\}, \end{array} \right\} \tag{145}$$

where $a(\tau) > 0$, eqn (144) may be written as

$$\left. \begin{array}{l} a' = -\lambda Ka \sin 2q + \epsilon Ka \left(-\dfrac{1}{2} \sin 2q \cos \tau - E \cos^2 q - \right. \\[3mm] \left. \quad - Da \cos^3 q \operatorname{sgn}(\cos q) - Aa^2 \sin^3 q \cos q \right), \\[3mm] \psi' = 2\lambda K \sin^2 q + \epsilon K \left(\sin^2 q \cos \tau + E \sin q \cos q + \right. \\[3mm] \left. \quad + Da \sin q \cos^2 q \operatorname{sgn}(\cos q) + Aa^2 \sin^4 q \right), \end{array} \right\} \tag{146}$$

where $q = K\tau + \psi(\tau)$.

It is now assumed that $a(\tau)$ and $\psi(\tau)$ are 'slowly' varying and that the right-hand sides of (146) may thus be replaced by their temporal means (see Section 1.2.2). The result of a choice of $K = \omega_0/\Omega_1 = \dfrac{1}{2}$ for the first-order instability region then results in

$$\left. \begin{array}{l} a' = -\dfrac{\epsilon}{8} a \sin 2\psi - \dfrac{2\epsilon}{3\pi} Da^2 - \dfrac{\epsilon}{4} Ea, \\[4mm] \psi' = -\dfrac{\epsilon}{8} \cos 2\psi + \dfrac{\lambda}{2} + \dfrac{3\epsilon}{16} Aa^2. \end{array} \right\} \tag{147}$$

Naturally, this system has the trivial solution $a \equiv 0$; but, in addition, there are also other stationary non-trivial solutions given by $a = a_0 = \text{const.}$, $\psi = \psi_0 = \text{const.}$ The non-trivial stationary solutions are investigated first.

The elimination of ψ_0 from eqns (147) easily yields the expression for the deviation λ of the frequency Ω from the nominal value Ω_1 in terms of the stationary amplitude a_0:

$$\lambda = -\frac{3\epsilon}{8} A a_0^2 \pm \epsilon \sqrt{\left(\frac{1}{16} - \frac{E^2}{4} - \frac{16}{9\pi^2} D^2 a_0^2 - \frac{4}{3\pi} DEa_0\right)}. \qquad (148)$$

Real values for λ are obtained when the expression under the radical is non-negative; two cases are to be distinguished. If $D = 0$, that is, no quadratic damping is present, then one obtains real values for λ as long as $E \leqslant 1/2$; a_0 may take on arbitrary values in this case. For $D > 0$ there exist non-trivial stationary solutions for all those values of a_0 which satisfy the inequality

$$a_0 \leqslant \frac{3\pi}{16D} (1 - 2E)$$

(see Fig. 2.14).

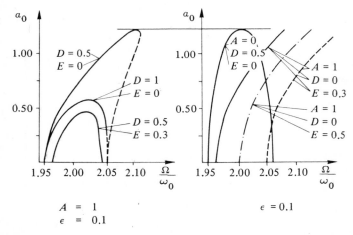

Fig. 2.14. Instability regions of the Mathieu-equation with linear and with quadratic damping and with cubic restoring term.

From (148) it is furthermore apparent that the values of λ become independent of the constants A and D for $a_0 \rightarrow 0$.

Next, the stability of the stationary solutions just treated will be considered. Toward this purpose, a and ψ in (147) are replaced by $a = a_0 + \bar{a}$ and $\psi = \psi_0 + \bar{\psi}$, where $\bar{a}$ and $\bar{\psi}$ represent the deviations from the stationary solution. Their substitution in (147) and the subsequent linearization of the equation with respect to $\bar{a}$ and $\bar{\psi}$ results in

$$\bar{a}' = \epsilon\left\{-\frac{1}{8}\sin 2\psi_0 - \frac{4D}{3\pi}a_0 - \frac{E}{4}\right\}\bar{a} - \epsilon\left(\frac{a_0}{4}\cos 2\psi_0\right)\bar{\psi},$$

$$\bar{\psi}' = \epsilon\frac{3A}{8}a_0\bar{a} + \epsilon\left\{\frac{1}{4}\sin 2\psi_0\right\}\bar{\psi}. \qquad \left.\right\} \qquad (149)$$

These equations may be used to investigate the stability of the stationary solutions a_0, ψ_0 of (147) by means of the method of the first approximation. An application of the Hurwitz-criterion then yields the stability conditions

$$\epsilon \left[\frac{2D}{\pi} a_0 + \frac{E}{2} \right] > 0, \tag{150}$$

$$A \frac{\lambda}{\epsilon} > -\frac{64}{27\pi^2} D^2 - \frac{8}{9\pi} \frac{DE}{a_0} - \frac{3}{8} A^2 a_0^2. \tag{151}$$

The inequality (150) is always satisfield as long as $\epsilon \neq 0$ and D and E are not simultaneously zero. When the values of λ resulting from (148) are substituted in (151), one obtains the condition

$$\pm A \sqrt{\left(\frac{1}{16} - \frac{E^2}{4} - \frac{16}{9\pi^2} D^2 a_0^2 - \frac{4}{3\pi} DE\, a_0 \right)} > -\frac{64}{27\pi^2} D^2 - \frac{8}{9\pi} \frac{DE}{a_0}. \tag{152}$$

For the upper sign, this inequality is always satisfied, that is, the corresponding branch of the resonance curve a_0 (λ) is always stable; it corresponds to the left (increasing) part of the resonance curve in Fig. 2.14. Generally, the condition (152) is also satisfied for the lower sign for certain values of a_0 which are, however, difficult to obtain explicitly. Eventually, one arrives at the following stability results:

- For $D = 0$, $0 < E < \frac{1}{2}$, $\epsilon > 0$ the right-hand part of the resonance curve in Fig. 2.14 is always unstable.
- For $A = 0$, all of the resonance curve is stable, as long as $D > 0$ and $\epsilon > 0$ are valid.
- For $E = 0$, the right-hand part of the resonance curve is stable for all a_0 which satisfy the inequality

$$a_0 > \frac{3\pi}{4D} \sqrt{\left(\frac{1}{16} - \frac{4096}{729\pi^4} \frac{D^4}{A^2} \right)}. \tag{153}$$

It follows that all of the right-hand part of the resonance curve is stable for $E = 0$ as long as $D^2 > A \,(27\pi^2/256)$ is the case.

The resonance curves corresponding to several values of A, D, E and ϵ have been depicted in Fig. 2.14. From the figure as well as from (148), it is apparent that the quadratic damping has no influence on the width of the interval which is cut out of the Ω/ω_0-axis by the resonance curve. The width of this interval clearly depends only on E. An essential difference between the resonance curves corresponding to the case of quadratic damping and that with only linear damping lies in the fact that with increasing values for D and decreasing values for A, the right-hand part of the curve also becomes stable. This is true up to a limiting value of a_0 where the curve has a vertical tangent perpendicular to the Ω/ω_0-axis; this may easily be deduced from (148) together with (152). A further difference consists of the fact that the resonance curves according to the first approximation now are closed, something which was not the case for linear damping.

Finally, the stability of the trivial solution will be investigated. With the substitution

$a \sin \psi = y$ and $a \cos \psi = z$

eqns (147) result in

$$y' = -\frac{\epsilon}{4} Ey + \left(-\frac{\epsilon}{8} + \frac{\lambda}{2} \right) z - \frac{2\epsilon}{3\pi} Dy \sqrt{(y^2 + z^2)} +$$

$$+ \frac{3\epsilon}{16} Az (y^2 + z^2),$$

$$z' = \left(-\frac{\epsilon}{8} - \frac{\lambda}{2} \right) y - \frac{\epsilon}{4} Ez - \frac{2\epsilon}{3\pi} Dz \sqrt{(y^2 + z^2)} - \frac{3\epsilon}{16} Ay (y^2 + z^2).$$

(154)

The Hurwitz-criterion may now be used to investigate the stability of the zero position by means of the first method of Liapounov, where only the linear part of eqns (154) need be considered. This results in the conditions $E > 0$ and $\lambda^2 > \frac{\epsilon^2}{16} (1 - 4E^2)$. It follows that the null position is always stable as long as $E > 1/2$ and that for $0 < E < 1/2$ the null position is stable for

$$\lambda > \frac{\epsilon}{4} \sqrt{(1 - 4E^2)} \quad \text{and} \quad \lambda < -\frac{\epsilon}{4} \sqrt{(1 - 4E^2)}$$

and is unstable for

$$\frac{\epsilon}{4} \sqrt{(1 - 4E^2)} > \lambda > -\frac{\epsilon}{4} \sqrt{(1 - 4E^2)}$$

(see Fig. 2.15).

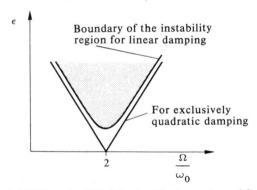

Fig. 2.15. Boundaries of the instability region of first order.

Only the linear damping enters into this result, that is, for $E > 0$ quadratic damping has no influence on the width of the instability region of first order.

The case $E = 0$ still needs to be investigated. The linearization of (154) with $E = 0$ yields

$$y' = \left(-\frac{\epsilon}{8} + \frac{\lambda}{2} \right) z,$$

$$z' = \left(-\frac{\epsilon}{8} - \frac{\lambda}{2} \right) y.$$

(155)

The instability of the trivial solution for $-\epsilon/4 < \lambda < \epsilon/4$ follows immediately.

For $\lambda > \epsilon/4$ and $\lambda < -\epsilon/4$ no conclusions based on (155) can be drawn, since the trivial solution of (155) is only stable but not asymptotically stable. This corresponds to the critical case, and stability therefore must be investigated by means of Liapounov's second method or the direct method of Liapounov.

For $D > 0$ the Liapounov function $V = \frac{1}{2}y^2 + \frac{1}{2}Bz^2$ may be employed successfully, where B is chosen so as to assure a vanishing of the second-order terms in V'. The use of (154) then yields

$$V' = -\frac{2D}{3\pi}\epsilon(y^2 + Bz^2)\sqrt{(y^2 + z^2)} + \frac{3A}{16}\epsilon yz(y^2 + z^2)(1 - B) \qquad (156)$$

with $B = (-\epsilon/8 + \lambda/2)/(\epsilon/8 + \lambda/2) > 0$. For $D > 0$ there always exists a neighbourhood of the point $y = z = 0$ in which (156) is negative definite. It follows that in this case the null position is stable for $\lambda > \epsilon/4$ and for $\lambda < -\epsilon/4$, that is, quadratic damping does not influence the stability of the null position even when $E = 0$.

2.6. Stability by the first approximation (aperiodic case)

In sections 2.4 and 2.5, it was shown that the asymptotic stability of the linear autonomous or periodic system implied the asymptotic stability of the trivial solution of the complete non-linear system. That this is no longer the case when the coefficients of the linear system are arbitrary functions of time is shown by the following counter-example.

Consider the linear system

$$\left.\begin{array}{l} \dot{x}_1 = -bx_1, \\[2mm] \dot{x}_2 = (\sin(\ln t) + \cos(\ln t) - 2b)x_2 \end{array}\right\} \qquad (157)$$

for $0 < t_0 \leqslant t$. It consists of two uncoupled differential equations with the solution

$$\left.\begin{array}{l} x_1(t) = x_{10}e^{-b(t-t_0)}, \\[2mm] x_2(t) = x_{20}e^{-(t_0 \sin(\ln t_0) - 2bt_0)}e^{(t \sin(\ln t) - 2bt)}. \end{array}\right\} \qquad (158)$$

As long as $b > \frac{1}{2}$ the trivial solution of (157) is obviously asymptotically stable. If one now adds a non-linear term in (157) in such a way that one obtains

$$\left.\begin{array}{l} \dot{x}_1 = -bx_1, \\[2mm] \dot{x}_2 = (\sin(\ln t) + \cos(\ln t) - 2b)x_2 + x_1^2 \end{array}\right\} \qquad (159)$$

then the general solution has the form

$$x_1(t) = x_{10}\, e^{-b(t - t_0)},$$

$$x_2(t) = e^{t \sin (\ln t) - 2b(t - t_0)} \cdot (x_{20}\, e^{-t_0 \sin (\ln t_0)} + \tag{160}$$

$$+\, x_{10}^2 \int_{t_0}^{t} e^{-t_1 \sin (\ln t_1)}\, dt_1),$$

a result which may easily be checked. The trivial solution of (159) however, is unstable, since

$$e^{t \sin (\ln t) - 2bt} \int_{t_0}^{t} e^{-t_1 \sin (\ln t_1)}\, dt_1$$

is unbounded as $t \to \infty$. For $t_n = e^{(2n + \frac{1}{2})\pi}, n$ an integer, with $t_n e^{-\pi} > t_0$, one has:

$$\int_{t_0}^{t_n} e^{-\bar{t} \sin (\ln \bar{t})}\, d\bar{t} > \int_{t_n e^{-\pi}}^{t_n e^{-\frac{2\pi}{3}}} e^{-\bar{t} \sin (\ln \bar{t})}\, d\bar{t} = \int_{e^{(2n-\frac{1}{2})\pi}}^{e^{(2n-\frac{1}{6})\pi}} e^{-\bar{t} \sin (\ln \bar{t})}\, d\bar{t} >$$

$$> \int_{e^{(2n-\frac{1}{2})\pi}}^{e^{(2n-\frac{1}{6})\pi}} e^{-\bar{t} \sin (-\frac{\pi}{6})}\, d\bar{t} > \int_{t_n e^{-\pi}}^{t_n e^{-\frac{2\pi}{3}}} e^{-t_n e^{-\pi} \sin (-\frac{\pi}{6})}\, d\bar{t} =$$

$$= e^{\frac{1}{2} t_n e^{-\pi}} \left\{ e^{-\frac{2\pi}{3}} - e^{-\pi} \right\} t_n .$$

For $t = t_n$ there thus follows:

$$e^{t_n \sin (\ln t_n) - 2b t_n} \int_{t_0}^{t_n} e^{-\bar{t} \sin (\ln \bar{t})}\, d\bar{t} > e^{t_n \sin (\ln t_n) - 2b t_n} \cdot$$

$$\left\{ e^{-\frac{2\pi}{3}} - e^{-\pi} \right\} t_n\, e^{\frac{1}{2} t_n e^{-\pi}} =$$

$$= \left\{ e^{-\frac{2\pi}{3}} - e^{-\pi} \right\} t_n\, e^{t_n (\sin (\ln t_n) - 2b + \frac{e^{-\pi}}{2})},$$

and this expression grows beyond all bounds as $n \to \infty$, as long as one has $1 + \frac{1}{2} e^{-\pi} > 2b$!

For $\frac{1}{2} < b < \frac{1}{2} + \frac{1}{4}\,e^{-\pi}$ one thus has the non-linear system (159) with unstable trivial solution and such that its linearized system is one with an asymptotically stable equilibrium position! It follows that the linearization theorems, as derived for autonomous and periodic systems, may not be generalized to the case with arbitrary time dependence without some additional assumptions!

However, even for systems of linear equations with arbitrary time dependent coefficients, one may define parameters which correspond to the real parts of the characteristic exponents defined in section 2.5, although with reversed sign: they are the *characteristic numbers* of Liapounov. These characteristic numbers may be used to describe the growth behaviour of a function $f(t)$. The *characteristic number z* of a function $f(t)$ is defined in the following manner: *the number z is that number for which the two conditions*

$$\left. \begin{array}{ll} \overline{\lim_{t \to \infty}} \, |f(t)| \, e^{(z + \epsilon)t} = +\infty, & \forall \epsilon > 0 \\[2mm] \lim_{t \to \infty} f(t) \, e^{(z - \epsilon)t} = 0, & \forall \epsilon > 0 \end{array} \right\} \qquad (161)$$

are satisfied.† It can be shown that (161) determines the characteristic number of a function $f(t)$ uniquely and that z may also be calculated by means of the expression

$$z = - \overline{\lim_{t \to \infty}} \, \frac{\ln|f(t)|}{t}. \qquad (162)$$

This definition may now be used to define the characteristic numbers of the solutions and consequently the characteristic numbers of a linear system and to obtain a number of stability results (see Malkin 1959).

As it turns out, one can obtain stronger linearization results for asymptotic stability than for instability. As indicated by Krasovskii (1963), this is due to the fact that *uniform* asymptotic stability is a *structural property* whereas instability is not.

A brief discussion of the concept of uniform stability follows. In the stability definition (eqn (2)), δ generally does not only depend on ϵ but also on t_0. If it is possible to obtain a function $\delta(\epsilon)$ such that the inequality (2) is satisfied for all t_0, the solution $x(a, t_0; t)$ is said to be *uniformly stable*. The solution $x(a, t_0; t)$ then is said to be *uniformly asymptotically stable* if $x(a, t_0; t)$ is uniformly stable and if one has $\lim_{t \to \infty} |x(x_0, t_0; t) - x(a, t_0; t)| = 0$ uniformly for all t_0 and for every x_0, $|x_0| < \delta$.

---

† $\overline{\lim}$ means 'lim sup'.

With this in mind, one may formulate the following linearization theorem, proven in Halanay (1966):

If the trivial solution of

$$\dot{\mathbf{x}} = \mathbf{A}(t)\,\mathbf{x}$$

is uniformly asymptotically stable, if $\mathbf{A}(t)$ *is bounded and if* $|\mathbf{h}(\mathbf{y}, t)| < c\,|\mathbf{y}|$ *(c is a sufficiently small positive constant which may depend on* $\mathbf{A}(t)$*), then the trivial solution of*

$$\dot{\mathbf{x}} = \mathbf{A}(t)\,\mathbf{x} + \mathbf{h}(\mathbf{x}, t)$$

is also uniformly asymptotically stable.

In the counter-example (eqns (157)-(160)) at the beginning of this section, the conditions for *uniform* asymptotic stability were not satisfied. There are numerous additional theorems concerning linearization and *structural properties* to be found in the literature. However, this interesting and by no means exhausted area will be pursued no further here.

2.7. Additional comments concerning stability

As was already indicated in the introduction, the Lagrange–Dirichlet theorem of mechanics provided the impetus to the development of Liapounov stability theory. Later works in stability theory also were often stimulated by questions from analytical mechanics. Thus, Chetayev spent more than twenty years on the converse of Lagrange's theorem. The development of stability theory occurred mainly in the Sovient Union, especially during the first half of this century (see Chetayev 1961; Malkin 1959; Krasovskii 1963). A simple introduction to the stability theorems of mechanics may be found in Gantmacher (1970), for example. Of the Western literature, only the two books by Hahn (1952, 1967) and the works of Bellman (1969), La Salle and Lefschetz (1967), Yoshizawa (1975), and Willems (1970) are cited here.

The special stability problems in Hamiltonian mechanics are emphasized by Moser (1973) (see also the works by Mettler (1959, 1965) and Hagedorn (1968, 1969, 1970a, b, c, 1971, 1974, 1975a, b)). The stability of a system with known first integrals is investigated by Risito (1975), who generalizes and extends the earlier results obtained by the Soviet researchers. The special case of a conservative mechanical system with gyroscopic forces is discussed in detail by Hagedorn (1975b). Specially adapted procedures for the investigation of stability have been developed in control theory; they may be found, for example, in Hahn (1967) and in Graham and McRuer (1971). Stability theorems for systems with delay terms are proven in Halanay (1966).

Besides those given here, there are many other stability definitions in the literature. Most of them are related to the Liapounov definitions which have proven to be extremely fruitful in applications. An important theorem concerning the orbital stability of a periodic solution of an autonomous system was proven by Andronov and Witt and is cited, for example, in Malkin (1959, p. 257). It was extended by Schräpel (1969) for a slightly altered definition of orbital stability which seemed more suited to a number of applications.

Detailed investigations concerning parametrically excited oscillations may be found in Bolotin (1961) and in Schmidt (1975).

In the last few years, a number of investigators have dealt with the connection between stability theory and bifurcation theory. In elastomechanics, for example, it has been quite common to use a so-called 'static stability theory'. Generally, one was satisfied there to obtain bifurcation points of stationary solutions (recall, for example, the 'stability' investigations of an Euler column), without treating the stability itself. An introduction and survey of this topic are given in Leipholz (1968). For some more recent theoretical results, see Kielhöfer (1972), for example.

Zubov (1964) extended Liapounov stability theory relatively early to much more general dynamical systems than the discrete systems governed by ordinary differential equations (to systems with infinitely many degrees of freedom, for example). Examples of applications for partial differential equations—where the Liapounov functions are replaced by Liapounov functionals—are given by Leipholz (1969) and by Plaut (1967), for example. The problem of stability concepts in continua is treated by Hagedorn (1975a).

References

Andronov, A. A., Witt, A. A., and Chaikin, S. E. (1965). *Theorie der Schwingungen* [*Theory of oscillations*], vols. 1 and 2. Akademie-Verlag, Berlin.

Bellman, R. (1969). *Stability theory of differential equations.* Dover, New York.

Bolotin, V. V. (1961). *Kinetische Stabilität elastischer Systeme* [*Kinetic stability of elastic systems*]. VEB Deutscher Verlag der Wissenschaften, Berlin.

Chetayev, N. G. (1961). *The stability of motion.* Pergamon Press, New York.

Forbat, N. (1966). *Analytische Mechanik der Schwingungen* [*Analytical mechanics of oscillations*]. VEB Deutscher Verlag der Wissenschaften, Berlin.

Gantmacher, F. (1970). *Lectures in analytical mechanics.* MIR Publishers, Moscow.

—— (1958). *Matrizenrechnung* [*Matrix algebra*], 2 Volumes. VEB Deutscher Verlag der Wissenschaften, Berlin.

Graham, D. and McRuer, D. (1971). *Analysis of nonlinear control systems.* Dover, New York.

Hagedorn, P. (1968). Zum Instabilitätsbereich erster Ordnung der Mathieugleichung mit quadratischer Dämpfung [Some contributions to the first-order instability region of the Mathieu equation with quadratic damping]. *Z. angew. Math. Mech.* **48**, T 256–T 259.

—— (1969). Kombinationsresonanz und Instabilitätsbereiche zweiter Art bei parametererregten Systemen mit nichtlinearer Dämpfung [Combination resonance and instability regions of the second kind in parameter-excited systems with non-linear damping]. *Ing.-Arch.* **38**, 80–96.

—— (1970a). Die Mathieugleichung mit nichtlinearen Dämpfungs- und Rück-stellgliedern [The Matieu equation with non-linear damping- and restoring-terms]. *Z. Angew. Math. Mech.* **50**, 321–4.

—— (1970b). On the destabilizing effect of nonlinear damping in nonconserv-ative systems with follower forces, *Int. J. non-linear Mech.* **5**, 341–59.

—— (1970c). Über Kombinationsresonanz bei parametererregten Systemen mit Coulombscher Dämpfung [Combination resonance in parameter-excited systems with Coulomb damping]. *Z. angew. Math. Mech.* **50**, T 228–T 231.

—— (1971). Die Umkehrung der Stabilitatssätze von Lagrange–Dirichlet und Routh [Converse theorems for the stability theorems of Lagrange–Dirichlet and Routh]. *Arch. rational Mech. Anal.* **42**, 281–316.

—— (1974). On the stability of equilibrium sets of discrete conservative mechanical systems. *AIAA J.* **12**, 1057–9.

—— (1975a). Some remarks on the string problem treated by Singh and Demin. *Celestial Mech.* **11**, 59–73.

—— (1975b). Über die Instabilität konservativer Systeme mit gyroskopischen Kräften [Some contributions to the instability of conservative systems with gyroscopic forces]. *Arch. rational Mech. Anal.* **58**, 1–9.

—— and Rizzi, P. (1972). Die Behandlung dynamischer Durchschlagprobleme mit der direkten Ljapunowschen Methode [The treatment of dynamic snap-through problems with Liapounov's direct method]. *J. appl. Math. Phys.* **23**, 852–7.

Hahn, W. (1952). *Theorie und Anwendungen der direkten Methode von Ljapunow* [*Theory and application of Liapounov's direct method*]. Springer, Berlin.

—— (1967). *Stability of motion.* Springer, Berlin.

Halanay, A. (1966). *Differential equations, stability, oscillations, time lags.* Academic Press, New York.

Herrmann, G. and Jong, I. C. (1965). On the destabilizing effect of damping in nonconservative elastic systems. *J. appl. Mech.* **32**, 592–7.

Kielhöfer, H. (1972). Hilbertraum-Theorie für fastlineare Anfangswertprobleme [Hilbertspace theory for quasi-linear initial value problems]. Dissertation, Ruhr-Universität, Bochum.

Knobloch, H. W. and Kappel, F. (1974). Gewöhnliche Differentialgleichungen [Ordinary differential equations]. B. G. Teubner, Stuttgart.

Krasovskii, N. N. (1963). *Stability of motion.* Stanford University Press, Stanford, California.

Lagrange, J. L. (1965). *Mécanique analytique* [*Analytical mechanics*]. Libraire Sc. Tech. A., Paris. [First published 1788].

La Salle, J. and Lefschetz, S. (1967). *Die Stabilitätstheorie von Ljapunow* [*Liapounov stability theory*]. Bibliographisches Institut, Mannheim.

Leipholz, H. (1968). *Stabilitätstheorie* [*Stability theory*]. Teubner, Stuttgart.

—— (1971). *Instability of continuous systems.* (IUTAM Symposium Herrenalb 1969). Springer, Berlin.

Lur'é. (1968). *Mécanique analytique* [*Analytical mechanics*]. Librairie Univers-itaire, Louvain.

Malkin, J. G. (1959). *Theorie der Stabilität einer Bewegung* [*Theory of the stability of motion*]. Akademie-Verlag, Berlin.

Mettler, E. (1959). Stabilitätsfragen bei freien Schwingungen mechanischer Systeme [Stability questions in the free oscillation of mechanical systems]. *Ing.-Arch.* **28**, 213–28.

—— (1965). Schwingungs- und Stabilitätsprobleme bei mechanischen Systemen mit harmonischer Erregung [Oscillation and stability problems for mechanical systems with harmonic excitation]. *Z. angew. Math. Mech.* **45**, 475–84.

Moser, J. (1973). *Stable and random motions in dynamical systems.* Annals of Mathematical Studies, Princeton University Press, Princeton, New Jersey.

Painlevé, P. (1897). Sur la réciproque du théorème de Lagrange [On the converse of Lagrange's theorem]. *Comptes Rendus* **25**, 1021–4.

Plaut, R. H. (1967). *A study of the dynamic stability of continuous elastic systems by Liapounov's direct method,* Rep. No. Am-67-3. Office of Research Services, University of California, Berkeley.

Pontryagin, L. S. (1965). *Gewöhnliche Differentialgleichungen* [*Ordinary differential equations*]. VEB Deutscher Verlag der Wissenschaften, Berlin.

Risito, C. (1975). Metodi per lo studio della stabilità di sistemi con integrali primi noti [Methods for the study of the stability of systems with first integrals]. *Annali Matematica pura appl.* **4**, 49–94.

Schmidt, G. (1975). *Parametererregte Schwingungen* [*Parametrically-excited oscillations*]. VEB Deutscher Verlag der Wissenschaften, Berlin.

Schräpel, H. D. (1969). Zur Problematik der Stabilitätsdefinition und zur Lösung des Stabilitätsproblems bei nichtlinearen schwingungsfähigen Systemen mit endlichem Freiheitsgrad [Contributions to questions of the definition of stability and of the solution of stability problems in non-linear oscillatory systems with finite degrees of freedom]. Dissertation, University of Stuttgart.

Willems, J. L. (1970). *Stability theory of dynamical systems.* Thomas Nelson and Sons, London.

Yoshizawa, T. (1975). *Stability theory and the existence of periodic solutions and almost periodic solutions.* Springer, Berlin.

Zubov, V. I. (1964). *The methods of Liapounov and their applications.* Noordhoff, Groningen.

Exercises

2.1. The stability of the singular point $x_1 = x_2 = 0$ is to be investigated in accordance with the first and with the second method of Liapounov and an estimate of the domains of attraction of the asymptotically stable equilibrium positions is to be obtained for the following systems:

(a) $\dot{x}_1 = -(x_1 - 3x_2)(1 - 2x_1^2 - 4x_2^2)$,

$\dot{x}_2 = -(x_1 + x_2)(1 - 2x_1^2 - 4x_2^2)$;

(b) $\dot{x}_1 = -x_1^3 - 3x_2$,

$\dot{x}_2 = 3x_1 - 5x_2^3$;

(c) $\dot{x}_1 = x_1^2 + x_2$,

$\dot{x}_2 = x_1 + x_2^2$;

(d) $\dot{x}_1 = x_1^2 - x_2^2,$

       $\dot{x}_2 = -2x_1 x_2 \,;$

(e) $\dot{x}_1 = x_2,$

       $\dot{x}_2 = -a_1 x_1 - a_2 x_2 - (b_1 x_2 + b_2 x_1)^2 x_2 \,,$

       $(a_1, a_2, b_1, b_2 \text{ const.}; \ a_1, a_2 > 0)\,;$

(f)   as in (e), however, with a_1, a_2, b_1, b_2 as functions of time.

2.2.   The direct method of Liapounov is to be used to show that the trivial solution of

$$\dot{x}_1 = 2(x_2 + y_1),$$

$$\dot{x}_2 = 8(x_1 + y_2^4) y_2^3,$$

$$\dot{y}_1 = -2[1 + e^{-\beta t}(2 - \sin \Omega t)]x_1 - 2(x_1 + y_2^4),$$

$$\dot{y}_2 = -2[1 + e^{-\beta t}(2 - \sin \Omega t)]x_2 - 2(x_2 + y_1)$$

is stable for $\Omega^2 < 3\beta^2, \beta > 0$.

2.3.   One of the many methods for the 'construction' of a Liapounov function is the method of *variable gradients* as described in Willems (1970). There, one assumes grad $V = \mathbf{k}(\mathbf{x})$ as an unknown vector-function and uses the necessary condition

$$\frac{\partial/h_i}{\partial x_j} = \frac{\partial/h_j}{\partial x_i},$$

$i, j = 1, 2, \ldots, n$ for the existence of V. Furthermore, conditions to assure the definiteness of $\dot{V}$ are introduced and one then attempts to choose the remaining free parameters in such a way that V also becomes definite.

       Use this procedure to construct a Liapounov function for

$$\dot{x}_1 = x_2,$$

$$\dot{x}_2 = -x_2 - x_1^3.$$

2.4. The double pendulum in Fig. 2.16 consists of two massless rods of length l and of the particles with masses $m_1 = 2m$, $m_2 = m$. Restoring couples $c(\varphi_2 - \varphi_1)$ and $c\varphi_1$ along with damping couples $b_2(\dot{\varphi}_2 - \dot{\varphi}_1)$ and $b_1\dot{\varphi}_1$ are acting at the hinges as indicated in the figure. The double pendulum is loaded by the *follower force* P which always acts along the direction of the upper rod.

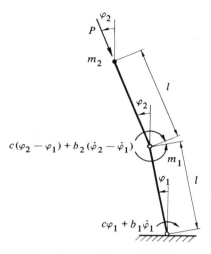

Fig. 2.16. Double pendulum with follower force.

Determine the equations of motion of the system and investigate the stability of the trivial solution for small values of the damping constants. Care must be taken to note that *follower forces* are not conservative, that is, they do not possess a potential. This problem was treated in detail by Herrmann and Jong (1965) (also, see Hagedorn 1970b).

2.5. Give an approximate treatment of the stability of the periodic solutions of

$$\ddot{x} + 2\delta\dot{x} + \omega_0^2 x + \mu x^3 = P \sin \Omega t$$

as determined in section 1.3.3.

2.6. Investigate the stability of the trivial solution $x = y = 0$ and its dependence on ϵ for the following system of differential equations

$$\dot{x} = \left(-\frac{1}{2} + \epsilon a \cos 2t\right)x + (1 - \epsilon a \sin 2t)y,$$

$$\dot{y} = (-1 - \epsilon a \sin 2t)x + \left(-\frac{1}{2} - \epsilon a \cos 2t\right)y$$

with periodic coefficients and with $a > 0$.

2.7. Investigate the stability of the trivial solution $x = y = 0$ of the system

$$\dot{x} = \quad y - x f(x, y, t),$$

$$\dot{y} = -x - y f(x, y, t),$$

where $f(0, 0, t) \equiv 0$, $\forall t \geqslant t_0$, and where $f \in C^1$.

2.8. Investigate the stability of the equilibrium positions and estimate the domain of attraction of the asymptotically stable equilibrium position for

$$\ddot{x} + a\dot{x} + 2bx + 3x^2 = 0,$$

where a and b are positive constants (La Salle and Lefschetz 1967).

2.9. Investigate the stability of the subharmonic oscillations determined in Exercise 1.9 for

$$\ddot{q} + \omega_0^2 (q + \beta q^2) = P \cos \Omega t.$$

2.10. State the conditions subject to which the Duffing eqn (1.139) has an (exact) subharmonic solution of the form $x = A \sin \frac{1}{3} \Omega t$ and investigate the stability of this solution.

3

SELF-EXCITED OSCILLATIONS

3.1. Basic concepts

In this chapter, the emphasis will be on the treatment of systems described by differential equations of the form

$$\ddot{x} + g(x,\dot{x}) = 0 , \tag{1}$$

an autonomous system with a single degree of freedom. The previously investigated systems of type (1) had the form

$$\ddot{x} + h(x)\dot{x} + f(x) = 0 , \tag{2}$$

where $f(x)$ represented the restoring force and $h(x)\dot{x}$ the damping of the system $(h(x) \geqslant 0)$.† With $T = \dot{x}^2/2$ and $U = \int f(x)\mathrm{d}x$, eqn (2) then yields

$$\frac{\mathrm{d}}{\mathrm{d}t}(T + U) = -h(x)\dot{x}^2 , \tag{3}$$

so that the energy $E = T + U$ is monotonically decreasing for free oscillations of the system, and the system tends asymptotically to the stable equilibrium position (provided, of course, that $U = \int f(x)\mathrm{d}x$ has a minimum). There are, however, numerous vibration problems where $h(x)$ does not take on only positive values but also negative ones. The energy of the system then does not necessarily decrease monotonically—it may also increase. In particular, there may also exist an *isolated* periodic solution in the phase plane, generally termed a *limit cycle*.

Considerable insight into such oscillation phenomena is obtained by assuming that the oscillations are quasi-harmonic, that is, that they are described by $x = a \sin (\omega t + \psi)$, where ω is constant and where $a(t)$ and $\psi(t)$ are 'slowly' changing parameters. It is also assumed that the physical process is of a type for which the damping terms can be separated from the excitation terms in $h(x)\dot{x}$. In that case, both the lost energy ΔE_D, due to damping during a full oscillation, and the energy ΔE_Z, provided by the excitation mechanism, may be computed as functions of the amplitude a. One has

---

†Eqn (2) is a special case of Liénard's equation.

$$\int_0^T h(x)\dot{x}^2 dt = \Delta E_D - \Delta E_Z$$

and for a periodic solution one must have $\Delta E_D(a) = \Delta E_Z(a)$, from which one then determines the amplitude (Fig. 3.1).

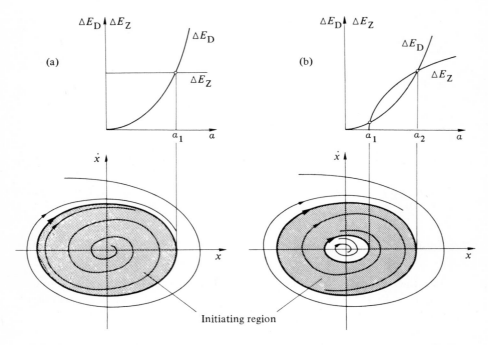

Fig. 3.1. Energy diagram and phase diagram of self-excited oscillations. (a) Soft self-excitation; (b) Hard self-excitation.

In any unsteady oscillation of the system, the amplitude will be increasing or decreasing depending on whether ΔE_Z or ΔE_D is dominating. For the linear damping assumed in Fig. 3.1, one has

$$\Delta E_D = \int_0^T 2\delta \dot{x}^2 dt = 2\delta a^2 \omega \pi, \tag{4}$$

so that $\Delta E_D(a)$ is represented by a parabola. In Fig. 3.1(a), the added excitation energy per full oscillation was assumed to be constant and independent of the amplitude. In Fig. 3.1(b), however, a certain non-linear dependence $\Delta E_Z(a)$ was chosen. In the first case, there clearly exists only a single periodic solution in the phase plane; it provides an approximation for the limit cycle of the system. Until now, there were no isolated periodic solutions for time-independent systems but always a multitude of periodic solutions (for the free oscillations of an undamped system). In Fig. 3.1(a), there is only one limit cycle and it is orbitally stable (generally, this is simply called a *stable limit cycle*). In Fig. 3.1(b), however, there are two limit cycles; the outer one is orbitally stable, the inner one is not.

The situation illustrated in Fig. 3.1(b), where the initial conditions must be sufficiently far from the equilibrium position for the occurrence of a motion which tends asymptotically toward the (outer) limit cycle, is termed *hard self-excitation*, whereas that illustrated in Fig. 3.1(a) is termed *soft self-excitation*. A limit cycle is called *semi-stable* if the phase curve approaches it from the outside (inside) and moves away from it on the inside (outside) (Fig. 3.2).

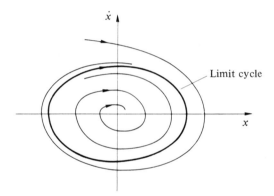

Fig. 3.2. Semi-stable limit cycle.

3.2. Self-excited oscillations in mechanical and electrical systems

Self-excited oscillations occur in many technically important systems. First, an easily grasped mechanical model will be investigated and other, more applications-oriented ones will be treated subsequently.

Consider a block of mass m resting on a conveyor belt moving horizontally with constant speed v (Fig. 3.3). The position of the block is denoted by x which is chosen in such a way that $x = 0$ corresponds to the unstressed state of the spring. The horizontal forces acting on the block are the spring force cx and the friction force R which is a function of the relative speed $v_{rel} = \dot{x} - v$ between the belt and the block. The equation of motion thus is given by

$$m\ddot{x} + cx + R = 0 \quad \text{with} \quad R = R(v_{rel}) = R(\dot{x} - v). \tag{5}$$

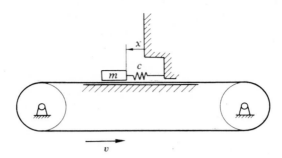

Fig. 3.3. Model of a mechanical system with self-excitation.

If Coulomb friction is assumed, one has

$$\left.\begin{array}{ll} R(v_{\text{rel}}) = R_G \; \text{sgn} \; v_{\text{rel}} & \text{for } v_{\text{rel}} \neq 0 , \\[2mm] |R| \leqslant R_{\text{H}} & \text{for } v_{\text{rel}} = 0 , \end{array}\right\} \quad (6)$$

where the friction force R_G is given by $R_G = \mu N$ with friction coefficient μ and normal force $N = mg$. The maximum static friction force is taken to be given by $R_{\text{H}} = \mu_{\text{H}} N$ where μ_{H} is the static friction coefficient. In actuality, the transition from 'adhesion' to 'slipping' is of course continuous and, generally, the graph of $R(v_{\text{rel}})$ is taken to be of the form shown in Fig. 3.4 (under certain circumstances, the kinetic friction force may also increase again for large values of v_{rel}). The absolute value of R is at most equal to the maximum static friction force R_{H}. If the relative velocity is zero, then R may take on any value in the interval $[-R_{\text{H}}, +R_{\text{H}}]$. For $\dot{x} - v = 0$ and $|cx| \leqslant R_{\text{H}}$ one has $R = cx$, whereas one has $|R| = R_{\text{H}}$ for $\dot{x} - v = 0$ and $|cx| > R_{\text{H}}$. Whenever the relative velocity is not equal to zero, then R takes on a value which is uniquely determined by the relative velocity. At any rate, the friction force R has values between R_{H} and the Coulomb friction force R_G for non-vanishing relative velocity.

Initially, the investigation of the motions of the system will be based on the simpler relationship (6) rather than the function $R(v_{\text{rel}})$ shown in Fig. 3.4. For $v_{\text{rel}} = \dot{x} - v > 0$ eqn (5) then takes on the form

$$\ddot{x} + \omega^2 x + R_G/m = 0 \qquad (7)$$

with solution

$$x(t) = -R_G/c + A \sin(\omega t + \alpha), \qquad (8)$$

that is, the phase trajectories in the $x, \dot{x}/\omega$-plane are circular arcs with centres at $(-R_G/c, 0)$. For $v_{\text{rel}} = \dot{x} - v < 0$, however, one obtains circular arcs about the

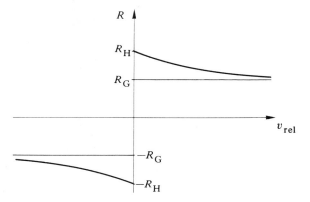

Fig. 3.4. The friction force and its dependence on the relative velocity.

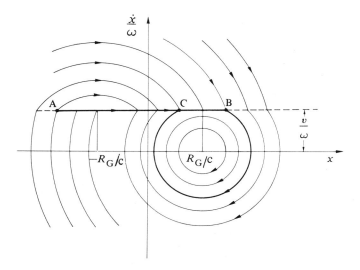

Fig. 3.5. Phase diagram of the simplified oscillator of Fig. 3.3.

the point $(+R_G/c, 0)$. In addition, the line segment AB is a part of the phase trajectories. The coordinates of the points A and B are given by $(-R_H/c, v/\omega)$ and $(R_H/c, v/\omega)$, respectively. From the phase diagram thus constructed, one may obtain a clear picture of the motion (Fig. 3.5). For the periodic motion which passes through the points B and C the block adheres to the belt until the force R_H is equal to the spring force at point B. Then it performs a harmonic motion, its velocity reverses, it moves to the left, eventually again adheres to the belt at C and is taken along to B. The block may even adhere to the belt over the larger length AB but, again, the motion just described will be observed if the block is released at point A. Because of the discontinuity in the differential equation, the solutions no longer depend continuously on the initial conditions.

Within the periodic solutions passing through B and C, there still are a number of other periodic solutions in the phase plane. However, these periodic solutions are no longer present when the function $R(v_{rel})$ given in Fig. 3.4 is used instead of the simplified expression (6). The periodic solution passing through B and C then becomes the stable limit cycle of Fig. 3.6. This case will not be investigated further here. However, it may be seen that there is self-excitation by investigating the equation of motion obtained from linearization about the equilibrium position $x = -R(-v)/c, \dot{x} = 0$. With

$$R(\dot{x} - v) \approx R(-v) + \dot{x} \left. \frac{dR}{dv_{rel}} \right| v_{rel} = -v,$$

$$\left. \frac{dR}{dv_{rel}} \right| v_{rel} = -v = -r, r > 0,$$

and

$$x = -R(-v)/c + \bar{x}, \ \dot{x} = \dot{\bar{x}}$$

(Fig. 3.7), one obtains

$$\ddot{\bar{x}} + \omega^2 \bar{x} - \frac{r}{m} \dot{\bar{x}} = 0 , \tag{9}$$

whose trivial solution is unstable, resulting in an increase of the amplitude of oscillation. The phase diagram in Fig. 3.6 thus contains only the one isolated periodic solution.

In mechanical systems, the cause of self-excited oscillations often is the non-linear relationship between the friction and the relative velocity. The transverse oscillations of violin strings excited by stroking a bow across them may be explained by this relationship, as may be the creaking of a door, the squeaking of brakes, and similar sounds which arise due to 'dry' friction. Other examples of important self-excited oscillations in mechanics are the 'shimmy' in the steering mechanism of a car, the flutter of an airplane wing, or the often observed wind-excited oscillations of transmission lines, bridges, and other structures. In all these cases, self-excitation is an undesirable phenomenon. Often, though, it also is a desirable one: one need only recall the oscillations of a clockwork balance, where one would like to obtain self-excited oscillations with a well-defined and as nearly as possible constant frequency.

Self-excited oscillations often occur in an oscillatory system which withdraws energy from an energy source at certain times which are themselves controlled

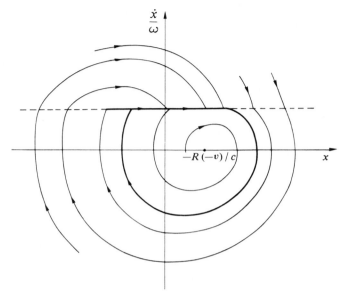

Fig. 3.6. Phase diagram of the oscillator of Fig. 3.3.

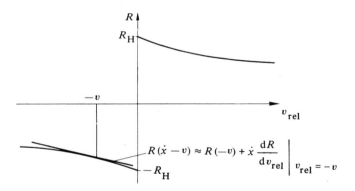

Fig. 3.7. Linearization of $R(\dot{x} - v)$ about the equilibrium position $\dot{x} = 0$.

by the system. These then are called *relaxation oscillations*. Examples of these are given by the balance of a clock, a steam engine, or something similar. In many other systems, the energy source, the oscillator, and the feedback are not so easily isolated.

Self-excited oscillations play an important part in electronics. Here, one uses non-linear networks to produce self-excited oscillations of certain frequencies. A simple example is given by the oscillator with a triode (Fig. 3.8). Let L be the inductance of the coil, C the capacity of the condenser, R the ohmian resistance, and let $M > 0$ be the mutual inductance; then one has

$$L\frac{\mathrm{d}i}{\mathrm{d}t} + Ri + \frac{1}{C}\int i\mathrm{d}t = M\frac{\mathrm{d}i_a}{\mathrm{d}t}\,, \tag{10}$$

where the currents i_a and i have the meaning indicated in Fig. 3.8. The grid voltage u_g is the same as the condenser voltage and the anode current $i_a(u_g)$ depends on this voltage in accordance with the tube characteristics. With the use of

$$i = C\frac{\mathrm{d}u_g}{\mathrm{d}t} \tag{11}$$

equation (10) then becomes

$$\frac{\mathrm{d}^2 u_g}{\mathrm{d}t^2} + \left(\frac{R}{L} - \frac{M}{LC}\frac{\mathrm{d}i_a}{\mathrm{d}u_g}\right)\frac{\mathrm{d}u_g}{\mathrm{d}t} + \frac{1}{LC}u_g = 0\,. \tag{12}$$

This equation is of type (2). The approximation of the tube characteristics $i_a(u_g)$ by a third-degree polynominal in a neighbourhood of $u_g = 0$ yields the differential equation

$$\frac{\mathrm{d}^2 u_g}{\mathrm{d}t^2} + \left(\frac{R}{L} + K + Au_g + Bu_g^2\right)\frac{\mathrm{d}u_g}{\mathrm{d}t} + \frac{1}{LC}u_g = 0\,. \tag{13}$$

Finally, if one assumes that the operating state of the tube is characterized by $A = 0, B > 0$, and $\frac{R}{L} + K < 0$, then one obtains a differential equation of the form

$$\ddot{x} + \mu(x^2 - 1)\dot{x} + \omega_0^2 x = 0 \tag{14}$$

with $\mu > 0$, and after u_g has been suitably normalized; this is the so-called Van der Pol (1922) equation about which there exists a wealth of analytical investigations (for example, see Minorsky 1962; Stoker 1950). It should be noted, however, that the coefficient A in eqn (13) generally may not vanish at the operating state of the tube, in which case eqn (14) must be replaced by a more complicated expression. In other vacuum tubes, as in pentodes, for example, the relationships are still more complicated (see Blaquière 1966, p. 49 ff.).

For small values of $|x|$ the expression in parentheses in eqn (14) is negative, so that one has 'negative damping' and energy is being supplied to the system. For large values of $|x|$, however, the system is damped. Thus, one may expect

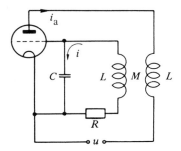

Fig. 3.8. Simple oscillator with triode.

to find a stable limit cycle in-between. In section 3.3, it will be investigated just how such a limit cycle may be approximately determined.

Other examples of self-excited systems with a single degree of freedom in electronics are Robinson's oscillator (see Blaquière 1966) or the RC-generator (see Magnus 1961). Instead of describing a large number of such systems, two examples will be given and the existence and approximate determination of limit cycles will be treated in the following sections.

Example: Aerodynamically-excited flutter oscillations. Consider a rigid plane body, for example, with wing profile which is subjected to a stationary plane flow with velocity v_∞ (v_∞ is the velocity of the undisturbed flow at a distance far away from the body). The flowing medium then exerts forces and moments on the body, depending on the angle α

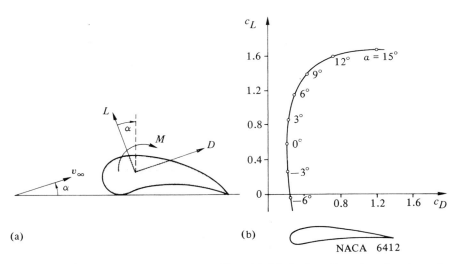

(a)   (b)

Fig. 3.9. (a) Flow-immersed wing profile with lift L, drag D, and angle of attack α. (b) Corresponding 'polar' characteristic (NACA Profile 6412, Reynolds number = 8×10^6).

(see Fig. 3.9). The forces usually are resolved into two components: the *drag* D in the direction of v_∞ and the *lift* L orthogonal to the v_∞-direction (the influence of the resultant moment will not be considered here). The components L and D are determined experimentally in a wind tunnel and thereafter are represented by the drag coefficient c_D and the lift coefficient c_L, both of which depend on α (Fig. 3.9(b)):

$$L = \frac{1}{2} \rho c_L (\alpha) \, l d v_\infty^2 \quad D = \frac{1}{2} c_D (\alpha) \, l d v_\infty^2 \tag{15}$$

where ρ is the mass density of the flowing medium, d is some characteristic diameter (which must be determined simultaneously with c_L and c_D), and l is the length of the profile under consideration.†

It is now assumed that only a vertical translation of the wing profile is admissible and that this motion is constrained by a linearly elastic spring with spring constant c. (See Fig. 3.10.)

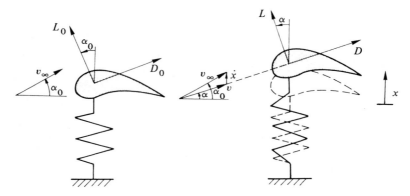

Fig. 3.10. Flutter oscillations of an unstable profile.

If the vertical velocity of the profile is given by $\dot{x}$, then one has

$$v = \sqrt{\{(v_\infty \cos \alpha_0)^2 + (v_\infty \sin \alpha_0 - \dot{x})^2\}} \tag{16}$$

as the flow velocity 'at infinity' with respect to a profile with angle of attack α_0 in the equilibrium position. However, not only the magnitude of the velocity is changing but also the relative angle of attack which determines L and D; one has

$$\alpha = \arctan \left(\frac{v_\infty \sin \alpha_0 - \dot{x}}{v_\infty \cos \alpha_0} \right) = \arctan \left(\tan \alpha_0 - \frac{\dot{x}}{v_\infty \cos \alpha_0} \right). \tag{17}$$

The lift and the drag again are given by (15) but with v_∞ replaced by v and with α satisfying the relationship (17). In accordance with Fig. 3.10, the equation of motion is obtained as

$$m\ddot{x} - L \cos \alpha - D \sin \alpha + cx = 0$$

†Orthogonal to the plane of the paper.

or, equivalently

$$m\ddot{x} - \rho \frac{ld}{2} v^2 c_L(\alpha) \cos \alpha - \rho \frac{ld}{2} v^2 c_D(\alpha) \sin \alpha + cx = 0 . \tag{18}$$

For small oscillations about the equilibrium position with $x = x_0 + \bar{x}, \dot{x} = \dot{\bar{x}}$, one has

$$v^2 \approx v_\infty^2 - 2v_\infty \dot{\bar{x}} \sin \alpha_0, \tag{19}$$

$$\alpha = \alpha_0 + \bar{\alpha} \approx \alpha_0 - \frac{\dot{\bar{x}}}{v_\infty \cos \alpha_0} . \tag{20}$$

The linearized form of eqn (18) thus is given by

$$m\ddot{\bar{x}} + \frac{\rho ld}{2} v_\infty \left[\left(\frac{dc_L}{d\alpha} + c_D \right) - \left(c_L - \frac{dc_D}{d\alpha} \right) \tan \alpha_0 + \right.$$
$$\left. + 2 (c_L \cos \alpha_0 + c_D \sin \alpha_0) \sin \alpha_0 \right] \dot{\bar{x}} + c\bar{x} = 0 \tag{21}$$

with equilibrium position defined by

$$x_0 = \frac{\rho ld}{2c} v_\infty^2 (c_L \cos \alpha_0 + c_D \sin \alpha_0). \tag{22}$$

Here, c_L and c_D and their derivatives in (21) and (22) must be evaluated at angle of attack $\alpha = \alpha_0$. The linearized equation of motion thus becomes

$$m\ddot{\bar{x}} + \frac{\rho}{2} ld \, v_\infty b\dot{\bar{x}} + c\bar{x} = 0, \tag{23}$$

where b has been used to denote the bracket in eqn (21). For the stability of the equilibrium position, one must have $b > 0$; for $b < 0$ the system is being excited. This stability criterion is simplified for $\alpha_0 = 0$ since one then has $b = \frac{dc_L}{d\alpha} + c_D$. In this form the stability criterion $\frac{dc_L}{d\alpha} + c_D > 0$ was already given by Den Hartog in 1932.

For a given angle of attack α_0 and given $c_L(\alpha_0)$ and $c_D(\alpha_0)$ one thus may determine theoretically whether self-excitation of the system is present or not. However, to obtain this result, some essential assumptions had to be made. For example, the functional values for $c_L(\alpha_0)$ and $c_D(\alpha_0)$ were initially determined in wind tunnel experiments for a stationary flow; they were used here in dynamic (non-stationary) investigations, and it is questionable as to how far this is permissible. A survey of flutter oscillations considering non-stationary flow conditions may be found in Garrick (1962) for example.

Whereas a profile in the shape of a circular cylinder always is stable in the above sense, this often is not the case for asymmetric profiles. Thus, one may easily set up experiments to observe the self-excited motions of a D-profile (a cylinder with semi-circular base).

In the wintertime, the cross-sections of high-voltage transmission lines become unsymmetrical because of ice deposits, so that one may observe self-excited oscillations, usually called 'galloping'. Because of the large amplitudes of oscillation, these often short-out the system and can lead to expensive breakdowns. These self-excited oscillations due to the asymmetry of the cross-sections should not be confused with the forced oscillations caused by Karman vortices (see Rocard 1957). For Karman vortex separation, the flowing medium exerts a periodically fluctuating force on the profile, a force which depends on the geometry and the flow conditions. The frequency of the exciting force there is given *a priori* and it generally differs from the eigenfrequency of the system. The self-excited oscillations observed here, however, are due to the 'negative damping' produced by the flow, eventually leading to oscillations of the system at its eigenfrequencies.

A much more complicated problem than the example treated here concerns the complete treatment of the flutter oscillations of an airplane wing, since the profile there may also rotate, resulting in coupled bending-torsional oscillations.

Example: Impulsively-excited systems. In mechanical clocks, mechanical oscillators (pendula or balances) are used, to which impulsive energy is supplied in certain states. The motion of such mechanisms may be approximately described by the differential equation of a simple linear oscillator with linear damping or with dry friction. The impulsive energy supply generally occurs once or twice per full oscillation. Two extreme cases have been particularly well investigated: the case of a fixed given velocity jump and that of a fixed given increase ΔE_Z of the kinetic energy at each impulse state. In comparison to the impulsive energy addition, that of a continuous energy supply over the total oscillation exhibits a number of technical disadvantages.

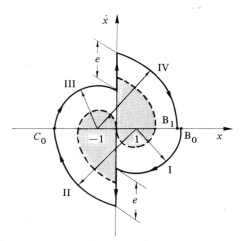

Fig. 3.11. Phase diagram of an impulsively excited system with constant velocity jump.

Consider then a system with Coulomb friction with equation of motion given by

$$\ddot{x} + x + \operatorname{sgn} \dot{x} = 0. \tag{24}$$

At every pass through the null position, the system is to be supplied a velocity impulse e. This means that the velocity $\dot{x}$ will be discontinuous at $x = 0$. If $x = 0$ at $t = \bar{t}$, then one has

$$\dot{x}(\bar{t}^{\,+}) = \dot{x}(\bar{t}^{\,-}) + e, \tag{25}$$

as long as $\dot{x}(\overline{t}^-) > 0$, and

$$\dot{x}(\overline{t}^+) = \dot{x}(\overline{t}^-) - e \qquad (26)$$

for $\dot{x}(\overline{t}^-) < 0$. It is known that the phase trajectories of this system are composed of circular arcs about the points $(1,0)$ and $(-1,0)$ (Fig. 3.11). The shaded region in this figure encompasses all motions which lead to a state of rest (in the interval $-1 \leqslant x \leqslant + 1$), without any sign change for x.

The point B_0 on the x-axis is mapped into the point B_1, as shown in Fig. 3.11, the mapping being completely defined by the phase trajectories. A periodic solution exists if the mapping has a fixed point, with B_1 identical to B_0 as a consequence. Because of symmetry, it suffices to consider the mapping from B_0 to C_0.

If the abscissas of the points B_0 and C_0 are designated by b and c, respectively, then one has

$$c = 1 - \sqrt{\left\{ \left[\sqrt{\{(b - 1)^2 - 1\}} + e \right]^2 + 1 \right\}}, \qquad (27)$$

as may easily be deduced from the phase diagram. A periodic solution corresponds to $c = -b$, and one may then solve eqn (27) for the amplitude

$$A = b = \frac{e^2}{2\sqrt{(e^2 - 4)}} \qquad (28)$$

of the limit cycle. Clearly, a limit cycle is possible only for $e > 2$. The amplitude A as a function of e is graphed in Fig. 3.12.

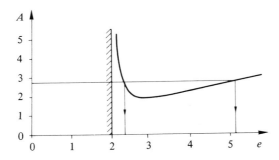

Fig. 3.12. The amplitude A of the limit cycle as a function of e.

For a given amplitude A one generally has two different values of e which lead to a corresponding limit cycle.

A brief discussion of the stability of the limit cycle follows. Toward this purpose, the limit cycle is 'disturbed' by setting $b = A + \bar{b}$. The mapping $b \to c$ then leads to $c = -A + \bar{c}$. The linearization of the mapping given by (27) with respect to $\bar{b}$ and $\bar{c}$ results in

$$\bar{c} = -h(A, e)\,\bar{b} \qquad (29)$$

with

$$h(A, e) = - \frac{(A-1)\,[\sqrt{\{(A-1)^2 - 1\}} + e]}{\sqrt{\left\{[\sqrt{\{(A-1)^2 - 1\}} + e]^2 + 1\right\}}\ \sqrt{\{(A-1)^2 - 1\}}} \tag{30}$$

The stability of the system now may be investigated by using the linearized mapping (29). It follows in a straightforward manner that the limit cycle is stable for $|h| < 1$ and unstable for $|h| > 1$.

However, the expression (30) together with (28) imply that one always has $|h| > 1$ and, thus, that the limit cycle is always unstable. Consequently, the model investigated here certainly does not accurately represent the dynamic behaviour of a mechanical clockwork.

A stable limit cycle is obtained by replacing the Coulomb damping in (24) with the usual linear damping. This will be done but it will also be assumed that the kinetic energy is instantaneously increased by a fixed amount ΔE_Z for each passage through the null position rather than the previously used velocity increase. A piecewise description of the system now is given by

$$\ddot{x} + 2D\dot{x} + x = 0 \tag{31}$$

with solution

$$x(t) = C\,e^{-Dt}\cos \nu t, \qquad \nu = \sqrt{(1 - D^2)}. \tag{32}$$

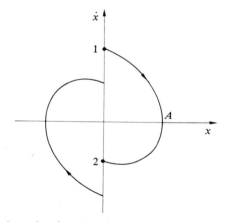

Fig. 3.13. Limit cycle of an impulsively-excited system with constant energy increase.

The phase diagram is composed of curves constructed in accordance with (32). For a given ΔE_Z and D only the amplitude A of the limit cycle will be computed here. Because of $x_1 = x_2 = 0$, the points 1 and 2 of Fig. 3.13 correspond to:

$$\left. \begin{array}{l} t_1 = -\dfrac{\pi}{2\nu}, \\[3mm] t_2 = \dfrac{\pi}{2\nu}, \end{array} \right\} \tag{33}$$

with velocities

$$\left.\begin{array}{l} \dot{x}_1 = C v e^{-Dt_1}, \\ \dot{x}_2 = -C v e^{-Dt_2}. \end{array}\right\} \tag{34}$$

The mechanical damping energy withdrawn from the system in its passage from 1 to 2 is obtained as

$$\Delta E_{12} = \frac{1}{2}(\dot{x}_1^2 - \dot{x}_2^2) = \frac{1}{2}C^2 v^2 (e^{-2Dt_1} - e^{-2Dt_2}) = C^2 v^2 \sinh \frac{\pi D}{v}. \tag{35}$$

Since one must have $\Delta E_Z = \Delta E_{12}$ for a limit cycle, it follows that

$$C = \frac{1}{v} \sqrt{\left(\frac{\Delta E_Z}{\sinh \frac{\pi D}{v}}\right)} \tag{36}$$

and eventually that the amplitude of the limit cycle is given by $A = x(t_0)$, where t_0 is the time at which $\dot{x}$ vanishes. From

$$\dot{x} = -C e^{-Dt} (D \cos vt + v \sin vt) \tag{37}$$

one obtains

$$t_0 = -\frac{1}{v} \arctan \frac{D}{v} \tag{38}$$

and, finally,

$$A = \frac{1}{v} \sqrt{\left(\frac{\Delta E_z}{\sinh \frac{\pi D}{v}}\right)} e^{-Dt_0} \cos vt_0. \tag{39}$$

For small damping ($D \ll 1$), one has $v \approx 1$, $t_0 \approx -D$, $e^{D^2} \approx 1$, $\cos vt_0 \approx 1$, and $\sinh(\pi D/v) \approx \pi D$, with

$$A \approx \sqrt{\left(\frac{\Delta E_Z}{\pi D}\right)}. \tag{40}$$

It may easily be shown that this limit cycle is stable.

3.3. Analytical approximation methods for the computation of self-excited oscillations

3.3.1. Perturbation methods

Consider the use of perturbation methods for the determination of the limit cycle of the Van der Pol equation

$$\ddot{x} + \mu (x^2 - 1)\dot{x} + \omega_0^2 x = 0 . \tag{41}$$

In order to be able to use Lindstedt's perturbation methods in the calculation of the circular frequency ω, the normalized time $\tau = \omega t$ is introduced. One then has

$$\omega^2 x'' + \mu\omega (x^2 - 1) x' + \omega_0^2 x = 0, \tag{42}$$

where the primes indicate derivatives with respect to the new 'dimensionless' time τ.† The expansion of ω and $x(\tau)$ in power series with respect to the 'small' parameter μ yields

$$\left. \begin{aligned} \omega &= \omega_0 + \mu\omega_1 + \mu^2\omega_2 + \dots , \\ x(\tau) &= x_0(\tau) + \mu x_1(\tau) + \mu^2 x_2(\tau) + \dots \end{aligned} \right\} \tag{43}$$

or, equivalently,

$$\left. \begin{aligned} \omega^2 &= \omega_0^2 + 2\mu\omega_0\omega_1 + \mu^2 (\omega_1^2 + 2\omega_0\omega_2) + \dots , \\ x^2 &= x_0^2 + 2\mu x_0 x_1 + \mu^2 (x_1^2 + 2x_0 x_2) + \dots . \end{aligned} \right\} \tag{44}$$

Substitution in eqn (42) then results in

$$\{\omega_0^2 + 2\mu\omega_0\omega_1 + \mu^2 (\omega_1^2 + 2\omega_0\omega_2) + \dots \}\{x_0'' + \mu x_1'' +$$
$$+ \mu^2 x_2'' + \dots \} + \mu (\omega_0 + \mu\omega_1 + \mu^2\omega_2 + \dots)\{x_0^2 - 1 +$$
$$+ 2\mu x_0 x_1 + \mu^2 (x_1^2 + 2x_0 x_2) + \dots \}(x_0' + \mu x_1' +$$
$$+ \mu^2 x_2' + \dots) + \omega_0^2 (x_0 + \mu x_1 + \mu^2 x_2 + \dots) = 0 . \tag{45}$$

An arrangement in accordance with the powers of μ and a comparison of the coefficients yields

$$\left. \begin{aligned} x_0'' + x_0 &= 0 , \\ x_1'' + x_1 &= -2\frac{\omega_1}{\omega_0} x_0'' + \frac{1}{\omega_0} (1 - x_0^2) x_0' , \end{aligned} \right\} \tag{46}$$

---

†Compare this time normalization with that used in section 1.1.1, eqns (22)–(24). The two approaches are equivalent even though they lead to different intermediate results.

and so on. The general solution of the first of eqns (46) is given by

$$x_0 = A_0 \cos \tau + B_0 \sin \tau .$$ (47)

Since eqn (42) is autonomous and since only the periodic solution is of interest, one may choose $x'(0) = 0$ and satisfy this condition by setting $x'_0(0) = x'_1(0) = \ldots = 0$. The introduction of $B_0 = 0$ in the second of eqns (46) provides

$$x''_1 + x_1 = 2 A_0 \frac{\omega_1}{\omega_0} \cos \tau - \frac{1}{\omega_0} (1 - A_0^2 \cos^2 \tau) A_0 \sin \tau$$

$$= 2 A_0 \frac{\omega_1}{\omega_0} \cos \tau - A_0 \frac{1}{\omega_0} (1 - A_0^2 + \frac{3}{4} A_0^2) \sin \tau +$$

$$+ \frac{1}{4} A_0^3 \frac{1}{\omega_0} \sin 3\tau .$$ (48)

If (48) is to have a periodic solution, resonance must be avoided by setting

$$A_0 \omega_1 = 0 ,$$

$$A_0 (1 - \frac{1}{4} A_0^2) = 0 .$$
(49)

These are the equations defining A_0 and ω_1. The trivial solution $A_0 = 0$ is of no interest, so that one obtains $A_0 = 2$ and $\omega_1 = 0$ from (49). Hence, eqn (48) takes on the form

$$x''_1 + x_1 = \frac{2}{\omega_0} \sin 3\tau$$ (50)

which has the general solution

$$x_1 = A_1 \cos \tau + B_1 \sin \tau - \frac{1}{4\omega_0} \sin 3\tau .$$ (51)

With $x'_1(0) = 0$, one now obtains $B_1 = 3/(4\omega_0)$. The value of A_1 remains undetermined for the moment; it is computed in the next step of the iteration. The intermediate calculations for the next step are omitted. Suffice it to note that the subsequent equation is given by

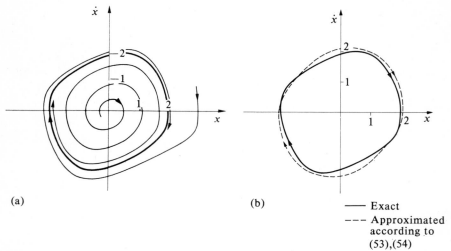

(a)   (b)   —— Exact
                                               --- Approximated
                                                 according to
                                                 (53),(54)

Fig. 3.14. The Van der Pol equation ($\mu = 0.3$; $\omega_0^2 = 1$). (a) Phase diagram; (b) exact and approximate limit cycle.

$$x_2'' + x_2 = \frac{5}{4\omega_0^2} \cos 5\,\tau - \frac{3}{2\omega_0^2} \cos 3\tau + \frac{3A_1}{\omega_0} \sin 3\tau$$

$$+ \left(4\frac{\omega_2}{\omega_0} + \frac{1}{4\omega_0^2} \right) \cos \tau + 2\frac{A_1}{\omega_0} \sin \tau . \tag{52}$$

The assumed periodicity of the solution requires $\omega_2 = -1/16\omega_0$ and $A_1 = 0$, so that the limit cycle now is approximated by

$$x(\tau) = 2 \cos \tau + \frac{3}{4\omega_0} \mu \sin \tau - \frac{1}{4\omega_0} \mu \sin 3\tau . \tag{53}$$

For the inverse transformation to the dimensional time $t = \tau/\omega$ the relationship

$$\omega = \omega_0 \left(1 - \frac{1}{16} \frac{\mu^2}{\omega_0^2} \right) \tag{54}$$

is used. Since it is impossible to obtain an analytically exact solution for (42), such approximation formulas are extremely valuable. Fig. 3.14 provides a comparison between the exact limit cycle as obtained by using an analogue computer and the approximate limit cycle provided by eqns (53) and (54).

3.3.2. Slowly changing phase and amplitude

In section 1.2.2, the differential equation

$$\ddot{x} + \omega_0^2 x = f(x,\dot{x}) \tag{55}$$

was replaced by the system

$$\left.\begin{array}{l} \dot{a} = \dfrac{1}{2\pi\omega_0} \displaystyle\int_0^{2\pi} f(a\sin(\theta+\psi), a\omega_0\cos(\theta+\psi))\cos(\theta+\psi)\,d\theta, \\[3mm] \dot{\psi} = -\dfrac{1}{a\,2\pi\omega_0} \displaystyle\int_0^{2\pi} f(a\sin(\theta+\psi), a\omega_0\cos(\theta+\psi))\sin(\theta+\psi)\,d\theta \end{array}\right\} \tag{56}$$

by the transformation

$$\left.\begin{array}{l} x = a\sin(\omega_0 t + \psi), \\[2mm] \dot{x} = a\omega_0\cos(\omega_0 t + \psi), \end{array}\right\} \tag{57}$$

and a subsequent averaging over a period of the motion. The same approximate system equations may also be used for self-excited systems. A solution with $\dot{a} \equiv 0$ corresponds to a limit cycle.

Example: The Van der Pol equation. For

$$\ddot{x} + \mu(x^2 - 1)\dot{x} + \omega_0^2 x = 0 \tag{58}$$

one has

$$f(x,\dot{x}) = -\mu(x^2 - 1)\dot{x}. \tag{59}$$

This results in

$$\left.\begin{array}{l} \dot{a} = \dfrac{a\mu}{2\pi} \displaystyle\int_0^{2\pi} \{1 - a^2\sin^2\phi\}\cos^2\phi\,d\phi, \\[3mm] \dot{\psi} = -\dfrac{\mu}{2\pi} \displaystyle\int_0^{2\pi} \{1 - a^2\sin^2\phi\}\cos\phi\sin\phi\,d\phi \end{array}\right\} \tag{60}$$

or, equivalently, in

$$\dot{a} = \mu \frac{a}{2} \left(1 - \frac{a^2}{4} \right) ,$$

$$\dot{\psi} = 0$$

$$\left. \right\} \quad (61)$$

with stationary solution $a_{st} = 2$. Within first approximations, the amplitude $A = a_{st} = 2$ of the limit cycle, as determined in this manner, corresponds to that obtained in section 3.3.1. Furthermore, it follows from the second of eqns (61) that the effect of the non-linear terms on the frequency is not yet apparent after the first approximation, since a time-independent frequency is obtained. From the expression for $\dot{a}$ it is apparent that the limit cycle is stable for positive μ ($\dot{a} > 0$ for $a < 2$, $\dot{a} < 0$ for $a > 2$).

3.3.3. Method of equivalent linearization

The method of equivalent linearization was already used in section 1.1.4; it is also suited for the approximate calculation of the amplitudes of limit cycles. In the form used here, it is closely related to the method of describing functions as used in control theory. Consider the differential equation

$$\ddot{x} + f(x, \dot{x}) = 0 \tag{62}$$

and determine its limit cycles. Assume that the limit cycle may be approximated by an harmonic oscillation of the form

$$x = A \cos \omega t ,$$

$$\dot{x} = -A \omega \sin \omega t ,$$

$$\left. \right\} \quad (63)$$

substitute (63) into the left side of (62), and expand the periodic function $f(A \cos \omega t, -A\omega \sin \omega t)$ in a Fourier series

$$f(A \cos \omega t, -A\omega \sin \omega t) = a_0 + \sum_{n=1}^{\infty} (a_n \cos n\omega t + b_n \sin n\omega t) . \tag{64}$$

The treatment will be restricted to such functions for which $a_0 = 0$; this is the case if $f(x, \dot{x})$ has certain symmetry properties. One thus has the first approximation

$$f(x, \dot{x}) \approx a_1 \cos \omega t + b_1 \sin \omega t = \frac{a_1}{A} x - \frac{b_1}{A\omega} \dot{x} = ax + b\dot{x} , \tag{65}$$

where a and b are computed from

$$a = \frac{1}{\pi A} \int_0^{2\pi} f(A \cos \omega t, -A \omega \sin \omega t) \cos \omega t \, d(\omega t),$$

$$b = -\frac{1}{\pi A \omega} \int_0^{2\pi} f(A \cos \omega t, -A \omega \sin \omega t) \sin \omega t \, d(\omega t). \tag{66}$$

The differential equation (62) is replaced by the linear equation

$$\ddot{x} + b(A, \omega)\dot{x} + a(A, \omega) x = 0 \tag{67}$$

and the amplitude and circular freqency of the limit cycle are computed from

$$b(A, \omega) = 0,$$

$$a(A, \omega) = \omega^2. \tag{68}$$

Note the similarity of this approach to the method of slowly-changing phase and amplitude. However, the method of equivalent linearization as described here can provide only the stationary solution; transient motions cannot be investigated by means of this method.

As an *example*, the limit cycle for

$$\ddot{x} + K(\dot{x}) + R(x) = 0 \tag{69}$$

will be determined, where the (discontinuous) functions $K(\dot{x})$ and $R(x)$ are illustrated in the diagrams of Fig. 3.15.

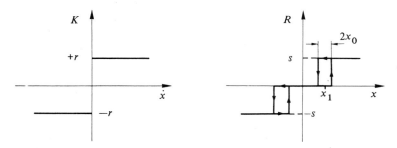

Fig. 3.15. The functions $K(\dot{x})$ and $R(x)$ for example (69).

The illustration of $R(x)$ contains a 'hysteresis loop', that is, $R(x)$ actually is not a single-valued function of the variable x, but it also depends on the sign of $\dot{x}$ (to be precise, one should write $R(x, \mathrm{sgn}\, \dot{x})$).

For the amplitude $A, A > x_0 + x_1$ is assumed since a periodic solution is not possible otherwise. With (63) and with $\omega t = \phi$ one then has

$$K^{\cdot}(-A\omega \sin \phi) = \begin{cases} -r, & \text{for} & 0 \leqslant \phi < \pi, \\ \\ +r, & \text{for} & \pi \leqslant \phi < 2\pi, \end{cases} \tag{70}$$

$$R(A\cos\phi) = \begin{cases} s, & \text{for} & 0 \leqslant \phi < \phi_1, \\ \\ 0, & \text{for} & \phi_1 \leqslant \phi < \phi_2, \\ \\ -s, & \text{for} & \phi_2 \leqslant \phi < \phi_3, \\ \\ 0, & \text{for} & \phi_3 \leqslant \phi < \phi_4, \\ \\ s, & \text{for} & \phi_4 \leqslant \phi < 2\pi \end{cases} \tag{71}$$

where

$$\left.\begin{aligned} \phi_1 &= \text{arc cos}\, \frac{x_1 - x_0}{A}, \\ \\ \phi_2 &= \text{arc cos}\left(-\frac{x_1 + x_0}{A}\right), \\ \\ \phi_3 &= \pi + \phi_1, \\ \\ \phi_4 &= \pi + \phi_2. \end{aligned}\right\} \tag{72}$$

These result in

$$\pi A a = -2r \int_0^\pi \cos\phi\, d\phi + 2s \int_0^{\phi_1} \cos\phi\, d\phi - 2s \int_{\phi_2}^\pi \cos\phi\, d\phi$$

$$= 2s\,(\sin\phi_1 + \sin\phi_2) \tag{73}$$

and

$$a = \frac{2s}{\pi A}\left[\sqrt{\left\{1 - \left(\frac{x_1 - x_0}{A}\right)^2\right\}} + \sqrt{\left\{1 - \left(\frac{x_1 + x_0}{A}\right)^2\right\}}\right]. \tag{74}$$

Analogously, one has

$$-b\pi A \omega = -2r \int_0^\pi \sin\phi\, d\phi + 2s \int_0^{\phi_1} \sin\phi\, d\phi - 2s \int_{\phi_2}^\pi \sin\phi\, d\phi \tag{75}$$

and

$$b = -4\,\frac{\dfrac{sx_0}{A} - r}{\pi A \omega}. \tag{76}$$

The conditions (68) then yield

$$A = \frac{s}{r} x_0 \qquad (77)$$

and

$$\omega^2 = \frac{2s}{\pi A} \left[\sqrt{\left\{ 1 - \left(\frac{x_1 - x_0}{A} \right)^2 \right\}} + \sqrt{\left\{ 1 - \left(\frac{x_1 + x_0}{A} \right)^2 \right\}} \right]. \qquad (78)$$

It can be shown that this limit cycle is stable.

3.4. Analytical criteria for the existence of limit cycles

Some analytical criteria for the occurrence of limit cycles will be given next. In place of the system (1), the somewhat more general system

$$\left.\begin{aligned} \dot{x}_1 &= P(x_1, x_2), \\ \dot{x}_2 &= Q(x_1, x_2) \end{aligned}\right\} \qquad (79)$$

will be treated with $P(x_1, x_2) = x_2$ as a special case.† It is well known that the differential eqns (79) determine a direction field in the x_1, x_2-plane. Some results obtained for (79) by Poincaré, Bendixson, and by Levinson (1955) and Smith will be presented; proofs, however, will be given in only a few cases.

In the following, the functions P and Q are assumed to be continuous in x_1 and x_2. Consider now a closed curve K with no self-intersections and without any critical points such that it surrounds exactly one critical point P_0. Every point of K is intersected by a phase trajectory whose directed tangent at the point of intersection forms an angle ϕ with respect to the x_1-axis (Fig. 3.16). The total change in the angle ϕ for a complete loop around K from any initial point evidently can only consist of an integral multiple of 2π since there always is a return to the initial direction.

It can be shown that the change in ϕ during one circuit depends only on the type of critical point and not on the special curve K which has been used. If the change in ϕ is denoted by $j2\pi$ then j is called the *index* of the critical point. Here, ϕ is measured in the mathematically positive sense and the interior of K is kept to the left in any tranversal of K. It is clear from an examination of Fig. 2.11 that the index for all critical points is $+1$, with the exception of the saddle point, for which it is -1.

---

†The system (79) really is more general than (1): for example, the system $\dot{x}_1 = x_1$ and $\dot{x}_2 = x_2$ cannot be written in the form (1).

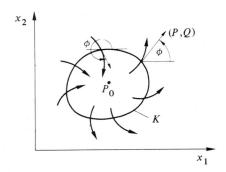

Fig. 3.16. The computation of the index of a critical point.

The index of a critical point may be determined directly by integration. From

$$\phi = \arctan \frac{\dot{x}_2}{\dot{x}_1} = \arctan \frac{Q(x_1, x_2)}{P(x_1, x_2)} , \qquad (80)$$

it follows that

$$j = \frac{1}{2\pi} \oint_K d\phi = \frac{1}{2\pi} \oint_K d\left(\arctan \frac{Q(x_1, x_2)}{P(x_1, x_2)} \right)$$

$$= \frac{1}{2\pi} \oint_K \frac{P\,dQ - Q\,dP}{P^2 + Q^2} , \qquad (81)$$

where K is an arbitrary curve surrounding only the single critical point in question.

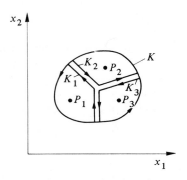

Fig. 3.17. Index of a closed curve.

Until now it was assumed that K surrounded only a single critical point. However, (81) may be computed for an arbitrary closed curve K surrounding any number of critical points, with the thus calculated value of j designated as the *index of the curve K*. If the closed curve K contains *no* critical point in its interior, then $j = 0$; however, if it encloses several critical points, then the index of the curve K is equal to the sum of the index values of the enclosed singular points. This may be seen by dividing K into several closed curves $K_1, K_2, \ldots,$ as illustrated in Fig. 3.17, in such a way that each of the curves K_i encloses only one singularity, where it may be necessary for some parts of the curves to be traversed twice. One then has:

$$j_K = \sum_{i=1}^{n} j_{P_i} ,$$ (82)

where j_{P_i} is the index of the critical point P_i ($i = 1, 2, \ldots, n$). If K now is taken to coincide with a closed phase trajectory (a periodic solution), then the index is $j_k = +1$ since the tangent to the curve K is identical to that of the phase trajectory. This has two important consequences which were proved by Poincaré:

(1) *A closed phase trajectory surrounds at least one singular point;*
(2) *The sum of the index values of the critical points within a phase trajectory is equal to + 1 or, expressed differently, within a closed phase trajectory, the number of saddle-points is always one less than the number of remaining critical points.*

The second statement follows without difficulty from (82) in the form

$$j_K = N + F + C - S ,$$ (83)

where N is the number of nodes, F is the number of foci, C is the number of centres, and S is the number of saddle points in the interior of the region surrounded by K.

Since limit cycles correspond to closed phase trajectories, a limit cycle must contain at least a node, a focus, or a centre in its interior.

Another important result concerning limit cycles is given by Bendixson's theorem:

If the expression

$$\frac{\partial P(x_1, x_2)}{\partial x_1} + \frac{\partial Q(x_1, x_2)}{\partial x_2}$$ (84)

does not take on positive and negative values on a domain D in phase space, then D cannot contain a limit cycle. This theorem is often also called Bendixson's *negative criterion.*† The proof is simple: in accordance with Gauss's theorem, one has

$$\iint_D \left(\frac{\partial P}{\partial x_1} + \frac{\partial Q}{\partial x_2} \right) dx_1 \, dx_2 = \oint_{\partial D} (P dx_2 - Q dx_1), \tag{85}$$

where ∂D is the boundary of the region D and where the area integral extends over the whole region D. Now, if ∂D is a phase trajectory, then the right-hand side of (85) vanishes in view of (79), and one obtains

$$\int_{t_1}^{t_2} \left(\frac{dx_1}{dt} \frac{dx_2}{dt} - \frac{dx_2}{dt} \frac{dx_1}{dt} \right) dt = 0; \tag{86}$$

here, the limit cycle is traversed precisely once in the time interval $[t_1, t_2]$. However, the left-hand side of (85) must also be equal to zero, which is not possible if (84) has the same sign everywhere in D. This proves the theorem.

As an *example*, consider the equation of the Lewis regulator (see Graham and McRuer 1971):

$$\ddot{x} + (1 - |x|)\dot{x} + x = 0, \tag{87}$$

which is similar to the Van der Pol eqn (58) for negative μ. Eqn (87) written as a first-order system has the form

$$\left. \begin{array}{l} \dot{x}_1 = P(x_1, x_2) = x_2, \\[2mm] \dot{x}_2 = Q(x_1, x_2) = -x_1 - (1 - |x_1|) x_2 \end{array} \right\} \tag{88}$$

resulting in

$$\frac{\partial P}{\partial x_1} + \frac{\partial Q}{\partial x_2} = -1 + |x_1|.$$

Since this expression takes on only negative values in the strip $-1 < x_1 < 1$ of the phase plane, the strip can contain no limit cycle. Krasovskii's theorem may also be used to obtain an estimate for the limit cycle in (87) in a manner similar to that of section 2.3.

Aside from the theorems of the type which have just been discussed, there are a number of other theorems which guarantee the existence of limit cycles for certain classes of differential equations. Only the theorem due to Levinson and Smith will still be cited here:

†It is assumed here that the derivatives contained in (84) exist and are continuous in D.

Consider the differential equation

$$\ddot{x} + f(x, \dot{x})\dot{x} + g(x) = 0 \qquad (89)$$

and assume that the following conditions hold:

(a) $xg(x) > 0$ *for all* $x > 0$,

(b) $\int_0^\infty g(x)dx = \infty$,

(c) $f(0, 0) < 0$, *and there exists an* $x_0 > 0$ *such that* $f(x, \dot{x}) \geqslant 0$ *for* $|x| > x_0$, *for every* $\dot{x}$,

(d) *there exists a constant* $M > 0$, *such that* $f(x, \dot{x}) \geqslant -M$ *for* $|x| \leqslant x_0$

(e) *there exists an* $x_1 > x_0$ *such that*

$$\int_{x_0}^{x_1} f[x, v(x)] \, dx \geqslant 10 M x_0$$

where $v(x)$ *is an arbitrary positive and monotonically decreasing function of* x,

then eqn (89) has at least one limit cycle.

The proof of this theorem leans heavily on Liapounov's method. It is easy to check that all of the hypotheses of the theorem are fulfilled for the Van der Pol equation, for example.

3.5. Forced oscillations in self-excited systems

When a self-excited system is subjected to an additional external excitation with circular frequency Ω, then the system may respond with periodic oscillations with circular frequence Ω under certain circumstances. This will be illustrated briefly for a Van der Pol oscillator with an additional external excitation. Consider the system

$$\ddot{x} + \mu (x^2 - 1)\dot{x} + \omega_0^2 x = p \sin \Omega t. \qquad (90)$$

For $\Omega \approx \omega_0$ and for sufficiently small values of μ the method of slowly-changing phase and amplitude, as it was used on page 44, will certainly yield useful results. If only periodic solutions with circular frequency Ω are of interest, the method of harmonic balance may also be used with $x \approx A \sin \Omega t + B \cos \Omega t$. For clarity, it is convenient here to choose the null point for t in such a way that

$$\ddot{x} + \mu(x^2 - 1)\dot{x} + \omega_0^2 x = p_1 \sin \Omega t + p_2 \cos \Omega t \qquad (91)$$

is valid instead of (90) and that the approximation

$$x = A \sin \Omega t \qquad (92)$$

is valid with a constant A. The introduction of (92) in (91) and some rearrangement yield

$$-A\Omega^2 \sin \Omega t + \mu A\Omega \left\{ \left(\frac{A^2}{4} - 1\right) \cos \Omega t + \frac{A^2}{4} \cos 3\Omega t \right\} +$$

$$+ \omega_0^2 A \sin \Omega t = p_1 \sin \Omega t + p_2 \cos \Omega t. \qquad (93)$$

Clearly, this algebraic equation has no solution for non-zero p_1, p_2, and μ. If one, however, compares only the terms in Ωt and thus satisfies equation (93) approximately, then one obtains

$$\left. \begin{aligned} A(\omega_0^2 - \Omega^2) &= p_1, \\[2mm] \mu\Omega A\left(\frac{A^2}{4} - 1\right) &= p_2, \end{aligned} \right\} \qquad (94)$$

and with $p^2 = p_1^2 + p_2^2$,

$$\frac{p^2}{4\mu^2\Omega^2} = \frac{A^2}{4} \left\{ \left(\frac{\omega_0^2 - \Omega^2}{\mu\Omega}\right)^2 + \left(\frac{A^2}{4} - 1\right)^2 \right\}. \qquad (95)$$

The *resonance curves* A^2 as a function of $(\omega_0^2 - \Omega^2)/\mu\Omega$ are illustrated in Fig. 3.18 for various values of the parameter $p^2/4\mu^2\Omega^2$. For sufficiently small values of the 'detuning' $(\omega_0^2 - \Omega^2)/\mu\Omega$ and for given $p^2/4\mu^2\Omega^2$ there are three different values of A^2.

A stability investigation by means of the method of slowly-changing phase and amplitude shows that the two smaller values of A in Fig. 3.18 correspond to the unstable solutions and the larger value to a stable oscillation. For larger detuning, only one stationary solution exists which may be stable in some regions and unstable in others. The boundaries of the region of stable solutions are indicated in Fig. 3.18; the unstable solutions lie within the shaded region.

Note that if ω_0 is sufficiently close to Ω then stable periodic solutions with frequency Ω exist only for given values of p, μ, and Ω. If the detuning is too large, however, then the excitation term is unable to take the system along with it.

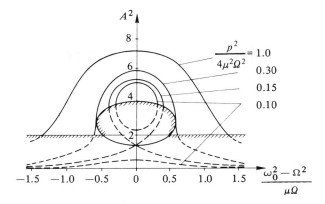

Fig. 3.18. Resonance curves for the forced oscillations of the
Van der Pol equation.

The investigation of the forced oscillations of self-excited systems thus is also
called the *theory of synchronization*. Synchronization, not only by means of
harmonic excitation terms but also by means of a periodic sequence of impulses,
for example, plays an important role in electronics (see Blaquière 1966, for
example). In the absence of synchronization, the motion of the system is a good
deal more complicated (see Kauderer 1958); generally, the motion then is
quasi-periodic.

3.6. Self-excited oscillations in systems with several degrees of freedom

In all of Chapter 1 and in the preceding part of Chapter 3, only systems
with a single degree of freedom were treated. In principle, the approximation
methods presented in Chapter 1 may also be used for systems with several
degrees of freedom, although this generally involves considerable computational
effort. These computations are carried out for a number of problems in
Blaquière (1966) and also in Malkin (1959), for example. To a large extent, the
results are analogous to those for systems with a single degree of freedom: the
frequencies of free oscillation depend on the amplitudes and for forced undamped
oscillations the amplitudes remain finite, even at resonance; corresponding to an
excitation frequency and given amplitude of the excitation force, there may
exist several stationary solutions, some of which may be stable and others
unstable.

Some of the familiar concepts from linear theory must be adjusted or
generalized. This especially affects the concept of normal modes for conservative
systems. For linear systems

$$\ddot{\mathbf{x}} + \mathbf{C}\mathbf{x} = \mathbf{0}, \tag{96}$$

where $\mathbf{C}$ is a constant symmetric positive definite matrix, the *normal modes* may be defined as solutions of the form

$$\mathbf{x} = \mathbf{a}_j \sin \omega_j t, \qquad j = 1, 2, \ldots n. \tag{97}$$

It is known that there exist n mutually orthogonal vectors $\mathbf{a}_j$ and n corresponding circular frequencies ω_j. For the non-linear system

$$\ddot{\mathbf{x}} + \mathbf{C}\mathbf{x} + \mathbf{f}(\mathbf{x}) = \mathbf{0} \tag{98}$$

the situation is different. In eqn (98), let $|\mathbf{f}(\mathbf{x})| < a|\mathbf{x}|^{1+\epsilon}$ for some fixed $a > 0$ and $\epsilon > 0$. A periodic solution $\mathbf{x}(t)$ here will be called a *normal mode* if the following statements are satisfied:

(a) Every component $x_i(t), i = 1, 2, \ldots, n$ has the same frequency;
(b) All the $x_i(t)$, $i = 1, 2, \ldots, n$ vanish at the same time, i.e., $x_i(\bar{t}) = 0$ implies in $x_1(\bar{t}) = x_2(\bar{t}) = \ldots = x_{i-1}(\bar{t}) = x_{i+1}(\bar{t}) = \ldots = x_n(\bar{t}) = 0$;
(c) All of the component functions $x_i(t)$ take on their extreme values at the same instant;
(d) For every $\bar{t}$ and for every $i, i = 1, \ldots, n$, the values $x_1(\bar{t}), \ldots, x_{i-1}(\bar{t})$, $x_{i+1}(\bar{t}), \ldots, x_n(\bar{t})$ are single-valued functions of $x_i(\bar{t})$.

This special definition of normal modes was given by Rosenberg (1962). However, there also are a number of other meaningful definitions of normal modes for non-linear systems.

Now, two self-excited systems with two degrees of freedom will be treated, rather than delving any deeper into the difficulties of the theory. Let the motion of the system in Fig. 3.19 be described by

$$m_1 \ddot{y}_1 - a\dot{y}_1 + e y_1^2 \dot{y}_1 + c_1 y_1 = 0 , \tag{99}$$

where a, e, and c_1 are positive constants. In this figure, S represents the excitation mechanism causing the force $a\dot{y}_1 - e y_1^2 \dot{y}_1$. It is known that the equilibrium position of this system is unstable and the possibility of stabilizing the system by means of an appropriate absorber is to be investigated.† For forced oscillations, absorbers have been treated extensively in the literature (for example, see Tong 1960, p. 138 ff.), whereas they have only recently been investigated for self-excited systems (see Mansour 1972). They are used, for

---

†For the usual absorber, for forced oscillation, damping is detrimental to the actual absorption effect. In the present case, however, the damping is essential to achieve stabilization. Thus, it might be more appropriate here to speak of a 'stabilizer' rather than an absorber.

example, in the construction of high-tension transmission lines where they are meant to absorb the self-excited oscillations due to the aerodynamic forces, the so-called 'galloping oscillations'.

When the absorber of Fig. 3.19(b) is included, then the system (99) must be replaced by

$$\left.\begin{array}{l} m_1\ddot{y}_1 - a\dot{y}_1 + ey_1^2\dot{y}_1 + c_1y_1 - b_2\dot{y}_2 - c_2y_2 = 0\,, \\[2mm] m_2(\ddot{y}_1 + \ddot{y}_2) + b_2\dot{y}_2 + c_2y_2 = 0\,. \end{array}\right\} \qquad (100)$$

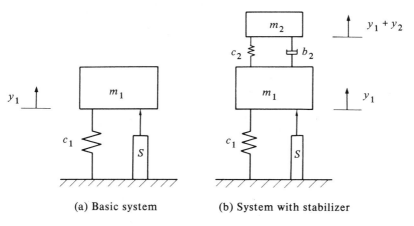

(a) Basic system   (b) System with stabilizer

Fig. 3.19. Self-excited system with stabilizer ('absorber').

If only the stability of the trivial solution is to be investigated, then it suffices to begin with the linearized system and to set $e = 0$ in eqns (100). With the abbreviations

$$\left.\begin{array}{l} c_1/m_1 = \omega_1^2\,, \qquad c_2/m_2 = \omega_2^2\,, \qquad \dfrac{a}{2\sqrt{(c_1m_1)}} = A\,, \\[4mm] \dfrac{b_2}{2\sqrt{(c_2m_2)}} = D\,, \qquad m_2/m_1 = \gamma\,, \qquad \omega_2/\omega_1 = \lambda\,, \end{array}\right\} \qquad (101)$$

along with the introduction of the new, dimensionless time $\tau = \omega_1 t$, for which one has

$$(\ \dot{}\ ) = \frac{\mathrm{d}}{\mathrm{d}t} = \omega_1\frac{\mathrm{d}}{\mathrm{d}\tau} = \omega_1\,(\ )'\,, \qquad (102)$$

the linearized system (100) may easily be transformed to the form

$$
\left.
\begin{aligned}
y_1'' - 2Ay_1' + y_1 - \gamma\lambda(2Dy_2' + \lambda y_2) &= 0, \\
y_2'' + (1 + \gamma)\lambda(2Dy_2' + \lambda y_2) + 2Ay_1' - y_1 &= 0.
\end{aligned}
\right\} \quad (103)
$$

The stability of the trivial solution depends only on the parameters A, D, γ, and λ and it may be investigated by means of the Hurwitz criterion. In the present case, this criterion results in relatively complicated analytical expressions which may only be evaluated numerically. In Fig. 3.20, the boundaries of stability and instability regions, respectively, have been presented, as they appear in the parameter plane, for a given mass-ratio γ and for several values of λ.

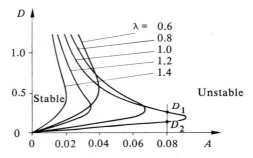

Fig. 3.20. Stability boundaries in the parameter plane (for $\gamma = 0.1$).

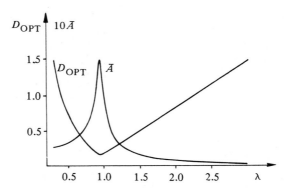

Fig. 3.21. Optimal damping D_{OPT} and maximal admissible excitation A
(for $\gamma = 0.1$).

For a given A, λ, and γ it is apparent from the figure that one has stability only for $D_2 > D > D_1$. Thus, the damping must not be too large either! But for every given frequency ratio $\lambda = \omega_2/\omega_1$ and for every given measure of damping

D, one also has a region of values of A for which the position of rest is stable. It now becomes of interest to discover that value of D for a given frequency ratio λ, which guarantees stability for the largest possible value of the excitation A. In each curve of Fig. 3.20, the value D_{OPT} corresponds to the point with vertical tangent. This results in a relationship between $D_{OPT}(\lambda)$ and the corresponding $\bar{A}(\lambda)$, as illustrated in Fig. 3.21.

For most of the applications, as for example for the initially mentioned high-tension line, the parameter a in eqn (100) and, correspondingly, A in (101) will be unknown. One would thus choose the damping D_{OPT} in such a way as to allow the largest possible excitation for which one still has stability and, for a given λ, one would then read off this value from the graph in Fig. 3.21. In applications to high-tension transmission lines, the calculations up to the present have been carried out with the cable (an infinite degree of freedom system), considered to be only a single lumped-mass system. This may be all right as long as one wishes to consider only one of the eigenmodes of the system. However, since the transmission line has an infinity of eigenmodes and eigenfrequencies, ω_1 is not given uniquely but could be any one of the eigenfrequencies of the system.

Systems with singular differential equations often occur in electronics. A simple example, conceived by Theodorchik (1948) and discussed by Blaquière (1966), is given by the system illustrated in Fig. 3.22. The differential equations describing the system are derived next.

An application of Kirchhoff's laws results in

$$\left.\begin{array}{c} L_1 \dfrac{di_1}{dt} + r_1 i_1 + \dfrac{1}{C_1} \int i_1 dt + \dfrac{1}{K} \int (i_1 - i_2) dt = M_1 \dfrac{di_a}{dt}, \\[3mm] L_2 \dfrac{di_2}{dt} + r_2 i_2 + \dfrac{1}{C_2} \int i_2 dt + \dfrac{1}{K} \int (i_2 - i_1) dt = M_2 \dfrac{di_a}{dt} \end{array}\right\} \quad (104)$$

with positive constants $L_1, L_2, r_1, r_2, C_1, C_2, K, L_1, L_2, M_1$, and M_2. If one introduces the new variables

$$x_1 = \frac{1}{C_1} \int i_1 dt, \qquad x_2 = \frac{1}{C_2} \int i_2 dt, \qquad (105)$$

and assumes that the tube characteristics may be approximated by $i_a = s_0 x_1 + s_2 x_1^3$, similar to the approach used in section 3.3, then the system (104) may also be written in the form

$$\ddot{x}_1 + 2\delta_1\dot{x}_1 + \omega_1^2 x_1 = \frac{M_1}{L_1 C_1} (s_0 + 3 s_2 x_1^2)\dot{x}_1 + \alpha_1 x_2 ,$$

$$\ddot{x} + 2\delta_2\dot{x}_2 + \omega_2^2 x_2 = \frac{M_2}{L_2 C_2} (s_0 + 3 s_2 x_1^2)\dot{x}_1 + \alpha_2 x_1 ,$$

(106)

where δ_1, δ_2, ω_1^2, ω_2^2, α_1, and α_2 are obtained from a suitable normalization of the previously introduced constants. If one has $s_0 > 0$ and $s_2 < 0$, then this system behaves in a manner similar to the sytem (100). Now, however, a completely different problem has been posed: in the example from mechanics the aim was the complete avoidance of the self-excited oscillations, whereas here a stable (non-trivial) limit cycle is precisely what is desired. The usual investigations are limited to the determination of the limit cycles and the corresponding stability observations. Both may be achieved with the previously introduced methods (see Blaquière).

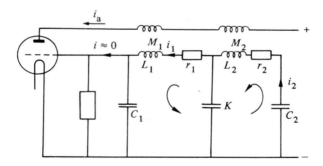

Fig. 3.22. Self-excited system with two degrees of freedom.

3.7. Additional comments concerning self-excited oscillations

In spite of the fact that self-excited oscillations have long been known, nearly all of the initial systematic investigations stem from the time right after the introduction of the vacuum tube; the fundamental work of Van der Pol appeared in 1922. Modern self-excited networks usually no longer contain vacuum tubes. Still, theoretical observations on oscillatory circuits with vacuum tubes are useful even today—at the very least, from a didactic viewpoint—since the phenomena stand out clearer here than they do for circuits with transistors. Modern circuits are discussed in Landvogt (1969), Blaquière (1966), (quartz-stabilized oscillator), and an introduction is given in Simonyi (1971), for example. In the classical work by Andronov, Witt, and Chaikin (1965), a number of self-excited systems are discussed in detail and a special chapter is devoted to the theory of clocks. Examples from mechanical engineering and control theory are treated in Magnus (1961), Den Hartog (1932, 1956), and Graham and McRuer (1971).

The aerodynamic self-excited oscillations of the galloping type should not be confused with the oscillations caused by Karman vortex separation (see Rocard 1957). A survey of the literature concerning oscillations of high tension wires may be found in Dubey (1973). Wind-excited oscillations of suspension bridges are discussed in numerous works (see Rocard 1957, Böhm 1969, for example).

Forced oscillations in systems with self-excitation are discussed in detail by Stoker (1950) and in the recently published monograph by Tondl (1975a). The 'absorption' of self-excited oscillations is treated in Mansour (1972) and Tondl (1975b, 1976a, b). The example in section 3.6 was dealt with independently by the author and by Mansour (1972); the discussion concerning 'optimal damping' is new.

A number of textbooks deal extensively with self-excited systems and the methods used in their investigation, among them Bogoliubov and Mitropolski (1965), Hayashi (1964), Kauderer (1958), Klotter (1951), Malkin (1959), Nayfeh (1973), Struble (1962), and Theodorchik (1948). Existence theorems, as given in section 3.4, may be found in Forbat (1966), for example.

References

Andronov, A. A., Witt, A. A., and Chaikin, S. E. (1965). *Theorie der Schwingungen* [*Theory of oscillations*], Volumes 1 and 2. Akademie-Verlag, Berlin.

Blaquière, R. (1966). *Nonlinear system analysis*. Academic Press, New York.

Böhm, F. (1969). Berechnung nichtlinearer aerodynamisch erregter Schwingungen von Hängebrücken [Computation of non-linear aerodynamically-excited oscillations of suspension bridges). *Der Stahlbau* **38**, 3–11.

Bogoliubov, N. N. and Mitropolski, J. A. (1965). *Asymptotische Methoden in der Theorie der nichtlinearen Schwingungen* [*Asymptotic methods in the theory of non-linear oscillations*]. Akademie-Verlag, Berlin.

Den Hartog, J. P. (1956). *Mechanical Vibrations*. McGraw-Hill, New York.

—— (1932). Transmission line vibrations due to sleet. *Trans. AIEE* **51**, 1074–6.

Dubey, R. N. (1973). Vibration of overhead transmission lines. *Shock and Vibration Digest* **5**, 1–7.

Forbat, N. (1966). *Analytische Mechanik der Schwingungen* [*Analytical mechanics of oscillations*]. VEB Deutscher Verlag der Wissenschaften, Berlin.

Garrick, I. E. (1962). Flutter. In *Handbook of engineering mechanics* (ed. W. Flügge). McGraw-Hill, New York.

Graham, D. and McRuer, D. (1971). *Analysis of nonlinear control systems*. Dover, New York.

Hale, J. K. (1963). *Oscillations in nonlinear systems*. McGraw-Hill, New York.

Hayashi, Ch. (1964). *Nonlinear oscillations in physical systems*. McGraw-Hill, New York.

Kauderer, H. (1958). *Nichtlineare Mechanik* [*Non-linear mechanics*]. Springer, Berlin.

Klotter, K. (1951). *Technische Schwingungslehre* [*Applied oscillation theory*], Vol. 1. Springer, Berlin.

Landvogt, G. F. (1969). Das elektrische Verhalten eines verallgemeinerten Van der Polschen Oszillatormodells [The electronic behaviour of a generalized Van der Pol oscillator model]. *Nachrichtentechnische Z.* **22**, 491–5.

Lefschetz, S. (1957). *Differential equations: geometric theory.* Interscience, New York.

Levinson, N. (1955). Theory of ordinary differential equations. McGraw-Hill, New York.

Magnus, K. (1961). *Schwingungen* [*Oscillations*]. B. G. Teubner, Stuttgart.

Malkin, I. G. (1959). *Some problems in the theory of nonlinear oscillations,* 2 Volumes. United States Atomic Energy Commission, AEC-tr-3766.

Mansour, W. M. (1972). Quenching of limit cycles of a Van der Pol oscillator. *J. Sound Vib.* **25** (3), 395–405.

Minorsky, N. (1962). *Nonlinear oscillations.* Princeton University Press, Princeton, New Jersey.

Nayfeh, A. H. (1973). *Perturbation methods.* John Wiley and Sons, New York.

Pontryagin, L. S. (1965). *Gewöhnliche Differentialgleichungen* [*Ordinary differential equations*]. VEB Deutscher Verlag der Wissenschaften, Berlin.

Rocard, Y. (1957). *Dynamic instability.* Crosby Lockwood and Son, London.

Rosenberg, R. M. (1962). The normal modes of nonlinear n-degree-of-freedom systems. *J. appl. Mech.* **29**, 7–14.

Simonyi, K. (1971). *Theoretische Elektrotechnik* [*Theoretical electronics*]. VEB Deutscher Verlag der Wissenschaften, Berlin.

Stoker, J. J. (1950). *Nonlinear vibrations.* Interscience, New York.

Struble, R. A. (1962). *Nonlinear differential equations.* McGraw-Hill, New York.

Theodorchik, K. F. (1948). *Auto-oscillating systems* [in Russian]. Moscow.

Tondl, A. (1975a). Quenching of self-excited vibrations: equilibrium aspects. *J. Sound Vib.* **42**, 251–60.

—— (1975b). Quenching of self-excited vibrations: one- and two-frequency vibrations. *J. Sound Vib.* **42**, 261–71.

—— (1976a). Quenching of self-excited vibrations: effect of dry friction. *J. Sound Vib.* **45**, 285–94.

—— (1976b). *On the interaction between self-excited and forced vibrations.* National Research Institute for Machine Design, Bechovice, Monographs and Memoranda, No. 20, Prague.

Tong, K. N. (1960). *Theory of mechanical vibrations.* John Wiley, New York.

Van der Pol, B. (1922). On a type of oscillation hysteresis in a simple triode generator. *Phil. Mag.* **43**, 177–93.

Exercises

3.1. Determine the limit cycle by means of the method of slowly-changing phase and amplitude and discuss its stability for the equation of the Lewis regulator,

$$\ddot{x} + (1 - |x|)\dot{x} + x = 0 . \tag{107}$$

3.2. Carry out the coordinate transformation

$$x_1 = x, \ x_2 = \dot{x} + \int_0^x f(\bar{x}) \, d\bar{x}$$

in Liénard's equation

$$\ddot{x} + f(x)\dot{x} + g(x) = 0, \qquad g(0) = 0 \tag{108}$$

and estimate the domain of attraction for the trivial solution as well as possible limit cycles, by means of a suitable Liapounov function.

3.3. Use the results of Problem 3.2 to analyse the Van der Pol equation and the Lewis equation.

3.4. Consider the system

$$\left.\begin{aligned} \dot{x}_1 &= x_2 + x_1 f(r^2), \\ \dot{x}_2 &= -x_1 + x_2 f(r^2) \end{aligned}\right\} \tag{109}$$

with $f(r^2) = \alpha + 2r^2 - r^4$, $r^2 = x_1^2 + x_2^2$ and determine:

(a) The location and the stability of the critical points;
(b) The possible limit cycles and their stability.

3.5. Use the negative criterion of Bendixson to analyse the system in Problem 3.4.

3.6. Consider the differential equation

$$\ddot{x} - \left(\frac{1}{10} - \frac{10}{3} \dot{x}^2 \right) \dot{x} + x - x^3 = 0 \tag{110}$$

and investigate:

(a) The stability behaviour of the equilibrium positions;
(b) The possible existence of limit cycles.

4

HAMILTONIAN SYSTEMS

4.1. Hamiltonian differential equations in mechanics

For a given continuously differentiable function $H(\mathbf{x}, \mathbf{y}, t)$: $\mathbb{R}^n \times \mathbb{R}^n \times \mathbb{R} \to \mathbb{R}$ one may form a system of differential equations of the type

$$
\left.
\begin{aligned}
\dot{\mathbf{x}} &= \mathbf{f}(\mathbf{x}, \mathbf{y}, t), \\[2mm]
\dot{\mathbf{y}} &= \mathbf{g}(\mathbf{x}, \mathbf{y}, t),
\end{aligned}
\right\}
\tag{1}
$$

where $\mathbf{f}$ and $\mathbf{g}$ are given by†

$$
\left.
\begin{aligned}
\mathbf{f}(\mathbf{x}, \mathbf{y}, t) &= \frac{\partial H}{\partial \mathbf{y}}, \\[3mm]
\mathbf{g}(\mathbf{x}, \mathbf{y}, t) &= -\frac{\partial H}{\partial \mathbf{x}}.
\end{aligned}
\right\}
\tag{2}
$$

Here, $H(\mathbf{x}, \mathbf{y}, t)$ is called the *Hamiltonian* and eqns (1) are designated as the *Hamiltonian differential equations* corresponding to $H(\mathbf{x}, \mathbf{y}, t)$. Such differential equations have a number of important characteristics. Thus, H is a first integral of eqn (1) if and only if $H(\mathbf{x}, \mathbf{y}, t)$ does not contain the time explicitly.

---

† Define $\left(\dfrac{\partial H}{\partial \mathbf{x}}\right)^{\mathrm{T}} = \left(\dfrac{\partial H}{\partial x_1}, \dfrac{\partial H}{\partial x_2}, \ldots, \dfrac{\partial H}{\partial x_n}\right)$ and use $\mathbf{f}^{\mathrm{T}}(\mathbf{x}, t) = (f_1, \ldots, f_n)$ to define

$$
\frac{\partial \mathbf{f}}{\partial \mathbf{x}} =
\begin{pmatrix}
\dfrac{\partial f_1}{\partial x_1} & \dfrac{\partial f_1}{\partial x_2} & \cdots & \dfrac{\partial f_1}{\partial x_n} \\[3mm]
\dfrac{\partial f_2}{\partial x_1} & \dfrac{\partial f_2}{\partial x_2} & \cdots & \dfrac{\partial f_2}{\partial x_n} \\[3mm]
\vdots & & & \\[3mm]
\dfrac{\partial f_n}{\partial x_1} & \dfrac{\partial f_n}{\partial x_2} & \cdots & \dfrac{\partial f_n}{\partial x_n}
\end{pmatrix}
$$

Namely, one then has

$$\dot{H} = \left(\frac{\partial H}{\partial \mathbf{x}}\right)^{\mathrm{T}}\dot{\mathbf{x}} + \left(\frac{\partial H}{\partial \mathbf{y}}\right)^{\mathrm{T}}\dot{\mathbf{y}} = \left(\frac{\partial H}{\partial \mathbf{x}}\right)^{\mathrm{T}}\left(\frac{\partial H}{\partial \mathbf{y}}\right) - \left(\frac{\partial H}{\partial \mathbf{y}}\right)^{\mathrm{T}}\left(\frac{\partial H}{\partial \mathbf{x}}\right) = 0 .$$

These differential equations, introduced by Hamilton in 1834, play a funda-mental role in analytical mechanics. To begin with, only the Hamiltonian equations of mechanics will be discussed and later, in Chapter 5, the discussion will be extended to problems in optimal control which also lead to such differ-ential equations. The objective in Chapter 4 is to transform a given Hamiltonian system into a simpler Hamiltonian system and to use the result to construct an iterative procedure for the determination of approximate solutions of the system (1). Toward this purpose, some of the fundamentals of Hamiltonian theory will be given first.

In mechanics, it is known that the equations of motion of a holonomic *conservative*† system with n degrees of freedom result from Lagrange's equations in the form

$$\frac{\mathrm{d}}{\mathrm{d}t}\frac{\partial L}{\partial \dot{q}_i} - \frac{\partial L}{\partial q_i} = 0 , \qquad i = 1, 2, \ldots, n . \tag{3}$$

Here, $\mathbf{q}^{\mathrm{T}} = (q_1, q_2, \ldots, q_n)$ is the matrix of the generalized coordinates and the Lagrangian $L(\mathbf{q}, \dot{\mathbf{q}}, t)$ is given by

$$L(\mathbf{q}, \dot{\mathbf{q}}, t) = T(\mathbf{q}, \dot{\mathbf{q}}, t) - U(\mathbf{q}, t) , \tag{4}$$

where T is the kinetic energy and U the potential function (if U is independent of the time, then one has $U(\mathbf{q})$ as the potential energy).

For *natural mechanical systems*, the kinetic energy is a positive definite quadratic form of the generalized velocities,

$$T(\mathbf{q}, \dot{\mathbf{q}}, t) = \frac{1}{2}\dot{\mathbf{q}}^{\mathrm{T}}\mathbf{A}(\mathbf{q}, t)\dot{\mathbf{q}} , \tag{5}$$

and eqn (3) then may always be written in the form

$$\ddot{\mathbf{q}} = \mathbf{f}(\mathbf{q}, \dot{\mathbf{q}}, t) . \tag{6}$$

Naturally, system (6) may also be written as a first-order system

$$\dot{\mathbf{y}} = \mathbf{g}(\mathbf{y}, t) \tag{7}$$

†*Conservative* here means that there exists a possibly time-dependent potential; it does not mean that the mechanical energy is necessarily conserved.

by introducing the coordinates and the velocities as new variables, for example. However, because of the associated symmetry properties it is often more appropriate to introduce Hamiltonian equations. In this context, one introduces the *generalized coordinates* q_i and the *generalized momenta* p_i ($i = 1, 2, \ldots, n$), defined by

$$p_i = \frac{\partial L}{\partial \dot{q}_i} \qquad i = 1, 2, \ldots, n, \tag{8}$$

as the new variables. Since T is quadratic in $\dot{q}$ the relationship between the p_i and the $\dot{q}_i$ is a linear one. Thus, the relations (8) may be used to determine $\mathbf{p}(\mathbf{q}, \dot{\mathbf{q}}, t)$ and from these $\dot{\mathbf{q}}(\mathbf{q}, \mathbf{p}, t)$ (because of the definiteness of $\mathbf{A}$ the coefficient determinant is non-zero). One now defines

$$H(\mathbf{q}, \mathbf{p}, t) = \mathbf{p}^T \dot{\mathbf{q}}(\mathbf{q}, \mathbf{p}, t) - L(\mathbf{q}, \dot{\mathbf{q}}(\mathbf{q}, \mathbf{p}, t), t) =$$

$$= \left(\frac{\partial L}{\partial \dot{\mathbf{q}}} \right)^T \dot{\mathbf{q}} - L, \tag{9}$$

where $\dot{\mathbf{q}}$ on the right-hand side of eqn (9) is expressed in terms of $\mathbf{q}$, $\mathbf{p}$, and t. Consider a variation of H with respect to $\mathbf{q}$ and $\mathbf{p}$ for a fixed time t (to which there, of course, corresponds a variation with respect to $\mathbf{q}$ and $\dot{\mathbf{q}}$) to obtain

$$\delta H = \mathbf{p}^T \delta \dot{\mathbf{q}} + \dot{\mathbf{q}}^T \delta \mathbf{p} - \left(\frac{\partial L}{\partial \mathbf{q}} \right)^T \delta \mathbf{q} - \left(\frac{\partial L}{\partial \dot{\mathbf{q}}} \right)^T \delta \dot{\mathbf{q}} =$$

$$= \dot{\mathbf{q}}^T \delta \mathbf{p} - \left(\frac{\partial L}{\partial \mathbf{q}} \right)^T \delta \mathbf{q} = \left(\frac{\partial H}{\partial \mathbf{q}} \right)^T \delta \mathbf{q} + \left(\frac{\partial H}{\partial \mathbf{p}} \right)^T \delta \mathbf{p}, \tag{10}$$

so that

$$\dot{\mathbf{q}} = \frac{\partial H}{\partial \mathbf{p}} \qquad \text{and} \qquad \frac{\partial L}{\partial \mathbf{q}} = -\frac{\partial H}{\partial \mathbf{q}} \tag{11}$$

follow. As a consequence of the conditions (3) together with (8), the definition of $\mathbf{p}$, one obtains

$$\dot{\mathbf{p}} = -\frac{\partial H}{\partial \mathbf{q}}. \tag{12}$$

Thus, one now has a system of differential equations of the form

$$\dot{\mathbf{q}} = \frac{\partial H}{\partial \mathbf{p}} \, ,$$

$$\dot{\mathbf{p}} = -\frac{\partial H}{\partial \mathbf{q}} \, . \tag{13}$$

Hence, it has been shown that (13) and (3) are equivalent as long as the Hamiltonian is defined by (9) together with the transformation (8).

In natural *scleronomic* (that is, time-independent) conservative systems, $H(\mathbf{q}, \mathbf{p})$ has a simple physical interpretation. In fact, one has

$$\mathbf{p}^{\mathrm{T}}\dot{\mathbf{q}} = \dot{\mathbf{q}}^{\mathrm{T}}\frac{\partial L}{\partial \dot{\mathbf{q}}} = \dot{\mathbf{q}}^{\mathrm{T}}\frac{\partial T}{\partial \dot{\mathbf{q}}} = 2\, T(\mathbf{q}, \dot{\mathbf{q}}) \, , \tag{14}$$

and, hence,

$$H = \mathbf{p}^{\mathrm{T}}\dot{\mathbf{q}}\,(\mathbf{q}, \mathbf{p}) - L\,(\mathbf{q}, \dot{\mathbf{q}}\,(\mathbf{q}, \mathbf{p})) = 2\,T - (T - U) =$$

$$= T\,(\mathbf{q}, \dot{\mathbf{q}}\,(\mathbf{q}, \mathbf{p})) + U\,(\mathbf{q}) \, . \tag{15}$$

For these systems, the Hamiltonian thus is the sum of the kinetic and the potential energy expressed in terms of the coordinates and the momenta. In such cases it is easy to determine the function $H(\mathbf{q}, \mathbf{p})$ by simply expressing the total mechanical energy $T + U$ in terms of $\mathbf{q}$ and $\mathbf{p}$. Furthermore, it follows from eqns (13) that the mechanical energy is a first integral of the equations of motion.

One may also obtain eqns (13) directly from *Hamilton's principle*

$$\delta \int_{t_0}^{t_1} L(\mathbf{q}, \dot{\mathbf{q}}, t)\,\mathrm{d}t = 0 \, . \tag{16}$$

If one carries out the indicated variation and expresses $\delta\dot{\mathbf{q}}$ in terms of $\delta\mathbf{q}$, then an integration by parts yields the Lagrangian equations (3) as a necessary condition for the solutions of (16). However, one may also formally introduce the new variables u_i which satisfy the constraints $\dot{q}_i - u_i = 0, i = 1, 2, \ldots, n$, where the u_i now may be independently varied. With the Lagrange multipliers $\lambda_i, i = 1, 2, \ldots, n$, eqn (16) may then be written in the form

$$\delta \int_{t_0}^{t_1} [L(\mathbf{q}, \mathbf{u}, t) + \lambda^{\mathrm{T}}(\dot{\mathbf{q}} - \mathbf{u})]\,\mathrm{d}t = 0 \, . \tag{17}$$

The multipliers λ_i are determined from the corresponding Euler–Lagrange equaticns

$$\frac{d}{dt}\frac{\partial[\,]}{\partial \dot{u}_i} - \frac{\partial[\,]}{\partial u_i} = 0 - \frac{\partial L}{\partial u_i} + \lambda_i = 0 , \tag{18}$$

as

$$\lambda_i = \frac{\partial L}{\partial u_i} , \qquad i = 1, 2, \ldots, n . \tag{19}$$

The variational eqn (17) thus takes on the form

$$\delta \int_{t_0}^{t_1} \left\{ L(\mathbf{q}, \mathbf{u}, t) + (\dot{\mathbf{q}}^T - \mathbf{u}^T) \frac{\partial L}{\partial \mathbf{u}} \right\} dt = 0 . \tag{20}$$

This is an unconstrained variational problem in the $2n$ variables $q_i, u_i, i = 1, 2, \ldots, n$. The introduction of the new variables p_i, with

$$p_i = \frac{\partial L}{\partial u_i} , \qquad i = 1, 2, \ldots, n \tag{21}$$

in eqn (20), results in

$$\delta \int_{t_0}^{t_1} \{L(\mathbf{q}, \mathbf{u}(\mathbf{q}, \mathbf{p}, t), t) + \dot{\mathbf{q}}^T \mathbf{p} - \mathbf{p}^T \mathbf{u}(\mathbf{q}, \mathbf{p}, t)\} dt = 0 , \tag{22}$$

and with

$$H(\mathbf{q}, \mathbf{p}, t) = \mathbf{p}^T \mathbf{u}(\mathbf{q}, \mathbf{p}, t) - L(\mathbf{q}, \mathbf{u}(\mathbf{q}, \mathbf{p}, t), t) \tag{23}$$

this may be written in the form

$$\delta \int_{t_0}^{t_1} [\mathbf{p}^T \dot{\mathbf{q}} - H(\mathbf{q}, \mathbf{p}, t)] dt = 0 . \tag{24}$$

The Euler–Lagrange equations for (24) are given by

$$\frac{d}{dt}\frac{\partial[\,]}{\partial \dot{\mathbf{q}}} - \frac{\partial[\,]}{\partial \mathbf{q}} = \frac{d}{dt}\,\mathbf{p} + \frac{\partial H}{\partial \mathbf{q}} = \mathbf{0}\,,$$

$$\frac{d}{dt}\frac{\partial[\,]}{\partial \dot{\mathbf{p}}} - \frac{\partial[\,]}{\partial \mathbf{p}} = -\dot{\mathbf{q}} + \frac{\partial H}{\partial \mathbf{p}} = \mathbf{0}\,,$$

$$\left.\begin{array}{c}\\[2ex]\\[2ex]\end{array}\right\} \quad (25)$$

which is the same as eqns (13).

Next, the Hamiltonian will be determined for a number of specific examples:

1. *The Hamiltonian for a particle in a force field (cylindrical coordinates).* Let the position of a particle with mass m be described in terms of the cylindrical coordinates r, φ, and z (Fig. 4.1).

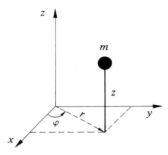

Fig. 4.1. Representation of the position of a particle in cylindrical coordinates.

One then has

$$T = \frac{1}{2}m\,(\dot{r}^2 + r^2\dot{\varphi}^2 + \dot{z}^2)\,,$$

$$U = U\,(r, \varphi, z)\,.$$

$$\left.\begin{array}{c}\\[2ex]\\[2ex]\end{array}\right\} \quad (26)$$

With $\mathbf{p} = \partial T/\partial \dot{\mathbf{q}}$ there results

$$p_r = m\dot{r}\,,\; p_\varphi = mr^2\dot{\varphi}\,,\; p_z = m\dot{z}\,,\tag{27}$$

and the Hamiltonian thus becomes

$$H = \frac{1}{2m}\,(p_r^2 + \frac{p_\varphi^2}{r^2} + p_z^2)\; + \; U\,(r, \varphi, z)\,.\tag{28}$$

2. *The Hamiltonian for a charged particle in an electromagnetic field.* When a constant mass (non-relativistic approach) is assumed, then the Lagrangian in Gaussian units is given by

$$L = \frac{m}{2}v^2 + \frac{e}{c}\mathbf{a}^T\mathbf{v} - e\,\phi\tag{29}$$

which becomes

$$L \doteq \frac{m}{2} (\dot{x}^2 + \dot{y}^2 + \dot{z}^2) + \frac{e}{c} (a_x \dot{x} + a_y \dot{y} + a_z \dot{z}) - e \phi (x, y, z) \tag{30}$$

in Cartesian coordinates. Here, x, y, and z are the coordinates of the particles, $\mathbf{v}^T = \dot{\mathbf{q}}^T = (\dot{x}, \dot{y}, \dot{z})$ is its velocity, m its mass, e the electric charge, c the speed of light, $\mathbf{a}^T = (a_x, a_y, a_z)$ the vector potential, and ϕ the scalar potential. The magnetic field $\mathbf{H}$, the electrostatic field $\mathbf{E}$, and the variables $\mathbf{a}$ and ϕ are related by

$$\mathbf{E} = - \operatorname{grad} \phi - \frac{1}{c} \frac{d\mathbf{a}}{dt} \,,$$

$$\mathbf{H} = \operatorname{rot} \mathbf{a} \,.$$

As a consequence, one has

$$p_x = \frac{\partial L}{\partial \dot{x}} = m\dot{x} + \frac{e}{c} a_x$$

as well as corresponding equations for p_y and p_z; collectively, these may also be written as

$$\mathbf{p} = m\mathbf{v} + \frac{e}{c} \mathbf{a} \,. \tag{31}$$

This is not a *natural* system in the sense mentioned earlier, since L contains terms which are linear in the velocities. The Hamiltonian, $H = \mathbf{p}^T \dot{\mathbf{q}} - L(\mathbf{q}, \dot{\mathbf{q}}(\mathbf{q}, \mathbf{p}, t), t)$, is calculated in accordance with (9) to obtain

$$H = \frac{1}{2m} \left(\mathbf{p} - \frac{e}{c} \mathbf{a} \right)^2 + e \phi \,. \tag{32}$$

This expression is often used in electrodynamics and quantum mechanics and it may also be generalized for the relativistic case (see Pars 1968, for example).

Here, as in many other problems, the expression for the Lagrangian contains terms which are linear in the generalized velocities (as opposed to the so-called *natural systems* where the velocities appear only as quadratic terms). These *gyroscopic terms* often arise as a consequence of the elimination of cyclic coordinates. The energies $U(\mathbf{q})$ and $T(\mathbf{q}, \dot{\mathbf{q}})$ are independent of these coordinates, as is the case for the angle of rotation about the axis of symmetry of a symmetric top, for example (see Pars 1968).

4.2. Canonical transformations

A given Hamiltonian system can often be simplified considerably by a suitable transformation of variables. A particular type of such transformations is discussed in this section.

In the Hamiltonian equations there are $2n$ dependent variables. Generally, a transformation of variables from $\mathbf{q}, \mathbf{p}$ to $\mathbf{q}^*, \mathbf{p}^*$ will be of the form

$$\mathbf{q}^* = \mathbf{q}^*(\mathbf{q}, \mathbf{p}, t),$$

$$\mathbf{p}^* = \mathbf{p}^*(\mathbf{q}, \mathbf{p}, t), \qquad\qquad (33)$$

with the corresponding transformed differential eqns (13) given by

$$\dot{\mathbf{q}}^* = \dot{\mathbf{q}}^*(\mathbf{q}^*, \mathbf{p}^*, t),$$

$$\dot{\mathbf{p}}^* = \dot{\mathbf{p}}^*(\mathbf{q}^*, \mathbf{p}^*, t). \qquad\qquad (34)$$

Consider now the special case where the system (34) again has the same symmetry properties as the system (13), that is, where there exists a function $H^*(\mathbf{q}^*, \mathbf{p}^*, t)$ such that the system (34) is generated by

$$\dot{\mathbf{q}}^* = \frac{\partial H^*}{\partial \mathbf{p}^*},$$

$$\dot{\mathbf{p}}^* = -\frac{\partial H^*}{\partial \mathbf{q}^*}. \qquad\qquad (35)$$

A transformation which transforms *every* system of Hamiltonian differential equations into another system of differential equations of the same type is called a *canonical transformation* or a *contact transformation*. With the assumption that the transformation (33) is univalent and invertible, it follows from this definition:

(1) *That the inverse of a canonical transformation is a canonical transformation;*
(2) *That the 'product' of two canonical transformations is itself a canonical transformation.*†

Such canonical transformations will now be investigated in more detail.

If the equations of motion in terms of the new variable take on the form (35), then it follows that not only

$$\delta \int_{t_1}^{t_2} \{\mathbf{p}^T\dot{\mathbf{q}} - H(\mathbf{q}, \mathbf{p}, t)\} \, \mathrm{d}t = 0 \qquad\qquad (36)$$

is satisfied, but also

---

†Note that the set of all canonical transformations forms a *group* under the composition operation.

$$\delta \int_{t_1}^{t_2} \{\mathbf{p}^{*T}\dot{\mathbf{q}}^* - H^*(\mathbf{q}^*, \mathbf{p}^*, t)\}\mathrm{d}t = 0. \tag{37}$$

The expressions (36) and (37) may be equivalent without the integrands being equal. The variational equations do not change for example if the integrand is multiplied by an arbitrary constant $c \neq 0$. Furthermore, the integrands may also differ by the total time-derivative of a function ϕ—in other words, by an exact differential. Choose $\mathbf{q}$, $\mathbf{q}^*$, and t as the independent variables in $\phi = \phi_1(\mathbf{q}, \mathbf{q}^*, t)$; then the variations (36) and (37) certainly are equivalent if

$$c\{\mathbf{p}^T\dot{\mathbf{q}} - H(\mathbf{q}, \mathbf{p}, t)\} = \mathbf{p}^{*T}\dot{\mathbf{q}}^* - H^*(\mathbf{q}^*, \mathbf{p}^*, t) + \frac{\mathrm{d}}{\mathrm{d}t}\phi_1(\mathbf{q}, \mathbf{q}^*, t) \tag{38}$$

holds, and the identity

$$\frac{\mathrm{d}}{\mathrm{d}t}\phi_1(\mathbf{q}, \mathbf{q}^*, t) = \frac{\partial \phi_1}{\partial t} + \left(\frac{\partial \phi_1}{\partial \mathbf{q}}\right)^T \dot{\mathbf{q}} + \left(\frac{\partial \phi_1}{\partial \mathbf{q}^*}\right)^T \dot{\mathbf{q}}^* \tag{39}$$

may be used to write eqn (38) in the form

$$\left(c\mathbf{p} - \frac{\partial \phi_1}{\partial \mathbf{q}}\right)^T \dot{\mathbf{q}} = \left(\mathbf{p}^* + \frac{\partial \phi_1}{\partial \mathbf{q}^*}\right)^T \dot{\mathbf{q}}^* + c\,H(\mathbf{q}, \mathbf{p}, t) -$$

$$- H^*(\mathbf{q}^*, \mathbf{p}^*, t) + \frac{\partial \phi_1}{\partial t}. \tag{40}$$

This equation is identically satisfied if

$$c\mathbf{p} = \frac{\partial \phi_1}{\partial \mathbf{q}}, \tag{41}$$

$$\mathbf{p}^* = -\frac{\partial \phi_1}{\partial \mathbf{q}^*}, \tag{42}$$

$$H^*(\mathbf{q}^*, \mathbf{p}^*, t) = c\,H(\mathbf{q}(\mathbf{q}^*, \mathbf{p}^*, t), \mathbf{p}(\mathbf{q}^*, \mathbf{p}^*, t), t) + \frac{\partial \phi_1}{\partial t} \tag{43}$$

are satisfied. These are the transformation equations for a given function ϕ_1, for, in principle, eqns (41) and (42) may be solved for $\mathbf{q}^*, \mathbf{p}^*$ or for $\mathbf{q}, \mathbf{p}$ provided the Jacobian determinant is non-zero. The function $\phi_1(\mathbf{q}, \mathbf{q}^*, t)$ is called the *generating function* of the transformation. As long as ϕ_1 does not depend explicitly on t, it follows from (43) that the new Hamiltonian may be obtained simply by expressing $\mathbf{q}$ and $\mathbf{p}$ in terms of $\mathbf{q}^*$ and $\mathbf{p}^*$ in $cH(\mathbf{q}, \mathbf{p}, t)$. In the future,

c in eqns (38)–(43) will always be taken to be equal to one since $c \neq 1$ provides no additional important results.

In eqn (38), instead of viewing ϕ as a function of $\mathbf{q}, \mathbf{q}^*, t$ one could equally well have chosen a function $\phi_2(\mathbf{q}, \mathbf{p}^*, t)$ of the variables $\mathbf{q}$, $\mathbf{p}^*$, and t. The *Legendre-transformation*† may be used to reduce this case to the one which has just been treated. Toward this purpose, consider (42) as a transformation from $\mathbf{q}^*$ to $-\mathbf{p}^*$ and determine the generating function for the inverse transformations from $\mathbf{p}^*$ to $\mathbf{q}^*$. In accordance with Legendre one has

$$\phi_2(\mathbf{q}, \mathbf{p}^*, t) = \phi_1(\mathbf{q}, \mathbf{q}^*, t) + \mathbf{p}^{*T}\mathbf{q}^* \tag{44}$$

(the signs which have been used here are those commonly used in analytical mechanics). The relationship (38) then may be replaced by the new relation

$$\mathbf{p}^T\dot{\mathbf{q}} - H(\mathbf{q}, \mathbf{p}, t) = \mathbf{p}^{*T}\dot{\mathbf{q}}^* - H^*(\mathbf{q}^*, \mathbf{p}^*, t) + \frac{\mathrm{d}}{\mathrm{d}t}(\phi_2 - \mathbf{p}^{*T}\mathbf{q}^*). \tag{45}$$

With

$$\frac{\mathrm{d}}{\mathrm{d}t}(\phi_2 - \mathbf{p}^{*T}\mathbf{q}^*) = \frac{\partial \phi_2}{\partial t} + \left(\frac{\partial \phi_2}{\partial \mathbf{q}}\right)^T \dot{\mathbf{q}} + \left(\frac{\partial \phi_2}{\partial \mathbf{p}^*}\right)^T \dot{\mathbf{p}}^* -$$

$$- \mathbf{p}^{*T}\dot{\mathbf{q}}^* - \mathbf{q}^{*T}\dot{\mathbf{p}}^* \tag{46}$$

one finally obtains

$$\mathbf{p} = \frac{\partial \phi_2(\mathbf{q}, \mathbf{p}^*, t)}{\partial \mathbf{q}}, \tag{47}$$

$$\mathbf{q}^* = \frac{\partial \phi_2(\mathbf{q}, \mathbf{p}^*, t)}{\partial \mathbf{p}^*}, \tag{48}$$

$$H^* = H + \frac{\partial \phi_2(\mathbf{q}, \mathbf{p}^*, t)}{\partial t} \tag{49}$$

for the transformation generated by $\phi_2(\mathbf{q}, \mathbf{p}^*, t)$. In a similar manner one obtains

---

†If the coordinate transformation $\mathbf{y} = \partial\phi(\mathbf{x})/\partial\mathbf{x}$ is given by the generating function $\phi(\mathbf{x})$ and if one wishes to obtain the generating function of the inverse transformation $\mathbf{x} = \mathbf{x}(\mathbf{y})$, then one may proceed in the following manner:
Write $\psi(\mathbf{y}) = \mathbf{y}^T\mathbf{x}(\mathbf{y}) - \phi(\mathbf{x}(\mathbf{y}))$ and form
$\frac{\partial \psi}{\partial \mathbf{y}} = \mathbf{x} + \left(\frac{\partial \mathbf{x}}{\partial \mathbf{y}}\right)^T \mathbf{y} - \left(\frac{\partial \mathbf{x}}{\partial \mathbf{y}}\right)^T \frac{\partial \phi}{\partial \mathbf{x}} = \mathbf{x}$, from which $\mathbf{x} = \frac{\partial \psi(\mathbf{y})}{\partial \mathbf{y}}$ indeed follows.

This pair, transformation and inverse transformation, is called the *Legendre transformation*.

$$\mathbf{q} = -\frac{\partial \varphi_3 \,(\mathbf{p}, \mathbf{q}^*, t)}{\partial \mathbf{p}} \,, \tag{50}$$

$$\mathbf{p}^* = -\frac{\partial \phi_3 \,(\mathbf{p}, \mathbf{q}^*, t)}{\partial \mathbf{q}^*} \,, \tag{51}$$

$$H^* = H + \frac{\partial \phi_3 \,(\mathbf{p}, \mathbf{q}^*, t)}{\partial t} \,, \tag{52}$$

for $\phi = \phi_3(\mathbf{p}, \mathbf{q}^*, t)$, and

$$\mathbf{q} = -\frac{\partial \phi_4 \,(\mathbf{p}, \mathbf{p}^*, t)}{\partial \mathbf{p}} \,, \tag{53}$$

$$\mathbf{q}^* = \frac{\partial \phi_4 \,(\mathbf{p}, \mathbf{p}^*, t)}{\partial \mathbf{p}^*} \,, \tag{54}$$

$$H^* = H + \frac{\partial \phi_4 \,(\mathbf{p}, \mathbf{p}^*, t)}{\partial t} \,, \tag{55}$$

for $\phi = \phi_4(\mathbf{p}, \mathbf{p}^*, t)$. The great generality of the canonical transformations expressed in the arbitrariness of the choice of generating functions often has the consequence that the distinct meaning of the generalized coordinates and momenta is completely lost. Consider the generating function $\phi = \phi_1 \,(\mathbf{q}, \mathbf{q}^*) = \mathbf{q}^T \mathbf{q}^*$, for example; then it follows from (41)–(43) that

$$\left.\begin{array}{l} \mathbf{p} \ = \dfrac{\partial \phi_1}{\partial \mathbf{q}} \ = \ \mathbf{q}^* \,, \\[3ex] \mathbf{p}^* \ = -\dfrac{\partial \phi_1}{\partial \mathbf{q}^*} \ = \ -\mathbf{q} \,, \\[3ex] H^* \,(\mathbf{q}^*, \mathbf{p}^*, t) \ = \ H\,(-\mathbf{p}^*, \mathbf{q}^*, t)\,, \end{array}\right\} \tag{56}$$

hold, that is, with the exception of a sign change the momenta and coordinates have been interchanged.

The simplest type of canonical transformation is that for which $\mathbf{q}^*(\mathbf{q}, \mathbf{p}, t)$ does not depend on $\mathbf{p}$ but only on $\mathbf{q}$ and possibly t. In that case, the coordinates are transformed only among themselves; this special kind of canonical transformation is called a *point transformation*. Whereas a canonical transformation normally destroys the distinct meaning of the coordinates and momenta (coordinates describe the position; momenta together with the coordinates, the velocity), this meaning is preserved for point transformations.

The transformation

$$\mathbf{q}^* = \mathbf{f}(\mathbf{q}, t) \tag{57}$$

of the coordinates among each other may be derived from the generating function

$$\phi = \phi_2(\mathbf{q}, \mathbf{p}^*, t) = \mathbf{f}^T(\mathbf{q}, t)\, \mathbf{p}^*, \tag{58}$$

for it follows from (47)–(49) that

$$\mathbf{p} = \frac{\partial \phi_2}{\partial \mathbf{q}} = \left(\frac{\partial \mathbf{f}}{\partial \mathbf{q}}\right)^T \mathbf{p}^*, \tag{59}$$

$$\mathbf{q}^* = \frac{\partial \phi_2}{\partial \mathbf{p}^*} = \mathbf{f}(\mathbf{q}, t), \tag{60}$$

$$H^* = H + \frac{\partial \mathbf{f}^T(\mathbf{q}, t)}{\partial t}\, \mathbf{p}^*, \tag{61}$$

is the case and that (60) again corresponds to (57).† For a given point transformation based on $\mathbf{f}(\mathbf{q}, t)$ eqns (59) and (61) provide the transformation of the momenta and of the Hamiltonian.

For a given transformation of the type (33), it generally is not immediately apparent whether it is canonical or not. It thus is desirable to have a criterion which may be used to determine if a transformation is canonical. Poisson brackets may be used toward this purpose. For given functions $f(\mathbf{q}, \mathbf{p}, t), g(\mathbf{q}, \mathbf{p}, t)$, both in C^1, the Poisson brackets are defined by

$$[f, g] = \left(\frac{\partial f}{\partial \mathbf{q}}\right)^T \left(\frac{\partial g}{\partial \mathbf{p}}\right) - \left(\frac{\partial f}{\partial \mathbf{p}}\right)^T \left(\frac{\partial g}{\partial \mathbf{q}}\right); \tag{62}$$

$[f, g]$ again is a scalar function of $\mathbf{q}$, $\mathbf{p}$, and t. It can be shown (see Lur'é 1968, for example) that the transformation (33) is canonical if and only if the conditions

$$[q_i^*, q_k^*] = 0, \quad [p_i^*, p_k^*] = 0, \quad [p_i^*, q_k^*] = \delta_{ik}, \quad i, k = 1, 2, \ldots, n \tag{63}$$

are satisfied, where δ_{ik} is the Kronecker delta.

†In (58) an arbitrary function $\lambda(\mathbf{q}, t)$ may still be added (see Teschner 1977).

Example. The linear harmonic oscillator. Consider the Hamiltonian of the linear harmonic oscillator,

$$H = \frac{p^2}{2} + \frac{\omega_0^2}{2} q^2 , \tag{64}$$

where ω_0^2 is constant. The equations of motion are

$$\left. \begin{aligned} \dot{q} &= p , \\ \dot{p} &= -\omega_0^2 q \end{aligned} \right\} \tag{65}$$

and they again result in $\ddot{q} + \omega_0^2 q = 0$. Now, the transformation generated by

$$\phi_1 \, (q, q^*) = \frac{\omega_0}{2} q^2 \cot q^* \tag{66}$$

is to be carried out. With (41), (42), and $c = 1$, one obtains

$$\left. \begin{aligned} p &= \frac{\partial \phi_1}{\partial q} = \omega_0 q \cot q^* , \\ p^* &= -\frac{\partial \phi_1}{\partial q^*} = \frac{\omega_0}{2} \frac{q^2}{\sin^2 q^*} , \end{aligned} \right\} \tag{67}$$

whose solution for q, p results in

$$\left. \begin{aligned} q &= \sqrt{\left(\frac{2}{\omega_0}\right)} \sqrt{(p^*)} \, \sin q^* , \\ p &= \sqrt{(2\,\omega_0)} \sqrt{(p^*)} \, \cos q^* . \end{aligned} \right\} \tag{68}$$

The new Hamiltonian is given by

$$H^*(q^*, p^*) = H \, (q \, (q^*, p^*), p \, (q^*, p^*)) = \omega_0 p^* , \tag{69}$$

and the system equations in terms of the new variables become

$$\left. \begin{aligned} \dot{q}^* &= \frac{\partial H^*}{\partial p^*} = \omega_0 , \\ \dot{p}^* &= -\frac{\partial H^*}{\partial q^*} = 0 , \end{aligned} \right\} \tag{70}$$

with the general solution

$$\left. \begin{aligned} q^* &= \omega_0 t + \alpha , \\ p^* &= \beta , \end{aligned} \right\} \tag{71}$$

where α and β are constants of integration. A transformation back to the original variables again yields the known solution

$$
\left.
\begin{aligned}
q &= \sqrt{\left(\frac{2\beta}{\omega_0}\right)} \, \sin\left(\omega_0 t + \alpha\right), \\[2mm]
p &= \sqrt{\left(2\,\omega_0\beta\right)} \, \cos\left(\omega_0 t + \alpha\right).
\end{aligned}
\right\}
\tag{72}
$$

4.3. The Hamilton–Jacobi differential equation

It has been shown that the canonical transformation

$$
\left.
\begin{aligned}
\mathbf{q^*} &= \mathbf{q^*}\,(\mathbf{q},\mathbf{p},t), \\[2mm]
\mathbf{p^*} &= \mathbf{p^*}\,(\mathbf{q},\mathbf{p},t),
\end{aligned}
\right\}
\tag{73}
$$

transforms the system with Hamiltonian $H(\mathbf{q}, \mathbf{p}, t)$ into one described by $H^*(\mathbf{q^*}, \mathbf{p^*}, t)$ so that one has

$$
H^*\,(\mathbf{q^*},\mathbf{p^*},t) = H\,(\mathbf{q}\,(\mathbf{q^*},\mathbf{p^*},t),\mathbf{p}\,(\mathbf{q^*},\mathbf{p^*},t),t) + \frac{\partial S}{\partial t},
\tag{74}
$$

where $S = \phi_1(\mathbf{q}, \mathbf{q^*}, t)$ is the generating function of the transformation (73).

In the new coordinates, the equations of motions are given by

$$
\left.
\begin{aligned}
\dot{\mathbf{q}}^* &= \frac{\partial H^*}{\partial \mathbf{p^*}}, \\[4mm]
\dot{\mathbf{p}}^* &= -\frac{\partial H^*}{\partial \mathbf{q^*}}.
\end{aligned}
\right\}
\tag{75}
$$

Consider now the particular case where $\mathbf{q^*}$ and $\mathbf{p^*}$ turn out to be constant, say, $\mathbf{q^*} = \boldsymbol{\alpha}$ and $\mathbf{p^*} = \boldsymbol{\beta}$. The inverse transformation then yields the motion $\mathbf{q}(\boldsymbol{\alpha}, \boldsymbol{\beta}, t)$, $\mathbf{p}(\boldsymbol{\alpha}, \boldsymbol{\beta}, t)$ in terms of these constants of integration, $\boldsymbol{\alpha}$ and $\boldsymbol{\beta}$. The quantities $\mathbf{q^*}$ and $\mathbf{p^*}$ are constant if H^* vanishes identically, as is easily seen from equations (75). Eqn (74) with $H^* \equiv 0$ yields

$$
H\,(\mathbf{q},\mathbf{p},t) + \frac{\partial S}{\partial t} = 0,
\tag{76}
$$

and by considering that (41) with $c = 1$ leads to $\mathbf{p} = \partial S/\partial \mathbf{q}$ it follows that the condition

$$H\left(\mathbf{q}, \frac{\partial S}{\partial \mathbf{q}}, t\right) + \frac{\partial S}{\partial t} = 0 \tag{77}$$

must be fulfilled.

For a given function $H(\mathbf{q}, \mathbf{p}, t)$ this is a first-order partial differential equation in the unknown function $S(\mathbf{q}, \boldsymbol{\alpha}, t)$. In the following, a solution of (77) is needed which depends on n arbitrary constants $\alpha_1, \alpha_2, \ldots, \alpha_n$ in such a way that the Jacobian determinant of $\partial S/\partial q_i$ with respect to the α_j satisfies

$$\left| \frac{\partial^2 S}{\partial q_i \, \partial \alpha_j} \right| \neq 0 . \tag{78}$$

Among others, the condition (78) excludes the possibility in which one of the n constants α_j is additive; that is, one must have

$$S\left(\mathbf{q}, \boldsymbol{\alpha}, t\right) \neq \overline{S}\left(\mathbf{q}, \alpha_1, \alpha_2, \ldots, \alpha_{n-1}, t\right) + \alpha_n . \tag{79}$$

A solution $S(\mathbf{q}, \boldsymbol{\alpha}, t)$ satisfying (78) is called a 'complete solution' of (77).

The differential equation (77) is the Hamilton–Jacobi partial differential equation (the Hamilton–Jacobi–Bellman differential equation of optimal control). The solution of this partial differential equation is equivalent to finding the solutions of the equations of motion (13). Conversely, the solution of (13) is nothing more than a solution of (77) using the method of characteristics. Generally, it is not essentially simpler to solve (77) instead of (13).

If a complete solution $S(\mathbf{q}, \boldsymbol{\alpha}, t)$ of (77) is known, then one has

$$\left.\begin{aligned} \frac{\partial S}{\partial \mathbf{q}} &= \mathbf{p} , \\[2mm] \frac{\partial S}{\partial \boldsymbol{\alpha}} &= -\boldsymbol{\beta} , \end{aligned}\right\} \tag{80}$$

in accordance with (41), (42), and $c = 1$. Also, since the condition (78) is satisfied, the second of the two algebraic equations (80) may be solved for $\mathbf{q}$ and the first may then be solved for $\mathbf{p}(\boldsymbol{\alpha}, \boldsymbol{\beta}, t)$. One thus has a canonical transformation from the constants $\boldsymbol{\alpha}, \boldsymbol{\beta}$ to $\mathbf{q}, \mathbf{p}$. From the definition of a canonical transformation, it then follows that the inverse transformation $\boldsymbol{\alpha} = \boldsymbol{\alpha}(\mathbf{q}, \mathbf{p}, t)$, $\boldsymbol{\beta} = \boldsymbol{\beta}(\mathbf{q}, \mathbf{p}, t)$ also is canonical.

Note, however, that if a general solution of (13) in the form $\mathbf{q} = \mathbf{q}(\boldsymbol{\gamma}, \boldsymbol{\delta}, t)$, $\mathbf{p} = \mathbf{p}(\boldsymbol{\gamma}, \boldsymbol{\delta}, t)$ is known, with constant vectors $\boldsymbol{\gamma}, \boldsymbol{\delta}$, then the correspondingly defined transformation from $\boldsymbol{\gamma}, \boldsymbol{\delta}$ to $\mathbf{q}, \mathbf{p}$ generally need not necessarily be canonical! An important special case is given by the situation where $\boldsymbol{\gamma}$ and $\boldsymbol{\delta}$ are precisely the initial values of $\mathbf{q}$ and $\mathbf{p}$, that is, if one has the relations

$$\left. \begin{array}{l} \mathbf{q} = \mathbf{q}\,(\mathbf{q}_0, \mathbf{p}_0, t)\,, \\[2ex] \mathbf{p} = \mathbf{p}\,(\mathbf{q}_0, \mathbf{p}_0, t) \end{array} \right\} \tag{81}$$

with $\mathbf{q}_0 = \mathbf{q}(\mathbf{q}_0, \mathbf{p}_0, t_0)$, $\mathbf{p}_0 = \mathbf{p}(\mathbf{q}_0, \mathbf{p}_0, t_0)$; as will be proven in section 4.4, the transformation from $\mathbf{q}_0$, $\mathbf{p}_0$ to $\mathbf{q}$, $\mathbf{p}$ is always canonical! Thus, every motion of an arbitrary Hamiltonian system corresponds to a one-parameter family of canonical transformations with t as the parameter.

An important special case arises when H does not depend on the time explicitly. The solution to (77) then may be formulated in the form

$$S\,(\mathbf{q}, \boldsymbol{\alpha}, t) = -ht + W\,(\mathbf{q}, \boldsymbol{\alpha}) \tag{82}$$

with $h = h(\boldsymbol{\alpha})$. The use of (82) in (77) yields

$$H\left(\mathbf{q}, \frac{\partial W}{\partial \mathbf{q}}\right) = h\,, \tag{83}$$

where h is the energy constant. For example, one may choose $h = \alpha_n$ so that

$$W = W(\mathbf{q}, \alpha_1, \alpha_2, \ldots, \alpha_{n-1}, h) \tag{84}$$

depends on $n - 1$ further arbitrary constants in addition to h. Recall that the Jacobian determinant with respect to the n coordinates and the n constants α_1, $\alpha_2, \ldots, \alpha_{n-1}, h$ may not vanish. Eqns (80) together with the formulation (82) now yield the system

$$\frac{\partial W}{\partial \alpha_i} = -\beta_i\,, \qquad i = 1, 2, \ldots, n-1, \tag{85}$$

$$\frac{\partial W}{\partial h} = t - \beta_n\,, \tag{86}$$

$$\frac{\partial W}{\partial \mathbf{q}} = \mathbf{p}\,. \tag{87}$$

The term $t - \beta_n$ in (86) follows directly from the fact that the system is autonomous. Indeed, one generally has: If $\dot{\mathbf{x}} = \mathbf{f}(\mathbf{x})$ is an arbitrary autonomous system with solution $\mathbf{x}(t)$, then $\mathbf{x}(t - \beta_n)$, with β_n arbitrary, is also a solution. Eqn (85) may be solved for $n - 1$ components of $\mathbf{q}$, say, for $q_1, q_2, \ldots, q_{n-1}$, resulting in

$$
\left.
\begin{aligned}
q_1 &= q_1 \ (\alpha_1, \alpha_2, \ldots, \alpha_{n-1}, h, \beta_1, \beta_2, \ldots, \beta_{n-1}, q_n), \\
q_2 &= q_2 \ (\alpha_1, \alpha_2, \ldots, \alpha_{n-1}, h, \beta_1, \beta_2, \ldots, \beta_{n-1}, q_n), \\
&\ \vdots \\
q_{n-1} &= q_{n-1} \ (\alpha_1, \alpha_2, \ldots, \alpha_{n-1}, h, \beta_1, \beta_2, \ldots, \beta_{n-1}, q_n).
\end{aligned}
\right\}
\tag{88}
$$

These equations describe the trajectories, but they no longer contain the time! The time is replaced by another parameter, in the present case, by q_n.

Two *examples* are now given to illustrate the use of the Hamilton–Jacobi theory for the integration of the equations of motion:

(1) *The linear harmonic oscillator.* Consider once more the example from section 4.2 with

$$
H = \frac{p^2}{2} + \frac{\omega_0^2}{2} q^2 .
\tag{89}
$$

The corresponding Hamilton–Jacobi equation is given by

$$
\frac{1}{2} \left(\frac{\partial S}{\partial q} \right)^2 + \frac{\omega_0^2}{2} q^2 + \frac{\partial S}{\partial t} = 0 .
\tag{90}
$$

With the initial formulation

$$
S(q, h, t) = -ht + W(q, h)
\tag{91}
$$

the complete solution is obtained from

$$
\frac{1}{2} \left(\frac{\partial W}{\partial q} \right)^2 + \frac{\omega_0^2}{2} q^2 = h
\tag{92}
$$

as

$$
W = \int \sqrt{(2h - \omega_0^2 q^2)} \, dq
\tag{93}
$$

and, consequently, one has

$$
S(q, h, t) = -ht + \int \sqrt{(2h - \omega_0^2 q^2)} \, dq.
\tag{94}
$$

From (86) and (87) one now obtains

$$
\left.
\begin{aligned}
p &= \frac{\partial W}{\partial q} = \sqrt{(2h - \omega_0^2 q^2)}, \\
t - \beta &= \frac{\partial W}{\partial h} = \int \frac{dq}{\sqrt{(2h - \omega_0^2 q^2)}} = \frac{1}{\omega_0} \arcsin \frac{q \omega_0}{\sqrt{(2h)}}
\end{aligned}
\right\}
\tag{95}
$$

and eventually

$$q = \frac{\sqrt{(2h)}}{\omega_0} \sin \omega_0 (t - \beta),$$

$$p = \sqrt{(2h)} \cos \omega_0 (t - \beta).$$

$\left.\vphantom{\begin{array}{c} \\ \\ \\ \\ \end{array}}\right\}$ (96)

Of course, there exist numerous other integrals besides the complete integral (94). For example,

$$S(q, \alpha, t) = \frac{1}{2} \omega_0 (q^2 + \alpha^2) \cot \omega_0 t - \frac{\omega_0 q \alpha}{\sin \omega_0 t},$$ (97)

is another such integral for which $\partial S/\partial \alpha = -\beta$ and $\partial S/\partial q = p$ result in

$$q = \frac{\beta}{\omega_0} \sin \omega_0 t + \alpha \cos \omega_0 t,$$

$$p = -\omega_0 \alpha \sin \omega_0 t + \beta \cos \omega_0 t.$$

$\left.\vphantom{\begin{array}{c} \\ \\ \\ \\ \end{array}}\right\}$ (98)

The connection between the integrals (97) and (94) is investigated by Pars (1968, p. 279 ff.), for example.

(2) *The elastic pendulum.* One end of a massless spring with spring constant c supports a particle of mass m whereas the other end is hinged at a fixed point P (Fig. 4.2).

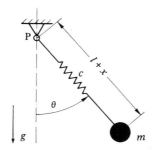

Fig. 4.2. The elastic pendulum.

Let l be the distance between P and the particle in the equilibrium position arising under the action of the gravitational force mg, and let x denote the additional elongation of the spring with respect to the equilibrium position. Then the kinetic and the potential energy may be written as

$$T = \frac{m}{2} \{\dot{x}^2 + (l + x)^2 \dot{\theta}^2\},$$

$$U = \frac{1}{2} \{cx^2 + 2mg (l + x) (1 - \cos \theta)\}$$

$\left.\vphantom{\begin{array}{c} \\ \\ \\ \\ \end{array}}\right\}$ (99)

or as

$$
T = \frac{ml^2}{2}\{\dot{q}_1^2 + (1 + q_1)^2\dot{q}_2^2\},
$$

$$
U = \frac{cl^2}{2}\{q_1^2 + 2\frac{mg}{cl}(1 + q_1)(1 - \cos q_2)\}
$$

$\left.\begin{array}{c}\\ \\ \end{array}\right\}$ (100)

in terms of the non-dimensional coordinates $q_1 = x/l$ and $q_2 = \theta$. With

$$
\frac{\partial T}{\partial \dot{q}_1} = ml^2\dot{q}_1 = p_1, \qquad \frac{\partial T}{\partial \dot{q}_2} = ml^2(1 + q_1)^2\dot{q}_2 = p_2, \tag{101}
$$

the Hamiltonian follows as

$$
H = \frac{1}{2ml^2}\left\{p_1^2 + \frac{p_2^2}{(1 + q_1)^2}\right\} +
$$

$$
+ \frac{cl^2}{2}\{q_1^2 + 2\frac{mg}{cl}(1 + q_1)(1 - \cos q_2)\}. \tag{102}
$$

The corresponding equations of motion are strongly non-linear and they cannot be solved analytically. Consider, for the moment, only the quadratic terms in the expression for H to obtain

$$
H_0 = \frac{1}{2ml^2}\left(p_1^2 + p_2^2\right) + \frac{cl^2}{2}\left(q_1^2 + \frac{mg}{cl}q_2^2\right); \tag{103}
$$

corresponding to the linear oscillations of the system.

From the reduced Hamiltonian (103), one obtains the Hamilton–Jacobi equation

$$
\frac{\partial S}{\partial t} + \frac{1}{2ml^2}\left\{\left(\frac{\partial S}{\partial q_1}\right)^2 + \left(\frac{\partial S}{\partial q_2}\right)^2\right\} + \frac{cl^2}{2}\left(q_1^2 + \frac{mg}{cl}q_2^2\right) = 0, \tag{104}
$$

for which a complete solution is to be obtained. The initial formulation

$$
S = -ht + W_1(q_1, \alpha_1) + W_2(q_2, \alpha_2) \qquad \text{with} \qquad h = \alpha_1 + \alpha_2 \tag{105}
$$

results in the non-linear differential equations

$$
\frac{1}{2ml^2}\left(\frac{\partial W_1}{\partial q_1}\right)^2 + \frac{cl^2}{2}q_1^2 = \alpha_1,
$$

$$
\frac{1}{2ml^2}\left(\frac{\partial W_2}{\partial q_2}\right)^2 + \frac{mgl}{2}q_2^2 = \alpha_2,
$$

$\left.\begin{array}{c}\\ \\ \end{array}\right\}$ (106)

which are satisfied by

$$W_1 = \int \sqrt{(2ml^2)} \sqrt{\left(\alpha_1 - \frac{cl^2}{2} q_1^2\right)} dq_1 ,$$

$$W_2 = \int \sqrt{(2ml^2)} \sqrt{\left(\alpha_2 - \frac{mgl}{2} q_2^2\right)} dq_2 . \tag{107}$$

The use of (105) together with (80) then yields

$$-\beta_1 = \frac{\partial S}{\partial \alpha_1} = -t + \int \frac{dq_1}{\sqrt{\left(\frac{2\alpha_1}{ml^2} - \omega_1^2 q_1^2\right)}} = -t + \frac{1}{\omega_1} \arcsin \frac{q_1 \omega_1}{\sqrt{\left(\frac{2\alpha_1}{ml^2}\right)}} ,$$

$$-\beta_2 = \frac{\partial S}{\partial \alpha_2} = -t + \int \frac{dq_2}{\sqrt{\left(\frac{2\alpha_2}{ml^2} - \omega_2^2 q_2^2\right)}} = -t + \frac{1}{\omega_2} \arcsin \frac{q_2 \omega_2}{\sqrt{\left(\frac{2\alpha_1}{ml^2}\right)}} , \tag{108}$$

$$\omega_1 = \sqrt{(c/m)}, \quad \omega_2 = \sqrt{(g/l)}$$

and, hence,

$$q_1 = \frac{1}{\omega_1} \sqrt{\left(\frac{2\alpha_1}{ml^2}\right)} \sin \omega_1 (t - \beta_1) ,$$

$$q_2 = \frac{1}{\omega_2} \sqrt{\left(\frac{2\alpha_2}{ml^2}\right)} \sin \omega_2 (t - \beta_2) \tag{109}$$

as well as

$$p_1 = \frac{\partial S}{\partial q_1} = \sqrt{(2ml^2)} \sqrt{\left(\alpha_1 - \frac{cl^2}{2} q_1^2\right)} = \sqrt{(2ml^2)} \sqrt{(\alpha_1)} \cos \omega_1 (t - \beta_1) ,$$

$$p_2 = \frac{\partial S}{\partial q_2} = \sqrt{(2ml^2)} \sqrt{\left(\alpha_2 - \frac{mgl}{2} q_2^2\right)} = \sqrt{(2ml^2)} \sqrt{(\alpha_2)} \cos \omega_2 (t - \beta_2) . \tag{110}$$

Naturally, the results (109) and (110) could equally well have been obtained directly as the solutions of the linearized ordinary differential equations. The non-linear problem will be discussed further in the next section and the advantages of the Hamiltonian formalism will then become apparent.

In (103) the function (102) has been replaced by a quadratic form. It is easy to see that the problem defined by

$$\bar{H}_0 = \frac{1}{2ml^2} (p_1^2 + p_2^2) + \frac{cl^2}{2} \left\{ q_1^2 + \frac{2mg}{cl} (1 - \cos q_2) \right\} \tag{111}$$

may also be completely solved, in spite of the fact that $\bar{H}_0$ contains terms of higher order than the second in q_2.

4.4. Canonical transformations and the motion

Let $H(\mathbf{q}, \mathbf{p}, t) \in C^1$ be an arbitrary function and let

$$\left.\begin{aligned} \mathbf{q} &= \mathbf{q}\,(\mathbf{q}_0, \mathbf{p}_0, t)\,, \\[1em] \mathbf{p} &= \mathbf{p}\,(\mathbf{q}_0, \mathbf{p}_0, t) \end{aligned}\right\} \tag{112}$$

be the general solution of the corresponding Hamiltonian equations with $\mathbf{q}_0$ $= \mathbf{q}(\mathbf{q}_0, \mathbf{p}_0, t_0)$, $\mathbf{p}_0 = \mathbf{p}(\mathbf{q}_0, \mathbf{p}_0, t_0)$, that is, $\mathbf{q}_0$ and $\mathbf{p}_0$ are the initial values of $\mathbf{q}$ and $\mathbf{p}$. Then (112) is a canonical transformation from $\mathbf{q}_0$, $\mathbf{p}_0$ to $\mathbf{q}(\bar{t})$, $\mathbf{p}(\bar{t})$ for every fixed $t = \bar{t}$. The motions of an arbitrary Hamiltonian system in the form (112) thus constitute a one-parameter family of canonical transformations. The proof is given by means of Hamilton's principle.

For the comparison of the value of the integral $\int_{t_0}^{t_1} L(\mathbf{q}, \dot{\mathbf{q}}, t)\,\mathrm{d}t$ along a trajectory $\mathbf{q}(t)$, $\dot{\mathbf{q}}(t)$ with that corresponding to a neighbouring trajectory given by $\mathbf{q}(t) + \delta\mathbf{q}(t)$, $\dot{\mathbf{q}}(t) + \delta\dot{\mathbf{q}}(t)$, it is known from the calculus of variations that

$$\delta \int_{t_0}^{t_1} L\,(\mathbf{q}, \dot{\mathbf{q}}, t)\,\mathrm{d}t = \int_{t_0}^{t_1} L\,(\mathbf{q} + \delta\mathbf{q}, \dot{\mathbf{q}} + \delta\dot{\mathbf{q}}, t)\mathrm{d}t - \int_{t_0}^{t_1} L\,(\mathbf{q}, \dot{\mathbf{q}}, t)\mathrm{d}t =$$

$$= \left(\frac{\partial L}{\partial \dot{\mathbf{q}}}\right)^{\mathrm{T}} \delta\mathbf{q}\ \Bigg|_{t_0}^{t_1} + \int_{t_0}^{t_1}\left(\frac{\partial L}{\partial \mathbf{q}} - \frac{\mathrm{d}}{\mathrm{d}t}\frac{\partial L}{\partial \dot{\mathbf{q}}}\right)^{\mathrm{T}} \delta\mathbf{q}\,\mathrm{d}t \tag{113}$$

is valid as long as t_0 and t_1 are fixed (see Gantmacher 1970, for example). If it is assumed, in addition, that $\delta\mathbf{q} = \mathbf{0}$ for $t = t_0$ and $t = t_1$, that is, only those trajectories in configuration space (the space of the generalized coordinates $\mathbf{q}$) with fixed end-points are admitted (just as hypothesized in Hamilton's principle), then Lagrange's equations (3) follow as necessary conditions for the actual motions.[†]

The motions (112) now are assumed known. For a given t_0 one may then compute the value of the integral $\int_{t_0}^{t} L(\mathbf{q}, \dot{\mathbf{q}}, \tau)\mathrm{d}\tau$ along an actual trajectory; the value of the integral depends only on the initial conditions $\mathbf{q}_0$, $\dot{\mathbf{q}}_0$, and t.

[†]Every solution of the equations of motion is designated as an *actual motion*. The term *possible motions*, however, is used to mean 'imagined' kinematically admissible 'motions' $\mathbf{q}(t)$ which generally need not be solutions of the equations of motion.

However, by using (112) the value of the integral may also be expressed in terms of $\mathbf{q_0}, \mathbf{p_0}, t$ or in terms of $\mathbf{q}, \mathbf{q_0}, t$.

In this manner, one defines the *principal function*

$$S(\mathbf{q}, \mathbf{q_0}, t) = \int_{t_0}^{t} L\left(\mathbf{q}(\mathbf{q_0}, \mathbf{p_0}, \tau), \dot{\mathbf{q}}(\mathbf{q_0}, \mathbf{p_0}, \tau), \tau\right) d\tau. \tag{114}$$

Observe that a change δS of the principal function during a transition from an actual motion to a neighbouring actual motion with different initial conditions may be calculated by means of (113). But the integral on the right-hand side of (113) vanishes, since both motions satisfy Lagrange's equations. One thus obtains

$$\delta S = \mathbf{p}^T \delta \mathbf{q} \Big|_{t_0}^{t} = \mathbf{p}^T \delta \mathbf{q} - \mathbf{p}_0^T \delta \mathbf{q_0} \tag{115}$$

and, hence,

$$\left. \begin{aligned} \frac{\partial S}{\partial \mathbf{q}} &= \mathbf{p}, \\[2mm] \frac{\partial S}{\partial \mathbf{q_0}} &= -\mathbf{p}_0. \end{aligned} \right\} \tag{116}$$

From a comparison of (116) and (41), (42), it is apparent that the principal function is the generating function for the transformation (112); it follows that (112) is a canonical transformation.

By taking the total derivative of (114) with respect to t, it is obvious that $S(\mathbf{q}, \mathbf{q_0}, t)$ satisfies the Hamilton–Jacobi equation. In fact, from (114) one obtains

$$\frac{dS}{dt} = L. \tag{117}$$

However, one also has

$$\frac{dS}{dt} = \frac{\partial S}{\partial t} + \left(\frac{\partial S}{\partial \mathbf{q}}\right)^T \dot{\mathbf{q}}, \tag{118}$$

which may be written in the form

$$\frac{\partial S}{\partial t} + \mathbf{p}^{\mathrm{T}}\dot{\mathbf{q}} - L = 0 \tag{119}$$

and, eventually, as

$$\frac{\partial S}{\partial t} + H\left(\mathbf{q}, \frac{\partial S}{\partial \mathbf{q}}, t\right) = 0 \tag{120}$$

by using the relations (116).

The integration of an arbitrary canonical system thus yields a canonical transformation $\mathbf{q}(\mathbf{q}_0, \mathbf{p}_0, t)$, $\mathbf{p}(\mathbf{q}_0, \mathbf{p}_0, t)$. Naturally, this transformation may be used on any other Hamiltonian system with the same number of degrees of freedom where the variables $\mathbf{q}$, $\mathbf{p}$, however, are no longer mapped into constant vectors.

4.5. Canonical perturbation theory

Consider now a system described by the Hamiltonian

$$H(\mathbf{q}, \mathbf{p}, t) = H_0(\mathbf{q}, \mathbf{p}, t) + H_1(\mathbf{q}, \mathbf{p}, t). \tag{121}$$

Let $H_0(\mathbf{q}, \mathbf{p}, t)$ be of a type for which the corresponding motions may be given analytically in closed form and let $H_1(\mathbf{q}, \mathbf{p}, t)$ represent a 'perturbation'. To be able to solve the problem corresponding to H_0 means that one may either cite the solutions $\mathbf{q}(\mathbf{q}_0, \mathbf{p}_0, t)$, $\mathbf{p}(\mathbf{q}_0, \mathbf{p}_0, t)$ of

$$\dot{\mathbf{q}} = \frac{\partial H_0}{\partial \mathbf{p}},$$

$$\dot{\mathbf{p}} = -\frac{\partial H_0}{\partial \mathbf{q}} \tag{122}$$

or that some complete integral $S_0(\mathbf{q}, \boldsymbol{\alpha}, t)$ of

$$\frac{\partial S_0}{\partial t} + H_0\left(\mathbf{q}, \frac{\partial S_0}{\partial \mathbf{q}}, t\right) = 0 \tag{123}$$

is known. One may then compute $\mathbf{q}(\boldsymbol{\alpha}, \boldsymbol{\beta}, t)$, $\mathbf{p}(\boldsymbol{\alpha}, \boldsymbol{\beta}, t)$ for the system (122) in the known manner in accordance with (80) with $\boldsymbol{\alpha}$ and $\boldsymbol{\beta}$ as constants of integration. The function $S_0(\mathbf{q}, \boldsymbol{\alpha}, t)$ may now be introduced as the generating function of a canonical transformation $(\mathbf{q}, \mathbf{p}) \rightarrow (\mathbf{q}^* = \boldsymbol{\alpha}, \mathbf{p}^* = \boldsymbol{\beta})$, which may then be used to transform the complete system (121). In accordance with (43), (121) then yields

$$H^*\left(\mathbf{q}^*, \mathbf{p}^*, t\right) = H_0 + H_1 + \frac{\partial S_0}{\partial t} \tag{124}$$

and, hence,

$$H^*\left(\mathbf{q}^*, \mathbf{p}^*, t\right) = H_1\left(\mathbf{q}\left(\mathbf{q}^*, \mathbf{p}^*, t\right), \mathbf{p}\left(\mathbf{q}^*, \mathbf{p}^*, t\right), t\right) \tag{125}$$

in view of (123), along with

$$\left.\begin{aligned}
\dot{\mathbf{q}}^* &= \frac{\partial H^*}{\partial \mathbf{p}^*}, \\[2mm]
\dot{\mathbf{p}}^* &= -\frac{\partial H^*}{\partial \mathbf{q}^*}.
\end{aligned}\right\} \tag{126}$$

In this connection, the constants of integration of the solutions of the 'simplified system' (122) are introduced as the new variables for the complete system.

This technique of a *variation of constants* is often used in the theory of differential equations. Here, however, the differential equations for the new variables (the 'constants of integration' $\boldsymbol{\alpha}, \boldsymbol{\beta}$) again assume the simple Hamiltonian form (126), since the generation of the transformation by means of the principal function S_0 ensures that $\boldsymbol{\alpha}$ and $\boldsymbol{\beta}$ are canonical conjugates of one another. If $\boldsymbol{\alpha}$ and $\boldsymbol{\beta}$ are not canonical conjugates but freely chosen constants of integration for (122), then (126) is replaced by differential equations which may be much more complicated (see Lur'é 1968, p. 557 ff., for example).

In principle, $H^*(\mathbf{q}^*, \mathbf{p}^*, t)$ may again be separated into two parts in accordance with (121), and this procedure may then be continued indefinitely. Because of computational considerations, the procedure will generally be limited to a small number of steps which may yield surprisingly good results for suitable choices of $\boldsymbol{\alpha}$ and $\boldsymbol{\beta}$. This is especially the case in celestial mechanics where a first approximation (H_0) to the n-body problem is assumed to be given by a number of two-body problems whose motions are the Keplerian ellipses (in general: conics). As constants of integration one chooses the six 'elements' of these ellipses, such as their eccentricity, length of the semi-major axis, and so on, and one then describes the motions of the n-body problem by means of 'slowly changing ellipses'. Non-canonical 'elements' also are often used in celestial mechanics.

Examples:

(1) *The Duffing equation.* Canonical perturbation theory is now used to obtain an approximate solution for the Duffing eqn (1.9). The Hamiltonian corresponding to

$$\ddot{q} + \omega_0^2 q + \mu q^3 = 0 \tag{127}$$

is given by

$$H(q, p) = \frac{1}{2}(p^2 + \omega_0^2 q^2) + \frac{1}{4}\mu q^4, \tag{128}$$

where the associations

$$\left. \begin{aligned} H_0 &= \frac{1}{2}(p^2 + \omega_0^2 q^2), \\[2mm] H_1 &= \frac{1}{4}\mu q^4, \end{aligned} \right\} \tag{129}$$

are made. The complete integral for

$$\frac{1}{2}\left\{\left(\frac{\partial S_0}{\partial q}\right)^2 + \omega_0^2 q^2\right\} + \frac{\partial S_0}{\partial t} = 0 \tag{130}$$

was already determined in (89)–(96), and it was given by

$$S_0(q, \alpha, t) = -\alpha t + \int \sqrt{(2\alpha - \omega_0^2 q^2)}\, dq, \tag{131}$$

where α has been used instead of h. The motion corresponding to H_0 thus is given by

$$\left. \begin{aligned} q &= \frac{\sqrt{(2\alpha)}}{\omega_0} \sin \omega_0 (t - \beta), \\[2mm] p &= \sqrt{(2\alpha)} \cos \omega_0 (t - \beta). \end{aligned} \right\} \tag{132}$$

The motion (132) now is interpreted as a canonical transformation between (q, p) and (α, β) generated by (131) to obtain

$$\begin{aligned} H^*(\alpha, \beta, t) &= H_1(q(\alpha, \beta, t), p(\alpha, \beta, t)) \\[2mm] &= \frac{\mu\alpha^2}{\omega_0^4} \sin^4 \omega_0(t - \beta), \end{aligned} \tag{133}$$

which may also be written in the form

$$H^*(\alpha, \beta, t) = \frac{\mu\alpha^2}{\omega_0^4}\left\{\frac{3}{8} - \frac{1}{2}\cos 2\omega_0(t - \beta) + \frac{1}{8}\cos 4\omega_0(t - \beta)\right\}. \tag{134}$$

In accordance with $H^* = H_0^* + H_1^*, H^*(\alpha, \beta, t)$ is separated into H_0^*, H_1^* with

$$\left. \begin{aligned} H_0^* &= \frac{3}{8}\frac{\mu\alpha^2}{\omega_0^4}, \\[2mm] H_1^* &= \frac{\mu\alpha^2}{8\omega_0^4}\left\{-4\cos 2\omega_0(t - \beta) + \cos 4\omega_0(t - \beta)\right\}, \end{aligned} \right\} \tag{135}$$

where H_0^* corresponds precisely to the temporal mean of (134) for fixed β. Now, neglect H_1^* and approximate H^* by H_0^*. Then one has

$$
\left.
\begin{aligned}
\dot{\alpha} &= \frac{\partial H_0^*}{\partial \beta} = 0 , \\[2em]
\dot{\beta} &= -\frac{\partial H_0^*}{\partial \alpha} = -\frac{3}{4}\frac{\mu\alpha}{\omega_0^4} ,
\end{aligned}
\right\}
\tag{136}
$$

with the solution $\alpha(t) = \alpha_0$, $\beta(t) = -\dfrac{3}{4}\dfrac{\mu\alpha_0}{\omega_0^4}\, t + \beta_0$, so that (132) eventually yields the approximate solution

$$
q = \frac{\sqrt{(2\alpha_0)}}{\omega_0} \sin\left\{ \omega_0\left(1 + \frac{3}{4}\frac{\mu\alpha_0}{\omega_0^4}\right) t - \omega_0\beta_0 \right\}.
\tag{137}
$$

This corresponds to the results obtained in Chapter 1.

    (2) *The elastic pendulum.* In (99)–(110) the linearized equations of motion of the elastic pendulum were treated. The Hamiltonian (102) now is approximated by $H = H_0 + H_1$ where H_0 corresponds to the expression (103) and where H_1 is given by

$$
H_1(q_1, q_2, p_1, p_2) = -\frac{1}{ml^2} q_1 p_2^2 + \frac{mgl}{2} q_1 q_2^2 ,
\tag{138}
$$

which contains all terms up to third order in the Taylor series expansion of (102). The substitution of (109), (110) in (138) yields

$$
H^*(\alpha, \beta, t) = -\frac{\alpha_2 \sqrt{(\alpha_1)}}{l\sqrt{(2c)}}\left[\sin \omega_1(t-\beta_1) + \frac{3}{2}\sin\{(\omega_1 + 2\omega_2)t - \right.
$$
$$
\left. - (\omega_1\beta_1 + 2\omega_2\beta_2)\} + \frac{3}{2}\sin\{(\omega_1 - 2\omega_2)t - (\omega_1\beta_1 - 2\omega_2\beta_2)\}\right].
\tag{139}
$$

The temporal mean of the right-hand side of (139) is zero, with the exception of $\omega_1 - 2\omega_2 \approx 0$, since $\sin\{(\omega_1 - 2\omega_2)t + (\omega_1\beta_1 - 2\omega_2\beta_2)\}$ then is essentially constant. Thus, when terms of third order are included in H, the approximate solutions for the elastic pendulum consist of the oscillations described by (109), (110) with constant α and β as long as there is no 'resonance' present. In order to deal with the 'resonance case' $\omega_1 = 2\omega_2$ in somewhat more detail, replace (139) by

$$
H_0^* = \frac{3}{2l\sqrt{(2c)}} \alpha_2 \sqrt{(\alpha_1)} \sin \omega_1(\beta_1 - \beta_2) .
\tag{140}
$$

This yields the equations of motion

$$\dot{\alpha}_1 = \frac{3\omega_1}{2l\sqrt{(2c)}} \ \alpha_2 \ \sqrt{(\alpha_1)} \cos \omega_1 \ (\beta_1 - \beta_2),$$

$$\dot{\alpha}_2 = -\frac{3\omega_1}{2l\sqrt{(2c)}} \ \alpha_2 \ \sqrt{(\alpha_1)} \cos \omega_1 \ (\beta_1 - \beta_2),$$

$$\dot{\beta}_1 = -\frac{3}{4l\sqrt{(2c)}} \ \frac{\alpha_2}{\sqrt{(\alpha_1)}} \ \sin \omega_1 \ (\beta_1 - \beta_2),$$

$$\dot{\beta}_2 = -\frac{3}{2l\sqrt{(2c)}} \ \sqrt{(\alpha_1)} \sin \omega_1 \ (\beta_1 - \beta_2).$$

$$(141)$$

These differential equations are integrated in Kane and Kahn (1968), for example. The integration of eqns (141) is omitted here; instead, the stability of the vertical oscillations ($q_2 \equiv 0$) of the pendulum will be investigated. Such oscillations, at any rate, are exact solutions of the complete non-linear system (102). They correspond to (109), (110) with $\alpha_2 = 0, \alpha_1 = \alpha_{10} > 0$.

From the previous discussion, it is known that they are stable in the non-resonance case within the approximation considered here. In Exercise 4.3, eqns (141) are used to investigate the stability of the stationary vertical oscillations for the resonance case $\omega_1 = 2\omega_2$. It turns out that these are always unstable: small perturbations in the initial conditions for α_2 lead to transverse oscillations (pendulous oscillations) with 'large' amplitudes.

It is easy to investigate experimentally how the energy wanders back and forth between the two eigenmodes of the linearized problem, and it must be emphasized that one is not dealing with the beat phenomenon known from the theory of linear oscillations. This wandering, which will not be investigated further here, is stated in detail in Kane and Kahn (1968). The case $\omega_1 - 2\omega_2 = \epsilon$, where ϵ is a small number, is treated by Heinbockel and Struble (1963), by Sethna (1965), and also by Nayfeh (1973).

4.6. General comments concerning Hamiltonian systems

The cited partial differential equation in section 4.3 was derived by Hamilton and by Jacobi during the past century. Further important results concerning Hamiltonian systems may be found in the classical works by Birkhoff (1927) and by Whittaker (1970), for example. From among the newer textbook authors, suffice it to cite Gantmacher (1970), Levi-Civita and Amaldi (1949), Lur'é (1968), and especially Pars (1968). Many important investigations, especially those concerning the existence of periodic solutions and applications in celestial mechanics in general, may be found in Poincaré (1957); newer results concerning celestial mechanics in a broader sense are given by Siegel and Moser (1971) as well as by Moser (1973).

Other than in the books cited above, detailed discussions of canonical perturbation theory may also be found in books by Giacaglia (1972) and by Nayfeh (1973). There, special consideration is also given to perturbation theory in accordance with Von Zeipel and with Lie. Only toward the end of the 1960s did various mathematicians use Lie series in canonical perturbation theory. In spite of the importance of Lie transformations, they are outside the framework of this book and the reader is referred to the above-mentioned authors.

An important problem of perturbation theory which here was dealt with only in passing concerns the 'external' and 'internal' resonances. External resonances are understood to be the case already treated in Chapter 1, where the excitation frequency is the same as the free oscillation frequency or, in a more general context, where they are rationally related—as for subharmonic resonance. One refers to internal resonance in systems with n degrees of freedom if there exist integers $m_1, m_2, \ldots, m_n$ such that there is a relation of the form $m_1\omega_1 + m_2\omega_2 + \ldots + m_n\omega_n = 0$ among the ω_i, where $\omega_1, \omega_2, \ldots, \omega_n$ are the eigenfrequencies of the linearized systems. Approximately, such equations may naturally be satisfied arbitrarily closely by using sufficiently large $m_i, i = 1, 2, \ldots, n$. Internal resonances cause difficulties in perturbation theory, particularly also in Hamiltonian systems because linear combinations of the frequencies occur in the denominators of the terms of the series expansions: in the case of internal resonance, one of these denominators may vanish and the series expansion thus becomes meaningless.

In this chapter the second approximation was treated for the case of inner resonance with $\omega_1 - 2\omega_2 = 0$, in Example 4.5 (the elastic pendulum). This example has been treated often and in much detail since behaviour typical for a whole group of mechanical systems may be clearly observed in terms of it. Other than Kane and Kahn (1968), a number of authors investigated the example; only Mettler (1975) and Heinbockel and Struble (1963) are mentioned here.

A representation of the theory of Hamiltonian systems in the light of the theory of non-linear oscillations is given by Forbat (1966). Hamiltonian theory is applied not only in classical mechanics but also in several problems of modern physics, as in the theoretical treatment of the synchrotron (R. Hagedorn 1956, 1957; R. Hagedorn, Hine, and Schoch 1956; Moser 1956), and in the treatment of problems in quantum mechanics by Schwinger.

References

Birkhoff, G. D. (1927). *Dynamical systems*. American Mathematical Society, Providence, Rhode Island.

Blaquière, A. (1966). *Nonlinear system analysis*. Academics Press, New York.

Forbat, N. (1966). *Analytische Mechanik der Schwingungen [Analytical mechanics of oscillations]*. VEB Deutscher Verlag der Wissenschaften, Berlin.

Gantmacher, F. (1970). *Lectures in analytical mechanics*. MIR Publishers, Moscow.

Giacaglia, G. E. O. (1972). *Perturbation methods in non-linear systems*. Springer, Berlin.

Hagedorn, R. (1956). Note on an instability of a difference resonance line. *CERN Symposium on high energy accelerators and pion physics*, Geneva, 1956, Vol. 1, pp. 293–4.

—— (1957). *Stability and amplitude ranges of two-dimensional non-linear oscillations with periodical Hamiltonian,* 2 Parts. CERN 57-1 Report, Proton Synchroton Division CERN, Geneva.

—— Hine, M. G. N., and Schoch, A. (1956). Non-linear orbit problems in synchrotons. *CERN Symposium on high energy accelerators and pion physics,* Geneva 1956, Vol. 1, pp. 237–53.

Hamel, G. (1949). *Theoretische Mechanik [Theoretical mechanics].* Springer, Berlin.

Heinbockel, J. H. and Struble, R. A. (1963). Resonant oscillations of an extensible pendulum. *Z. angew. Math. Phys.* **14**, 262–9.

Kane, T. R. and Kahn, M. E. (1968). On a class of two-degree-of-freedom oscillations. *J. appl. Mech.* **35**, 547–52.

Levi–Cevita, T. and Amaldi, V. (1949). *Lezioni di meccanica razionale [Lectures on rational mechanics],* 2 Volumes. Zanichelli editore, Bologna. [First edn 1922.]

Lur'é. (1968). *Mécanique analytique [Analytical mechanics].* Librairie Universitaire, Louvain.

Mettler, E. (1975). Über höhere Näherungen in der Theorie des elastischen Pendels mit innerer Resonanz [Some remarks about higher approximations in the theory of the elastic pendulum with inner resonance]. *Z. angew. Math. Mech.* **55**, 69–82.

Moser, J. (1956). The resonance lines for the synchrotron. *CERN symposium on high energy accelerators and pion physics,* Geneva 1956, Vol. 1, pp. 290–2.

—— (1973). *Stable and random motions in dynamical systems.* Annals of Mathematical Studies, Princeton University Press, Princeton, New Jersey.

Nayfeh, A. H. (1973). *Perturbation methods.* John Wiley and Sons, New York.

Pars, L. A. (1968). *A treatise on analytical dynamics.* Heinemann, London.

Poincaré, H. (1957). *Les méthodes nouvelles de la mécanique céleste [The new methods in celestial mechanics],* 3 Volumes. Dover, New York. [First edn 1892.]

Sethna, P. R. (1965). Vibrations of dynamical systems with quadratic nonlinearities. *J. appl. Mech.* **32**, 576–82.

Siegel, C. L. and Moser, J. K. (1971). *Lectures on celestial mechanics.* Springer, Berlin.

Teschner, W. (1977). Zur Instabilität konservativer Systeme mit gryroskopischen Kräften [The instability of conservative systems with gyroscopic forces], *Z. angew. Math. Mech.* **57**, T92–T94.

Whittaker, E. T. (1970). *A treatise on the analytical dynamics of particles and rigid bodies.* Cambridge University Press, Cambridge. [First edn 1904.]

Exercises

4.1. Use the condition (4.38) to determine whether

$$q^* = \alpha_1 q + \beta_1 p,$$

$$p^* = \alpha_2 q + \beta_2 p,$$

with $\alpha_1, \alpha_2, \beta_1, \beta_2$ constant and $(\alpha_1\beta_2 - \alpha_2\beta_1) \neq 0$ is a canonical transformation or not, and determine the principal function (Gantmacher 1970).

4.2. Use Poisson brackets to determine whether the following transformations are canonical or not:

(a) $q^* = q \cos p$,

$p^* = q \sin p$,

(b) $q^* = \ln(\frac{1}{q} \sin p)$,

$p^* = q \cos p$,

(c) $q^* = \ln(1 + \sqrt{q} \cos p)$,

$p^* = 2(1 + \sqrt{q} \cos p) \sqrt{q} \sin p$.

4.3. Obtain the solutions for the approximate eqns (4.141) for the example of the elastic pendulum in section 4.5 and investigate the stability of the vertical harmonic oscillations.

4.4. Use canonical perturbation theory to investigate the stability of the trivial solution of the Mathieu equation

$$\ddot{q} + (\omega_0^2 + \mu \cos 2t) q = 0$$

for small μ and $\omega_0^2 \approx 1$ (Nayfeh 1973).

4.5. The plane motion of a particle with mass m in a central force field is described by the Hamiltonian

$$H(r, \theta, p_r, p_\theta) = \frac{1}{2m} \left(p_r^2 + \frac{p_\theta^2}{r^2} \right) + U(r),$$

where r and θ are the polar coordinates of the location of the particle and $U(r)$ is the potential energy. Use Hamilton–Jacobi theory to obtain the solution of the equations of motion.

4.6. Every arbitrary differential equation may be imbedded in a Hamiltonian system by adjoining additional ('adjoint') variables. Do this for the oscillator with cubic damping

$$\ddot{x} + x + \mu\dot{x}^3 = 0$$

and use canonical perturbation theory to obtain an approximate solution.

5

INTRODUCTION TO THE THEORY OF OPTIMAL CONTROL

5.1. Control problems, controllability

Consider a system of the form

$$\dot{\mathbf{x}} = \mathbf{f}(\mathbf{x}, \mathbf{u}, t) \tag{1}$$

with $\mathbf{x} \in \mathbb{R}^n$, $\mathbf{u} \in \mathbb{R}^m$. With the introduction of a given function of time $\mathbf{u}(t)$ into the right-hand side of eqn (1), one obtains an ordinary, generally non-linear, differential equation. In many physical processes described by differential equations, the time dependence of the process may be influenced in some manner. This is generally referred to as a steering of the process: it is implemented in eqn (1) by means of the *steering function* or *control function* $\mathbf{u}(t)$. The variable $\mathbf{x}$ is called the *state variable* in control theory. Consider, for example, a spaceship; then the components of the vector $\mathbf{x}$ may refer to position and velocity and $\mathbf{u}^T = (u_1, u_2, \ldots, u_m)$ may represent the controllable thrusts of the individual engines as well as their directions of action insofar as the engines are gimballed. If a system is to be transferred from a given state $\mathbf{x}_0$ to another state $\mathbf{x}_1$ there often exist numerous control functions with which this may be accomplished. Not all of these will be suitable and the question arises as to how one might determine a most suitable one—for example, that one which minimizes the fuel consumption, or that which minimizes the travel time. Problems from other areas also may lead to similar mathematical problems, as in a market economy, for example, where a conglomerate of producers has the 'control variables' price and amount of production at its disposal in order to 'control' the market (state variable). A number of other examples will also be introduced in this chapter.

The solutions of the system (1) depend on the function $\mathbf{u}(\cdot)$ and one often writes them in the form $\mathbf{x}(\mathbf{x}_0, t_0; \mathbf{u}(\cdot), t)$.† A typical question in control theory then is the following: For a given $\mathbf{x}_0, t_0$, and $\mathbf{x}_1$, does there exist a $t_1 > t_0$ and a function $\mathbf{u}(\cdot)$ such that $\mathbf{x}(\mathbf{x}_0, t_0; \mathbf{u}(\cdot), t_1) = \mathbf{x}_1$, that is, does there exist a function $\mathbf{u}(\cdot)$ which steers the system from $\mathbf{x} = \mathbf{x}_0$ to $\mathbf{x} = \mathbf{x}_1$? If the answer to this question is affirmative, then one also says that the system (1) is *controllable* from $\mathbf{x}_0$ to $\mathbf{x}_1$.

---

†The notation $\mathbf{u}(\cdot)$ here is used to designate a function defined on the interval $[t_0, t]$.

An important special case is that of the linear system with constant coefficients:

$$\dot{\mathbf{x}} = \mathbf{Ax} + \mathbf{Bu}, \tag{2}$$

where $\mathbf{A}$ is an $n \times n$ matrix and $\mathbf{B}$ is an $n \times m$ matrix. For linear systems, it is meaningful to define *complete controllability*:

The system (2) is completely controllable if and only if for every $\mathbf{x}_0$ *there exists a function* $\mathbf{u}(\cdot)$ *which steers the system to* $\mathbf{x}_1 = \mathbf{0}$.

For the system (2) there exists a simple criterion for controllability. The system (2) is completely controllable if and only if

$$\text{rank } (\mathbf{B}, \mathbf{AB}, \ldots, \mathbf{A}^{n-1}\mathbf{B}) = n \tag{3}$$

holds (for a proof, see Knobloch and Kappel 1974).

Examples:

(1) *Satellite in a central gravitational field.* With kinetic energy $T = \frac{1}{2} m \, (\dot{r}^2 + r^2 \dot{\varphi}^2)$ and potential energy $U = -\gamma m/r$, the equations of motion are obtained as

$$\left. \begin{aligned} \ddot{r} &= -\frac{\gamma}{r^2} + r\dot{\varphi}^2, \\[2ex] \ddot{\varphi} &= -2\frac{\dot{\varphi}\dot{r}}{r}. \end{aligned} \right\} \tag{4}$$

Here m is the mass of the satellite, γ is the product of the gravitational constant with the mass of the planet, and r and φ are the polar coordinates of the satellite, idealized as a particle, in the xy-plane (Fig. 5.1). A particular solution is given by the motion in a circular orbit with $r = R$, $\dot{\varphi} = \omega = \sqrt{(\gamma/R^3)}$. Deviations from this orbit are to be corrected by two rocket engines with thrust vectors in the directions $\mathbf{e}_r$ and $\mathbf{e}_\varphi$, respectively, so that the equations of motion now have the form

$$\left. \begin{aligned} \ddot{r} &= r\dot{\varphi}^2 - \frac{\gamma}{r^2} + u_1, \\[2ex] \ddot{\varphi} &= -2\frac{\dot{\varphi}\dot{r}}{r} + \frac{1}{r}u_2, \end{aligned} \right\}$$

where u_1 and u_2 are the accelerations in the radial and normal directions, respectively, as produced by the corresponding engines. The expressions 'radial' and 'tangential' here refer to the circular orbit. The introduction of the new variables

$$\left. \begin{aligned} x_1 &= r - R, \\[1.5ex] x_2 &= \dot{x}_1 = \dot{r}, \\[1.5ex] x_3 &= (\varphi - \omega t)R, \\[1.5ex] x_4 &= \dot{x}_3 = (\dot{\varphi} - \omega)R, \end{aligned} \right\} \tag{5}$$

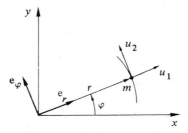

Fig. 5.1. Satellite in a gravitational field.

which represent the (small) deviations from the reference motion and the subsequent linearization lead to differential equations of the form (2) with

$$\mathbf{A} = \begin{pmatrix} 0 & 1 & 0 & 0 \\ 3\omega^2 & 0 & 0 & 2\omega \\ 0 & 0 & 0 & 1 \\ 0 & -2\omega & 0 & 0 \end{pmatrix}, \quad \mathbf{B} = \begin{pmatrix} 0 & 0 \\ 1 & 0 \\ 0 & 0 \\ 0 & 1 \end{pmatrix}, \tag{6}$$

providing a first approximation to the controlled motions in a neighbourhood of the reference orbit. To investigate the controllability of the system, the rank of $(\mathbf{B}, \mathbf{AB}, \mathbf{A}^2\mathbf{B}, \mathbf{A}^3\mathbf{B})$ must be computed. One has

rank $(\mathbf{B}, \mathbf{AB}, \mathbf{A}^2\mathbf{B}, \mathbf{A}^3\mathbf{B})$

$$= \text{rank} \begin{pmatrix} 0 & 0 & 1 & 0 & 0 & 2\omega & -\omega^2 & 0 \\ 1 & 0 & 0 & 2\omega & -\omega^2 & 0 & 0 & -2\omega^3 \\ 0 & 0 & 0 & 1 & -2\omega & 0 & 0 & -4\omega^2 \\ 0 & 1 & -2\omega & 0 & 0 & -4\omega^2 & 2\omega^3 & 0 \end{pmatrix} = 4,$$

and it follows that the system indeed is completely controllable.

If one assumes that only radial thrust is available, then $\mathbf{B}^T = (0, 1, 0, 0)$ follows and the system no longer is completely controllable, as may easily be checked. If one, however, admits only tangential thrust with $\mathbf{B}^T = (0, 0, 0, 1)$, then complete controllability is maintained.

(2) *The concept of pervasive damping.* The linear oscillations of a damped discrete mechanical system about a stable equilibrium position are described by

$$\mathbf{A}\ddot{\mathbf{x}} + \mathbf{B}\dot{\mathbf{x}} + \mathbf{C}\mathbf{x} = \mathbf{0} \tag{7}$$

where $\mathbf{A}^T = \mathbf{A}$ and $\mathbf{C}^T = \mathbf{C}$ are positive definite constant matrices (see also section 2.2). If the damping matrix $\mathbf{B}^T = \mathbf{B}$ also is positive definite, then (7) is 'completely damped' and the trivial solution is asymptotically stable. This is a sufficient but by no means necessary condition for asymptotic stability. More specifically, the system may be asymptotically stable even when **B** is only semi-definite; the latter case is referred to as *pervasive damping*. It is easy to show that the complete controllability of the system

$$\mathbf{A\ddot{x}} + \mathbf{Bu} + \mathbf{Cx} = 0 \tag{8}$$

(written as a first-order system) together with the positive semi-definiteness of **B** is a necessary and sufficient condition for asymptotic stability. The transformation of the system (8) to the principal coordinates of the undamped system results in

$$\ddot{y}_i + \omega_i^2 y_i + \mathbf{l}_i^{\mathrm{T}} \mathbf{u} = 0 \,, \qquad i = 1, 2, \ldots, n \,, \tag{9}$$

where the $\mathbf{l}_i \in \mathbf{R}^m$ are constant vectors. If the vector $\mathbf{l}_i$ vanishes for some i then the corresponding subsystem (9) is not completely controllable and the corresponding eigenmode is undamped. It follows that complete controllability is a necessary condition for pervasive damping; that it also is a sufficient condition may be shown by another approach (see Müller and Schiehlen 1976).

5.2. The Pontryagin maximum principle

Consider again the system (1) and assume that it is desired to transfer the system from the given state $\mathbf{x}_0$ to the terminal state $\mathbf{x}_1$, which is also specified. Furthermore, the control function $\mathbf{u}(t)$ is assumed to be piecewise continuous and it is to take on values in the so-called 'control set' U. A solution of the control problem then is a pair of functions $\mathbf{u}(t)$, $\mathbf{x}(t)$ satisfying eqns (1), with $\mathbf{u}(t) \in U$, $t_0 \leqslant t \leqslant t_1$ and $\mathbf{x}(t_0) = \mathbf{x}_0$, $\mathbf{x}(t_1) = \mathbf{x}_1$. The corresponding function $\mathbf{u}(t)$ is called an admissible control function. The instant t_1 and possibly also the instant to here generally have not been specified *a priori*.

The control set U is assumed to be a closed bounded set as, for example, the 'unit ball' $\|\mathbf{u}\| \leqslant 1$ or the 'unit sphere' $\|\mathbf{u}\| = 1$; but the control set may also be specified in terms of several equations or inequalities of the form $g(\mathbf{u}, \mathbf{x}, t) \leqslant 0$. In applications, these constraints arise from simple physical limitations imposed on the acceleration, velocity, or force, for example.

The question concerning the existence of a solution for the control problem formulated above will not be treated here. Rather, it will be assumed that solutions exist and necessary conditions for the 'optimal' solution will be formulated. An optimal solution of the control problem here is one for which the functional ('cost')

$$J = \int_{t_0}^{t_1} f_0(\mathbf{x}(t), \mathbf{u}(t), t) \, \mathrm{d}t \tag{10}$$

takes on its smallest possible value. Here, f_0 is a given function of $\mathbf{x}$, $\mathbf{u}$, and t. Note again, that t_1 is not specified but that it depends on whichever control function $\mathbf{u}(t)$ is chosen. In particular, f_0 may be identically equal to unity so that the optimal solution for the control problem is that which yields the shortest transit time from $\mathbf{x}_0$ to $\mathbf{x}_1$ (one then speaks of time-optimal control).

The optimal control problem may also be formulated in a somewhat different manner by introducing the additional variable x_0† and dealing with the system

$$\dot{x}_i = f_i(x_1, \ldots, x_n, \mathbf{u}, t), \qquad i = 0, 1, 2, \ldots, n . \tag{11}$$

The given quantities are assumed to be the point $(0, x_1(t_0), x_2(t_0), \ldots, x_n(t_0))$ in $\mathbb{R}^{n+1}$ as well as the straight line $x_1(t_1), x_2(t_1), \ldots, x_n(t_1)$ parallel to the x_0-axis, where t_1 is as yet undetermined. Determine that control function $\mathbf{u}(t)$ whose corresponding solution of eqns (11) cuts the straight line as close as possible to the hyperplane $x_0 = 0$ (Fig. 5.2).

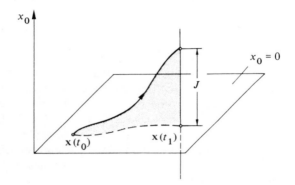

Fig. 5.2. The problem of optimal control.

Necessary conditions for the optimality of a solution of the control problem are supplied by the Pontryagin *maximum principle*, which is cited here without proof:‡

Let $(\bar{\mathbf{u}}(t), \mathbf{x}(t))$ *be a solution of the boundary-value problem defined by the system (1),* $\mathbf{x}_0$ *and* $\mathbf{x}_1$ *with free terminal time, and minimizing the functional (10). Then there exist continuous piecewise differentiable functions* $y_0(t)$, $y_1(t), \ldots, y_n(t)$ *which satisfy the following conditions:*

(a) *The functions* $x_i(t), y_i(t)$ *satisfy the differential equations*

$$\dot{x}_i = \frac{\partial H}{\partial y_i}, \tag{12}$$

†The additional variable x_0 should not be confused with the initial state $\mathbf{x}(t_0) = \mathbf{x}_0$.
‡In the statement of the theorem, only the presumed optimality of the control has been emphasized by an overbar on $\mathbf{u}(t)$. Strictly speaking, such an overbar should be placed on both the state variables and the adjoint variables also, since the statement of the theorem refers to all of the quantities evaluated at the optimal control $\bar{\mathbf{u}}(t)$.

$$\dot{y}_i = -\frac{\partial H}{\partial x_i}, \qquad i = 0, 1, 2, \ldots, n, \tag{13}$$

with

$$H(x_1, \ldots, x_n; y_0, \ldots, y_n; \overline{\mathbf{u}}(t), t) =$$

$$\sum_{i=0}^{n} y_i f_i(x_1, \ldots, x_n; \overline{\mathbf{u}}(t), t); \tag{14}$$

(b) the $y_0, y_1, \ldots, y_n$ are not all simultaneously zero, and y_0 is a constant $\leqslant 0$;

(c) one has

$$H(x_1(t), \ldots, x_n(t); y_0(t), \ldots, y_n(t); \overline{\mathbf{u}}(t), t) =$$

$$= \max_{\mathbf{u} \in U} H(x_1(t), \ldots, x_n(t); y_0(t); \mathbf{u}(t), t), \tag{15}$$

that is, the optimal control function at each instant assumes those values which maximize H;

(d) in terms of the optimal solution, H is a continuous function of the time and one has $H(t_1) = 0$. If the functions f_i, $i = 0, 1, 2, \ldots, n$ do not depend on t explicitly, then H is a constant and equal to zero.

Clearly, eqns (12) and (13) describe a Hamiltonian system where the x_i correspond to the generalized coordinates and where the additionally introduced adjoint variables y_i correspond to the generalized momenta. Recall also that the Hamiltonian is a first integral for autonomous systems, taking on the value zero in the case of an optimal control, as indicated by the assertion (d) of the theorem.

If (1), (10), and $\mathbf{x}_0, \mathbf{x}_1$ are given, the next step would be to form the function (14). The optimal controls are determined from (15) in their dependence on the $x_1, \ldots, x_n; y_0, \ldots, y_n;$ and t. Subsequently, one would then attempt to use $\overline{\mathbf{u}}(t)$ as obtained therefrom to determine the solution of the eqns (12) and (13) subject to the given boundary conditions on $\mathbf{x}$. It is immediately apparent from eqn (13) that y_0 must be constant, since H is independent of x_0 by definition. Since (14) is linear homogeneous in $y_0, y_1, \ldots, y_n$ and since y_0 is constant, there is no loss in generality in choosing $y_0 = -1$ for non-vanishing y_0.†

---

† $y_0 = 0$ corresponds to the so-called abnormal problem in optimal control. In general, this possibility must also be considered. A usual approach consists of attempting to show that $y_0 = 0$ would result in a simultaneous vanishing of all of the adjoint functions, a contradiction of the necessary conditions for optimality.

Equation (12) for $i = 0$ corresponds to the differentiated form of (10) and it is independent of the remaining eqns (12) and (13). Thus, eqns (12) and (13) need be considered only for $i = 1, \ldots, n$.

Note that if one were to take a completely rigorous approach, there would be three main aspects to be considered in a control problem: existence of an optimal control, necessary conditions which it must satisfy, and sufficient conditions to assure that any candidates which have been found are in fact optimal. In practice, existence is often taken for granted from physical considerations, and extremal quantities (satisfying only necessary conditions) are referred to as optimal. Now, if an optimal solution can be shown to exist, then the extremal control which yields the lowest cost is, in fact, optimal; and if an extremal pair $(\bar{\mathbf{u}}(t), \mathbf{x}(t))$ is unique, then optimality also follows immediately. It would lead too far here to deal with all of these aspects in detail; thus, the adjective 'optimal' will be used throughout, although 'extremal' might be more appropriate. The reader is referred to the literature for existence and sufficiency theorems in optimal control.

In addition, the differential eqns (12) and (13) will generally be non-linear so that it will not be possible to obtain analytical, closed-form solutions; rather, it will be necessary to seek refuge in numerical and analytical approximation methods.

Examples.

(1) *Time-optimal motion of a particle with bounded acceleration (Pontryagin).* Assume that the control function $u(t)$ in the equation

$$\ddot{x} = u \tag{16}$$

is subject to the constraint $|u| \leqslant 1$. For given initial conditions $x(0)$ and $\dot{x}(0)$, that control function is to be found which transfers the system to $x(t_1) = 0, \dot{x}(t_1) = 0$ in as short a time as possible. The cost functional J here is given by

$$J = \int_0^{t_1} \mathrm{d}t. \tag{17}$$

Eqn (16) now is written as a first-order system

$$\left. \begin{aligned} \dot{x}_1 &= x_2, \\ \dot{x}_2 &= u \end{aligned} \right\} \tag{18}$$

and the function H is defined in accordance with (14) as

$$H = y_0 + x_2 y_1 + u y_2. \tag{19}$$

Based on (13), the adjoint equations are given by

$$\dot{y}_0 = 0 ,$$

$$\dot{y}_1 = 0 , \qquad\qquad\qquad\qquad\qquad (20)$$

$$\dot{y}_2 = -y_1 .$$

They have the solutions

$$y_0 = C_0 ,$$

$$y_1 = C_1 , \qquad\qquad\qquad\qquad\qquad (21)$$

$$y_2 = C_2 - C_1 t .$$

$C_0 \leqslant 0$ follows from the maximum principle, and one may here choose $C_0 = -1$ without loss of generality. The optimal control is given by

$$\bar{u}(t) = \text{sgn } y_2(t) = \text{sgn} (C_2 - C_1 t) . \qquad\qquad (22)$$

The optimal control function thus is piecewise constant and assumes only the values $+1$ and -1. Furthermore, it is apparent that the function $\bar{u}(t)$ has at most one point of discontinuity, since the function $C_2 - C_1 t$ clearly has only one zero.

For the time interval for which $u \equiv +1$ holds, eqns (18) yield

$$x_1 = \frac{1}{2} t^2 + s_2 t + s_1 = \frac{1}{2} (t + s_2)^2 + \left(s_1 - \frac{1}{2} s_2^2 \right) ,$$

$$x_2 = t + s_2 \qquad\qquad\qquad\qquad\qquad (23)$$

with s_1 and s_2 as constants of integration. The elimination of t yields

$$x_1 = \frac{1}{2} x_2^2 + \left(s_1 - \frac{1}{2} s_2^2 \right) . \qquad\qquad (24)$$

For $u \equiv +1$ the optimal trajectories thus coincide with the parabolas shown in Fig. 5.3.

In an analogous manner, $u \equiv -1$ yields

$$x_1 = -\frac{1}{2} t^2 + \bar{s}_2 t + \bar{s}_1 = -\frac{1}{2} (t - \bar{s}_2)^2 + \left(\bar{s}_1 + \frac{1}{2} \bar{s}_2^2 \right)$$

$$x_2 = -t + \bar{s}_2 \qquad\qquad\qquad\qquad\qquad (25)$$

and

$$x_1 = -\frac{1}{2} x_2^2 + \left(\bar{s}_1 + \frac{1}{2} \bar{s}_2^2 \right) . \qquad\qquad (26)$$

The corresponding optimal trajectories are shown in Fig. 5.4.

It has been shown already that the optimal control takes on only the values ± 1 and exhibits only one switching point. If $\bar{u}(t)$ first takes on the value $+1$ and then the value -1, then the optimal trajectory must be of the type indicated in Fig. 5.5(a). Conversely, if

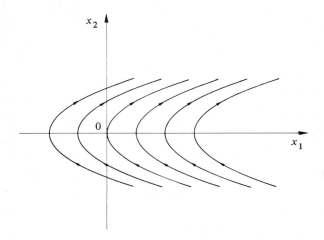

Fig. 5.3. The family of optimal trajectories for $u \equiv +1$.

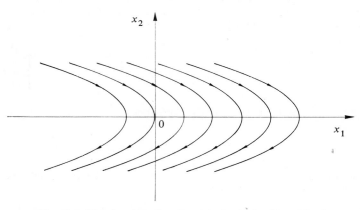

Fig. 5.4. The family of optimal trajectories for $u \equiv -1$.

$\bar{u}(t)$ is first equal to -1 and then $+1$, then the optimal trajectory must be of the type indicated in Fig. 5.5(b). The totality of optimal trajectories has been represented in Fig. 5.6. The heavy curve AOB is called the switching curve for the control function; its upper half OB is given by $x_1 = -\frac{1}{2} x_2^2$ and its lower half OA by $x_1 = \frac{1}{2} x_2^2$.

The maximum principle supplies necessary conditions for optimality. Thus, only the trajectories depicted in Fig. 5.6 qualify as candidates for optimal trajectories. Only one such trajectory passes through every initial point. If it is known that there exists an optimal control for given initial conditions—as can indeed be shown in the present case—then the field of trajectories shown in Fig. 5.6 actually is that of the optimal trajectories.

The solution of the control problem as presented here may also be interpreted in a somewhat different manner. Let a function $v(x_1, x_2)$ be defined by

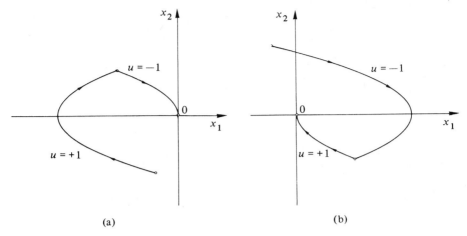

(a)   (b)

Fig. 5.5. Typical optimal trajectories.

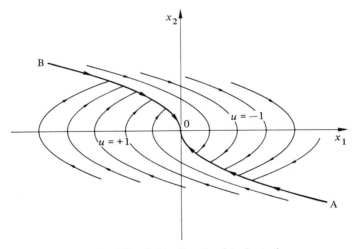

Fig. 5.6. The field of optimal trajectories.

$$v(x_1, x_2) = \begin{cases} +1 \text{ for points below the curve A0B and on A0,} \\ -1 \text{ for points above the curve A0B and on B0.} \end{cases}$$

Then the optimal control may be written in the form $\bar{u}(t) = v(x_1(t), x_2(t))$. When given in terms of the state variables the control function $v(x_1, x_2)$ is called a 'closed loop control function', as opposed to $u(t)$ ('open loop control function'). Correspondingly, the differential eqns (18) may be replaced by $\dot{x}_1 = x_2$ and $\dot{x}_2 = v(x_1, x_2)$.†

---

†The process of generating an optimal feedback control from a known optimal open-loop control is called the 'synthesis of optimal control'.

(2) *Active time-optimal control of an oscillator.* Consider the differential equation

$$\ddot{x} + x = u,\tag{27}$$

and write it as the first-order system

$$\left.\begin{aligned}\dot{x}_1 &= x_2,\\\dot{x}_2 &= -x_1 + u.\end{aligned}\right\}\tag{28}$$

Assume that the control function satisfies $|u| \leqslant 1$. For given initial conditions $u(t)$ again is to be determined in such a way that the system is transferred to a position of rest in as short a time as possible. With $y_0 = -1$ the function H thus is given by

$$H = -1 + y_1 x_2 - y_2 x_1 + y_2 u,\tag{29}$$

and the adjoint equations are obtained as

$$\left.\begin{aligned}\dot{y}_1 &= y_2,\\\dot{y}_2 &= -y_1.\end{aligned}\right\}\tag{30}$$

The solution of eqns (30) is

$$\left.\begin{aligned}y_1(t) &= -A \cos(t - \alpha_0),\\y_2(t) &= A \sin(t - \alpha_0),\end{aligned}\right\}\tag{31}$$

where $A > 0$ and α_0 are constants of integration. Based on the maximum principle, one obtains

$$\bar{u} = \operatorname{sgn} y_2 = \operatorname{sgn}[A \sin(t - \alpha_0)] = \operatorname{sgn}[\sin(t - \alpha_0)],\tag{32}$$

so that $\bar{u}(t)$ is a piecewise constant function with period 2π.

For $\bar{u} \equiv +1$, the general solution of eqns (28) is given by

$$\left.\begin{aligned}x_1 &= B \sin(t - \beta_0) + 1,\\x_2 &= B \cos(t - \beta_0),\end{aligned}\right\}\tag{33}$$

where B and β_0 are constants of integration. The elimination of t yields the first integral

$$(x_1 - 1)^2 + x_2^2 = B^2.\tag{34}$$

In an analogous manner, $\bar{u} \equiv -1$ yields

$$\left.\begin{aligned}x_1 &= \bar{B} \sin(t - \bar{\beta}_0) - 1,\\x_2 &= \bar{B} \cos(t - \bar{\beta}_0)\end{aligned}\right\}\tag{35}$$

and

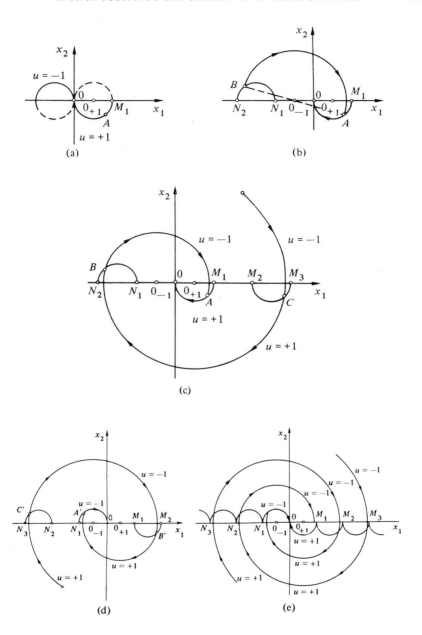

Fig. 5.7. Construction of the optimal trajectories.

$$(x_1 + 1)^2 + x_2^2 = \bar{B}^2 . \tag{36}$$

The phase trajectories for (28) thus consist of circular arcs with centres at $(1,0)$ and $(-1,0)$, respectively. Since the optimal control function $\bar{u}(t)$ is piecewise constant and takes on only the values $+1$ and -1, the optimal trajectory is composed only of a sequence of such circular arcs. These trajectories now may easily be constructed. Note first of all that only the two semicircles, with radius equal to one, reach the origin in Fig. 5.7(a). All other trajectories thus must eventually connect to these two semicircles. The function $\bar{u}(t)$, however, is periodic with period 2π and changes its sign at least once in any time interval of length greater than π; this is apparent from (32). Therefore, the point describing the motion in state space will move through an angle π, at most, on one of the two circular arcs of Fig. 5.7(a). To begin with, assume that the point on the circular arc $M_1 0$ with $\bar{u} = +1$ reaches the origin. If the control function $\bar{u}(t)$ changes its sign at the point A of the circular arc OM_1 then the continuation here is given by a circular arc with centre at $(-1,0)$. Continuing backwards along the trajectory generated by $\bar{u}(t)$ one notes that the sign now remains the same for a time interval of length π. At the point B of Fig. 5.7(b), $\bar{u}(t)$ again changes sign. Moving the point A on the circular arc OM_1 results in a tracing of the circular arc $N_1 N_2$ by B. This construction may be continued as indicated in Fig. 5.7(c).

The optimal trajectories corresponding to $\bar{u} = -1$ and terminating on the circular arc $N_1 0$ may be obtained in a similar manner (Fig. 5.7(d)). The superpositioning of these two cases finally yields the phase diagram shown in Fig. 5.7(e). The optimal control function is equal to -1 for all points in the phase plane which lie above the curve $\ldots N_3 N_2 N_1 0$ $M_1 M_2 M_3 \ldots$ as well as those which lie on the curve $N_1 0$. It is equal to $+1$ below the curve $\ldots N_3 N_2 N_1 0 M_1 M_2 M_3 \ldots$ and on OM_1.

Here also the control problem may again be written in 'closed-loop' form with $v(x_1, x_2)$:

$$\left. \begin{aligned} \dot{x}_1 &= x_2 , \\ \dot{x}_2 &= -x_1 + v\,(x_1, x_2) \end{aligned} \right\} \tag{37}$$

with a corresponding definition of the optimal control function $v(x_1, x_2)$.

When the control function $\bar{u}(t)$ takes on only its extreme values and jumps back and forth between them, as was the case in Examples 1 and 2, it is generally referred to as 'bang-bang' control.

(3) *Minimum time paths through a region with position-dependent velocity vector.* Consider a ship navigating in the $x_1 x_2$-plane and assume that the motion occurs in a region where a strong current is active. The current has the velocity component $u(x_1, x_2)$ in the direction x_1 and $v(x_1, x_2)$ in the direction of the x_2-axis; the magnitude of the velocity of the ship relative to the water is given by w and the direction of the relative velocity is given by the angle φ of the velocity vector with respect to the x_1-axis. The angle here is the control which is to be chosen in such a way as to minimize the time of travel from a given point A to another given point B (Fig. 5.8). One then has the equations

$$\left. \begin{aligned} \dot{x}_1 &= w \cos \varphi + u\,(x_1, x_2) , \\ \dot{x}_2 &= w \sin \varphi + v\,(x_1, x_2) , \end{aligned} \right\} \tag{38}$$

where u, v are known functions of x_1, x_2 and where φ is the control function yet to be determined. With $y_0 = -1$, the Hamiltonian has the form

$$H = -1 + y_1\,(w \cos \varphi + u) + y_2\,(w \sin \varphi + v) . \tag{39}$$

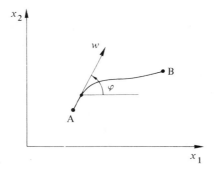

Fig. 5.8. Navigation in the presence of a position-dependent current.

The adjoint equations are given by

$$
\dot{y}_1 = -\frac{\partial H}{\partial x_1} = -y_1 \frac{\partial u}{\partial x_1} - y_2 \frac{\partial v}{\partial x_1} ,
$$

$$
\dot{y}_2 = -\frac{\partial H}{\partial x_2} = -y_1 \frac{\partial u}{\partial x_2} - y_2 \frac{\partial v}{\partial x_2} ,
$$

$$\left.\right\} \quad (40)$$

and the optimal control is obtained from

$$
\frac{\partial H}{\partial \varphi} = w(-y_1 \sin \varphi + y_2 \cos \varphi) = 0 \tag{41}
$$

in the implicit form

$$
\tan \varphi = y_2/y_1 . \tag{42}
$$

From (39) with $H = 0$, together with (42), it is easy to compute

$$
y_1 = \frac{\cos \varphi}{w + u \cos \varphi + v \sin \varphi} ,
$$

$$
y_2 = \frac{\sin \varphi}{w + u \cos \varphi + v \sin \varphi} .
$$

$$\left.\right\} \quad (43)$$

The elimination of y_1 and y_2 in (40) and (42) yields

$$
\dot{\varphi} = \sin^2\varphi \, \frac{\partial v}{\partial x_1} + \sin \varphi \cos \varphi \left(\frac{\partial u}{\partial x_1} - \frac{\partial v}{\partial x_2} \right) - \cos^2\varphi \, \frac{\partial u}{\partial x_2} . \tag{44}
$$

Finally, the simultaneous solution of (38) and (44) then results in the optimal trajectories.

An important special case is that in which u and v depend only on the coordinate x_2. The first of eqns (40) then results in $\dot{y}_1 = 0$ and hence $y_1 = $ const. and from the first of eqns (43) one obtains

$$
\frac{\cos \varphi}{w + u(x_2) \cos \varphi + v(x_2) \sin \varphi} = \text{const.} . \tag{45}
$$

Thus, in this case, it was possible to determine the control function φ implicitly as a function of the coordinates. The relationship (45) for a current depending only on x_2 corresponds to Snell's refraction law in optics.

5.3. Transversality conditions and problems with target sets

Consider again the optimal control problem specified by (1) and (10). Assume, however, that the end-points x_0 and x_1 are no longer specified but, instead, that all which is known about them is that they are located on two continuously differentiable manifolds S_0 and S_1. Each of these manifolds is assumed to have been specified by a system of algebraic equations of the form

$$\left.\begin{aligned} g_1(x_1, x_2, \ldots, x_n) &= 0, \\ g_2(x_1, x_2, \ldots, x_n) &= 0, \\ &\vdots \\ g_r(x_1, x_2, \ldots, x_n) &= 0 \end{aligned}\right\} \tag{46}$$

with $r = r_0$ for S_0 and $r = r_1$ for S_1. The dimension of the manifold defined by (46) is $n - r$, that is, it is $n - r_0$ for S_0 and $n - r_1$ for S_1.

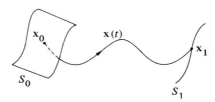

Fig. 5.9. Optimal control with initial and terminal manifolds.

The optimal control problem now consists of the selection of a trajectory and corresponding control function, leading from S_0 to S_1, as a solution of eqn (1) in such a way that the cost functional (10) is minimized (Fig. 5.9). In this context, x_0 and x_1 on S_0 and S_1, respectively, also have to be selected with this goal in mind. If x_0 and x_1 were known, then one would be dealing with the previously treated problem. It follows that the maximum principle again is a necessary condition. For the end-points, there are some additional conditions. Since S_0 has the dimension $n - r_0$, just as many additional equations are needed for the determination of x_0 and, analogously, $n - r_1$ equations are needed for the determination of x_1. These additional conditions are embodied in the *transversality conditions:*

Let $u(t)$, $t_0 \leqslant t \leqslant t_1$ *be an admissible control guiding the state of system (1)* *from some point $\mathbf{x}_0 \in S_0$ to another point $\mathbf{x}_1 \in S_1$, and let $\mathbf{x}(t)$ be the corresponding solution of (1). If $\mathbf{u}(t)$, $\mathbf{x}(t)$ is to be a solution of the problem defined by (1), (10), S_0 and S_1, the optimal control problem with initial and terminal manifold, then it is necessary that:*

(a) *There exists a function $\mathbf{y}(t)$ satisfying all of the conditions of the maximum principle laid down in section 5.2;*

(b) *The vector $\mathbf{y}(t_0)$ be orthogonal to S_0 and that $\mathbf{y}(t_1)$ be orthogonal to S_1.*

It is clear that the condition (b) of the theorem provides precisely the $n - r_0$ and $n - r_1$ algebraic equations needed for the determination of $\mathbf{x}_0$ and $\mathbf{x}_1$.†

If, in some problem, the terminal time t_1 is not free but has been specified, then the problem may always be reduced to one with a free terminal time by introducing the additional variable x_{n+1} with $\dot{x}_{n+1} = 1$. In this new problem, the value of the new terminal time $\bar{t}_1$ is left open and x_{n+1} is restricted by $x_{n+1} (\bar{t}_0) = t_0$ and $x_{n+1} (\bar{t}_1) = t_1$. It is easy to check that all of the conditions of the maximum principle apply directly to the problem with a given terminal time with the exception of condition (d), $H(t_1) = 0$. For autonomous systems, H is still equal to a constant but this constant is no longer zero, in general.

Example. Energy-minimal acceleration (Lee and Markus 1967). The system

$$\ddot{x} = u \tag{47}$$

or, equivalently,

$$\left. \begin{array}{l} \dot{x}_1 = x_2, \\[2mm] \dot{x}_2 = u \end{array} \right\} \tag{48}$$

with $u(t)$ unconstrained (generally taken to mean $|u(t)| < \infty$), is to be guided from the point $(0, -3)$ to the unit circle about the origin in a time interval $[0,1]$ in such a way that

$$J = \frac{1}{2} \int_0^1 u^2 \, dt \tag{49}$$

takes on its minimum value (Fig. 5.10). With y_0 arbitrarily chosen as -1 the Hamiltonian is given by

$$H = -\frac{1}{2} u^2 + y_1 x_2 + y_2 u . \tag{50}$$

†Often the manifolds S_0 and S_1 are such that the values of some of the variables involved in their specification, such as $x_m, x_{m+1}, \ldots, x_n$ are given, whereas the remaining $x_1, x_2, \ldots, x_{m-1}$ may take on arbitrary values. It then follows from the transversality conditions that the values of the functions $y_i(t)$, $i = 1, 2, \ldots, m-1$ at the corresponding end-points must be zero. For, as a consequence of the transversality conditions, $\mathbf{y}(t_1)$ ($\mathbf{y}(t_0)$) must be orthogonal to all of the tangents of S_1 (S_0) at $\mathbf{x}(t_1)$ ($\mathbf{x}(t_0)$). These tangents here are given by $\mathbf{x}^T = (s_1, s_2, \ldots, s_{m-1}, x_m, x_{m+1}, \ldots, x_m)$, where $s_1, s_2, \ldots, s_{m-1}$ are free parameters. Now, if $\mathbf{x}^T(t_1) \, \mathbf{y}(t_1)$ ($\mathbf{x}^T(t_0) \, \mathbf{y}(t_0)$) is to vanish for all values of these parameters, then it follows that $y_1, y_2, \ldots, y_{m-1}$ must be equal to zero.

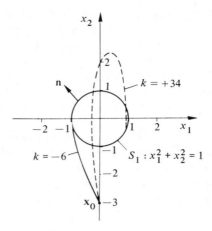

Fig. 5.10. The problem of energy-minimal acceleration.

The adjoint equations corresponding to the system (48) follow as

$$\dot{y}_1 = 0 \,,$$
$$\dot{y}_2 = -y_1 \,. \tag{51}$$

For an open control set $U(|u(t)| < \infty)$, the condition $\partial H/\partial u = 0$ yields an optimal control $u = y_2$; it is easily seen that this control indeed maximizes H. Since the terminal point is not specified but must lie on S_1, the transversality condition must be satisfied for $t = 1$. With S_1 specified by $x_1^2 + x_2^2 = 1$, an outward normal to S_1 at a point (x_1, x_2) is given by $\mathbf{n} = (x_1, x_2)$; $(y_1(1), y_2(1))$ is required to be parallel to $\mathbf{n}$. As a consequence, one has to solve the problem

$$
\begin{aligned}
\dot{x}_1 &= x_2 \,, & \dot{y}_1 &= 0 \,, & x_1(0) &= 0 \,, \\
\dot{x}_2 &= y_2 \,, & \dot{y}_2 &= -y_1 \,, & x_2(0) &= -3 \,, \\
\begin{pmatrix} y_1(1) \\ y_2(1) \end{pmatrix} &= k \begin{pmatrix} x_1(1) \\ x_2(1) \end{pmatrix} \,, & & & x_1^2(1) + x_2^2(1) &= 1 \,.
\end{aligned}
\tag{52}
$$

If y_{10} and y_{20} are taken to be the initial values for y_1, y_2 then one has

$$
\begin{aligned}
y_1(t) &= y_{10} \,, & y_2(t) &= -y_{10}t + y_{20} \,, \\
x_1(t) &= \frac{-y_{10}t^3}{6} + \frac{y_{20}t^2}{2} - 3t \,, & x_2(t) &= -\frac{y_{10}t^2}{2} + y_{20}t - 3 \,,
\end{aligned}
\tag{53}
$$

where the initial conditions for $\mathbf{x}$ have already been taken into consideration.
From the conditions for $t = 1$ one obtains

$$y_1(1) = y_{10} = k\,x_1(1) = k\left(-\frac{1}{6}y_{10} + \frac{1}{2}y_{20} - 3\right),$$

$$y_2(1) = -y_{10} + y_{20} = k\,x_2(1) = k\left(-\frac{1}{2}y_{10} + y_{20} - 3\right) \tag{54}$$

and

$$y_{10}^2 + (-y_{10} + y_{20})^2 = k^2. \tag{55}$$

The simultaneous solution of eqns (54) for y_{10} and y_{20} yields

$$y_{10} = \frac{36\,(k^2/2 - k)}{k^2 - 16\,k + 12}, \tag{56}$$

$$y_{20} = \frac{12\,(k^2 - 6\,k)}{k^2 - 16\,k + 12}, \tag{57}$$

and their substitution in (55) results in the equation

$$k^4 - 32\,k^3 - 80\,k^2 + 480\,k - 2448 = 0. \tag{58}$$

This equation has two real roots, $k = -6$ and $k = 34$. It is a simple matter now to compute the value of the cost functional (49) for both of these roots. With

$$\frac{1}{2}\int_0^1 u^2 \, dt = 72\,\frac{\frac{1}{4}k^4 - 3\,k^3 + 21\,k^2}{(k^2 - 16\,k + 12)^2}$$

one obtains $J = 6$ for $k = -6$ and $J \approx 44.46$ for $k = 34$. Thus, the fuel-minimal solution is obtained with $k = -6$; corresponding thereto one obtains $y_{10} = 6, y_{20} = 6$, and $u(t) = -6t + 6, 0 \le t \le 1$. The terminal point then follows as $x_1(1) = -1, x_2(1) = 0$; the optimal trajectory is depicted in Fig. 5.10.†

5.4. Canonical perturbation theory in optimal control

It was shown in section 5.2 that necessary conditions for optimality resulted in differential equations of Hamiltonian type. Everything that was said about Hamiltonian systems in Chapter 4 may now be applied to problems in optimal control. The Hamiltonian in this connection always has a very special form: it is always linear in the 'adjoint' variables which were designated as generalized momenta in Chapter 4.

---

†For linear quadratic control problems (control problems with linear differential equations and quadratic cost functional) with target sets, Lee and Markus (1967) quite generally show that the constant k in the system (52) must be negative for optimal control.

The Hamilton–Jacobi partial differential equation now takes on the form

$$\frac{\partial S}{\partial t} + \sum_{i=0}^{n} \frac{\partial S}{\partial x_i} f_i(x_1, \ldots, x_n; \mathbf{u}, t) = 0 \tag{59}$$

where $\mathbf{u}$ may be obtained as a function of the state variables, the adjoint variables, and the time, all in accordance with the maximum principle. In the present context, this equation is also known as Bellman's equation, obtained as the limiting case in the theory of 'dynamic programming' (see Lee and Markus 1967, for example).

Canonical perturbation theory, as it was explained in Chapter 4, also may be used on problems in optimal control. This is important, since the differential equations for the adjoint variables and for the state variables generally are non-linear and cannot be solved in closed form. Naturally, all the other (non-canonical) variants of perturbation theory may also be used on control problems.

An important special case arises when the system (1) to be controlled is itself of Hamiltonian type and if the corresponding optimal control is piecewise constant. The results from canonical perturbation theory may then be used to deduce the solution of the adjoint differential equations directly from the solutions of the state equations. For additional detail concerning this topic, see Hagedorn (1978).

Example. *Energy-optimal control of a non-linear oscillator.* The system

$$\ddot{x} + \omega_0^2 x + \mu x^3 = u \tag{60}$$

with $u(t)$ unconstrained, is to be steered from an arbitrary given point in the phase plane to the origin in such a way that

$$J = \frac{1}{2} \int_{t_0}^{t_1} u^2 \, dt \tag{61}$$

is minimized, where t_1 is unspecified. When the system (60) is written as the first-order system

$$\left. \begin{array}{l} x_1 = x_2, \\[2mm] \dot{x}_2 = -\omega_0^2 x_1 - \mu x_1^3 + u, \end{array} \right\} \tag{62}$$

then $y_0 = -1$ yields a Hamiltonian of the form

$$H = -\frac{1}{2} u^2 + y_1 x_2 + y_2(-\omega_0^2 x_1 - \mu x_1^3 + u) . \tag{63}$$

The use of the maximum principle together with $\partial H/\partial u = 0$ results in an optimal control $u = y_2$ as well as in the adjoint equations

$$\dot{y}_1 = \omega_0^2 y_2 + 3\mu x_1^2 y_2 , \left.\vphantom{\begin{array}{c}1\\1\end{array}}\right\} \quad (64)$$
$$\dot{y}_2 = -y_1 .$$

The equations resulting from a linearization of (62) and (64) may be solved without difficulty. Here, however, a treatment of the linearized problem will be postponed; for computational reasons, a substitute problem containing only some of the linear terms of (62) and (64) will be discussed first. In line with this approach, let $H = H_0 + H_1$ with

$$H_0 = y_1 x_2 - \omega_0^2 y_2 x_1 , \tag{65}$$

$$H_1 = -\mu y_2 x_1^3 + \frac{1}{2} y_2^2 . \tag{66}$$

A complete solution of the Hamilton–Jacobi equation

$$\frac{\partial S}{\partial x_1} x_2 - \omega_0^2 \frac{\partial S}{\partial x_2} x_1 + \frac{\partial S}{\partial t} = 0 \tag{67}$$

corresponding to (65), is given by

$$S = x_1 p_1 \sin(\omega_0 t + p_2) + \frac{x_2}{\omega_0} p_1 \cos(\omega_0 t + p_2) , \tag{68}$$

where p_1, p_2 are contants of integration. The function (68) now is used together with $q_i = \frac{\partial S}{\partial p_i}$ and $y_i = \frac{\partial S}{\partial x_i}$, $i = 1, 2$ to generate the canonical transformation

$$x_1 = q_1 \sin(\omega_0 t + p_2) + \frac{q_2}{p_1} \cos(\omega_0 t + p_2) , \left.\vphantom{\begin{array}{c}1\\1\\1\\1\\1\\1\\1\\1\\1\\1\\1\end{array}}\right\}$$

$$x_2 = -\frac{q_2}{p_1} \omega_0 \sin(\omega_0 t + p_2) + q_1 \omega_0 \cos(\omega_0 t + p_2) ,$$

$$y_1 = p_1 \sin(\omega_0 t + p_2) , \qquad\qquad\qquad (69)$$

$$y_2 = \frac{p_1}{\omega_0} \cos(\omega_0 t + p_2) ,$$

where q_1, q_2 are the new generalized coordinates and p_1, p_2 are the new generalized momenta. The system $H^*(\mathbf{q}, \mathbf{p}, t) = H(\mathbf{x}(\mathbf{q}, \mathbf{p}, t), \mathbf{y}(\mathbf{q}, \mathbf{p}, t))$ now is described in terms of these new variables (see section 4.5). After some algebraic manipulation, this results in

$$H^*(\mathbf{q}, \mathbf{p}, t) = \frac{1}{4\omega_0^2} p_1^2 - \frac{3\mu}{8\omega_0}\left(q_1^2 q_2 + \frac{q_2^3}{p_1^2}\right) + \frac{p_1^2}{4\omega_0^2}\cos 2(\omega_0 t + p_2) - $$

$$- \frac{\mu p_1}{8\omega_0}\left\{\left(2q_1^3 + 6\frac{q_1 q_2^2}{p_1^2}\right)\sin 2(\omega_0 t + p_2)\right.$$

$$+ 4\frac{q_2^3}{p_1^3}\cos 2(\omega_0 t + p_2) +$$

$$+ \left(3\frac{q_1 q_2^2}{p_1^2} - q_1^3\right)\sin 4(\omega_0 t + p_2) +$$

$$\left.+ \left(\frac{q_2^3}{p_1^3} - 3\frac{q_1^2 q_2}{p_1}\right)\cos 4(\omega_0 t + p_2)\right\}, \tag{70}$$

and there is no difficulty in expressing the differential equations in terms of these new variables. These, however, cannot be solved in closed form. An approximate solution can be computed by omitting all sums containing trigonometric functions in (70). This approach corresponds to calculating the temporal mean of (70) for a fixed p_2. One thus replaces H^* by

$$H_0^*(\mathbf{q}, \mathbf{p}, t) = \frac{1}{4\omega_0^2} p_1^2 - \frac{3\mu}{8\omega_0}\left(q_1^2 q_2 + \frac{q_2^3}{p_1^2}\right) \tag{71}$$

to obtain

$$\dot{q}_1 = \frac{1}{2\omega_0^2} p_1 + \frac{3\mu}{4\omega_0}\frac{q_2^3}{p_1^3},$$

$$\dot{q}_2 = 0,$$

$$\dot{p}_1 = \frac{3\mu}{4\omega_0} q_1 q_2, \tag{72}$$

$$\dot{p}_2 = \frac{3\mu}{8\omega_0} q_1^2 + \frac{9\mu}{8\omega_0}\frac{q_2^2}{p_1^2}.$$

Since q_2 is constant, the first and the third of eqns (72) may be combined and integrated, the result substituted into the last equation, which may then be integrated to obtain $p_2(t)$. If (72) is to be solved only for the given boundary conditions, then some additional simplifications are possible. A particular solution of (72) is obtained by setting $t_1 = 0$ with $x_1(0) = 0, x_2(0) = 0$, and $t_0 < 0$ as a consequence. Eqns (69) then imply $q_1(0) = 0, q_2(0) = 0$. The condition $H(\mathbf{x}, \mathbf{y}, \bar{\mathbf{u}}) = 0$ furthermore yields $y_2(0) = 0$ and hence $p_2(0) = \pi/2$. A solution of (72) which satisfies these conditions is given by

$$q_1 = \frac{p_1(0)}{2\omega_0^2} t ,$$

$$q_2 = 0 ,$$

$$p_1 = p_1(0) ,$$

$$p_2 = \frac{\pi}{2} + \frac{\mu}{32\omega_0^5} p_1^2(0) t^3 ,$$

(73)

which results in $x_1(t), x_2(t)$ of the form

$$x_1(t) = \frac{p_1(0)}{2\omega_0^2} t \cos \left\{ \left(\omega_0 + \frac{\mu}{32\omega_0^5} p_1^2(0) t^2 \right) t \right\} ,$$

$$x_2(t) = -\frac{p_1(0)}{2\omega_0^2} t \sin \left\{ \left(\omega_0 + \frac{\mu}{32\omega_0^5} p_1^2(0) t^2 \right) t \right\}$$

(74)

with constant of integration $p_1(0)$. In an illustration of the trajectories in the phase plane, $p_1(0)$ serves as the parameter which fixes a particular member of the family of trajectories. A comparison of the exact solutions of the problem with the approximate solutions (74) is given in Fig. 5.11.

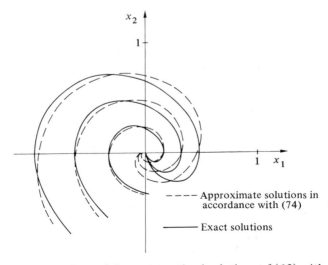

Fig. 5.11. A comparison of the exact optimal solutions of (62) with the approximate solutions (74) ($\omega_0 = 1, \mu = -1/6$).

To continue the canonical perturbation process, eqns (72) must be solved for arbitrary initial conditions rather than the specific ones used here; in this manner, one then obtains the new canonical transformation $(\mathbf{q}, \mathbf{p}) \rightarrow (\mathbf{q}_0, \mathbf{p}_0)$.

In this example, an investigation of the existence and uniqueness of the solutions leads to some interesting results (see Otterbein 1976).

5.5. Additional comments concerning the theory of optimal control

The problem of optimal control investigated in this chapter—the minimization of the functional (10) subject to the differential eqns (1) and with $\mathbf{u} \in U$—is a generalization of the Lagrangian problem in the calculus of variations. Whereas the set of control values is an open set in the classical calculus of variations, it is quite permissible for this set to be closed in the theory of optimal control. In the case of 'bang-bang' control, the Euler–Lagrange equations of the calculus of variations certainly do not suffice to determine the optimal controls, since the optimal control here takes on only values on the boundary of U (U is closed). If the methods of the classical calculus of variations are used for such a problem, then one arrives at the erroneous result that no optimal controls exist, since the calculus of variations supplies necessary conditions for the optimality of control functions which only take on values in the interior of U! For the case of an open control set U, the maximum principle yields the Euler–Lagrange equations if $\partial H/\partial \mathbf{u} = \mathbf{0}$ is used as a necessary condition for the maximization of H.

The theory of optimal control is relatively new: the most important results by Pontryagin and his associates appeared in the Soviet Union in the mid-1950s. It must be mentioned that western scientists, in particular, Bellman (1957) and Isaacs (1965), independently obtained similar results at about the same time. Aside from the classical book by Pontryagin, Boltyanski, Gamkrelidze, and Mischenko (1967), excellent textbooks on optimal control are those by Athans and Falb (1966) as well as Lee and Markus (1967). From the German literature, let it suffice to cite Knobloch and Kappel (1974). Numerous interesting technical applications may be found in Bryson and Ho (1969). The connections between the classical calculus of variations and optimal control are discussed by Young (1969) and more recently in an article by McShane (1978).

An important problem in mechanics which gave impetus to many innovations in control theory was the problem of determining the optimal (fuel minimal) trajectories of a spaceship in a central force field, as treated in the well-written book of Lawden (1963) and by Tolle (1975). Additional new results about this topic may be found in Bell and Jacobson (1975). A number of other interesting problems of optimal control occur in connection with space travel, as, for example, the fuel-minimal rotation of a rigid body about a body-fixed axis, as investigated by Sagirow (1974).

In spite of the fact that Hamiltonian mechanics and the theory of optimal control obviously are closely related, only a few authors make use of canonical perturbation theory in control problems (Fraeijs de Veubeke 1965, 1966;

Ozgoren, Longman, and Cooper 1975; Hagedorn 1978). Here, the use of Lie series for the computation of the optimal control functions, as attempted by Ozgoren *et al.* (1975), appears to be especially interesting. Special results are obtained when the system which is to be controlled is itself of Hamiltonian type (see Hagedorn 1978). Other concepts from theoretical mechanics have been interpreted in the light of control theory by Djukic (1973).

References

Athans, M. and Falb, P. L. (1966). *Optimal control.* McGraw-Hill, New York.

Bell, D. J. and Jacobson, D. H. (1975). *Singular optimal control processes.* Academic Press, London.

Bellman, R. (1957). *Dynamic programming.* Princeton University Press, Princeton, New Jersey.

Bryson, A. E. and Ho, Yu-Chi. (1969). *Applied optimal control.* Ginn, Waltham, Massachusetts.

Djukic, D. J. S. (1973). An analytical mechanics contribution to optimum control theory. *Int. J. Control* **17**, 1287–92.

Fraeijs de Veubeke, B. (1965). Canonical transformations and the thrust–coast–thrust optimal transfer problem. *Astronaut. Acta* **11**, 271–82.

—— (1966). Optimal steering and cutoff–relight programs for orbital transfers. *Astrononaut. Acta* **12**, 323–8.

Hagedorn, P. (1978). Canonical transformations in the optimal control of mechanical systems. *Int. J. non-linear Mech.* **13**, 103–16.

Isaacs, R. (1965). *Differential games.* Wiley, New York.

Knobloch, H. W. and Kappel, F. (1974). *Gewöhnliche Differentialgleichungen* [*Ordinary differential equations*]. Teubner, Stuttgart.

Lawden, D. F. (1963). *Optimal trajectories for space navigation.* Butterworths, London.

Lee, E. B. and Markus, L. (1967). *Foundations of optimal control theory.* John Wiley, New York.

McShane, E. J. (1978). The calculus of variations from the beginning through optimal control theory. In *Optimal control and differential equations.* Academic Press, Inc., New York.

Müller, P. C. and Schiehlen, W. O. (1976). *Lineare Schwingungen* [*Linear oscillations*]. Akademische Verlagsgesellschaft, Wiesbaden.

Otterbein, S. (1976). *Studienarbeit* [*A study*]. Institut für Mechanik, TH Darmstadt.

Ozgoren, M. K., Longman, R. W., and Cooper, C. A. (1975). *Application of Lie transform-based canonical perturbation method to the optimal control of bilinear systems.* AAS/AIAA Astrodynamics Specialists Conference, Nassau, Bahamas, July 28–30, 1975.

Pontryagin, L. S., Boltyanski, V. G., Gamkrelidze, R. V., and Mischenko, E. F. (1967). *Mathematische Theorie optimaler Prozesse* [*Mathematical theory of optimal processes*]. R. Oldenburg, Munich.

Sagirow, P. (1974). Verbrauchsoptimale Drehungen um eine körperfeste Achse [Fuel-optimal rotations about a body-fixed axis]. In *Gyrodynamics, Euromech 38 Colloquium* (ed P. Y. Willems). Springer, Berlin.

Tolle, H. (1975). *Optimization methods.* Springer, Berlin.

Young, L. C. (1969). *Lectures on the calculus of variations and optimal control theory.* W. B. Saunders, Philadelphia.

Exercises

5.1. A particle is to move smoothly on a fixed path from 0 to B under the influence of gravity (Fig. 5.12). How must the path between the fixed given points 0 and B be chosen if the particle, after being released at 0 with initial velocity v_0, is to arrive at B in as short a time as possible?[†]

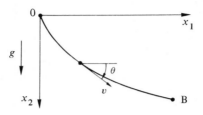

Fig. 5.12. Exercise 5.1.

5.2. In Example 3 of section 5.2 (minimum time paths through a region with position-dependent current velocity), let $u(x_1, x_2)$ and $v(x_1, x_2)$ in eqn (38) be defined by

$$u(x_1, x_2) = -w\frac{x_2}{h},$$

$$v(x_1, x_2) = 0,$$

where h is a positive constant. Determine the optimal trajectory initiating at the point $(3.66h, -1.86h)$ and terminating at the origin (Bryson and Ho 1969).

5.3. Consider a car moving with constant velocity w in the $x_1 x_2$-plane (Fig. 5.13). Its equations of motion are given by

$$\dot{x}_1 = w\cos\theta,$$

$$\dot{x}_2 = w\sin\theta,$$

$$\dot{\theta} = \frac{w}{\rho},$$

[†] This problem of the 'brachistrochrone' was posed in 1696 by John Bernoulli, and it was solved by Newton (1642–1727), Leibniz (1646–1716), James Bernoulli (1654–1705), and L'Hospital (1661–1704).

where θ is the angle between the velocity vector and the x_1-axis and ρ is the radius of curvature of the path. Assume that the minimum turning radius for the car is R so that one has $-1 \leqslant R/\rho \leqslant 1$. Determine the time optimal trajectories between two given points A and E.

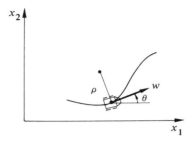

Fig. 5.13. Exercise 5.3.

5.4. Consider the system

$$\dot{x} = x + u$$

on the time interval $[0,1]$ with $x(0) = x_0$ and $x(1) = 0$. Determine the unconstrained ($|u| < \infty$) control function $u(t)$ and corresponding solution $x(t)$ which minimize the cost functional

$$J = \frac{1}{4} \int_0^1 u^4 \, \mathrm{d}t$$

(Lee and Markus 1967).

5.5. A hovercraft (aircushion vehicle) is moving in a horizontal plane. If the air resistance is neglected in comparison to the thrust, then a first approximation to the motion is given by that of a particle moving in the plane and subjected to a thrust $S(S \leqslant S_{\max})$. The controls here are the direction and the absolute value of the thrust vector.

Write the equations of motion for the system and determine that thrust which transfers the vehicle from a state with initial velocity v_0 in the direction θ_0 to one with velocity v_1 and direction θ_1 in minimum time (θ here is the angle between the direction of the velocity vector and some fixed reference axis). The position of the vehicle at the end of the manoeuvre is not prescribed.

5.6.   Consider the system

$$\ddot{x} + \omega_0^2 x + ax^3 = u, \qquad |u| \leqslant 1.$$

The system is to be transferred from an arbitrary initial point to the point $x = 0$ and $\dot{x} = 0$ in minimum time. Show how the problem may be solved by means of canonical perturbation theory.

SOLUTIONS FOR THE EXERCISES

1.1. The equations of motion are given by

$$m_1\ddot{q}_1 = -f_1(q_1) + f_2(q_2) + m_1 g,$$

$$m_2\ddot{q}_3 = -f_2(q_2) + m_2 g, \tag{1}$$

where $q_3 = q_1 + q_2$ is the displacement of m_2. In this manner one obtains the system of non-linear differential equations

$$m_1\ddot{q}_1 = -c_1 q_1 (1 + \alpha_1^2 q_1^2) + c_2 q_2 (1 + \alpha_2^2 q_2^2) + m_1 g,$$

$$m_2 (\ddot{q}_1 + \ddot{q}_2) = -c_2 q_2 (1 + \alpha_2^2 q_2^2) + m_2 g. \tag{2}$$

An application of the transformation

$$x_1 = \alpha_1 q_1, \qquad x_2 = \alpha_2 q_2, \qquad \tau = \sqrt{\left(\frac{c_1}{m_1}\right)} t \tag{3}$$

yields

$$x_1'' + x_1 (1 + x_1^2) - 4 x_2 (1 + x_2^2) = 2,$$

$$x_1'' + 8 x_2'' + x_2 (1 + x_2^2) = 2, \tag{4}$$

where the primes designate derivatives with respect to τ. For the equilibrium position $\mathbf{x}_{st}$ one has

$$x_{1st} (1 + x_{1st}^2) - 4 x_{2st} (1 + x_{2st}^2) = 2,$$

$$x_{2st} (1 + x_{2st}^2) = 2 \tag{5}$$

and, hence, $x_{1st} = 2, x_{2st} = 1$ as the only real solution.
   The substitution of

$$x_1 = x_{1st} + \bar{x}_1, \qquad x_2 = x_{2st} + \bar{x}_2 \tag{6}$$

in the equations of motion and the subsequent neglect of the non-linear terms in

$\bar{x}_1$ and $\bar{x}_2$ yield

$$\bar{x}_1'' + 13\,\bar{x}_1 - 16\,\bar{x}_2 = 0\,,$$
$$\bar{x}_1'' + 8\,\bar{x}_2'' + 4\,\bar{x}_2 = 0\,. \tag{7}$$

An assumed solution of the form $\bar{x}_i = A_i \cos{(\omega\tau + \alpha_i)}, i = 1, 2$, leads to

$$(13 - \omega^2)\,A_1 \qquad\qquad - 16\,A_2 = 0\,,$$
$$-\omega^2 A_1 + (4 - 8\,\omega^2)\,A_2 = 0\,. \tag{8}$$

If this homogeneous linear system of algebraic equations in A_1 and A_2 is to have a non-trivial solution, then the coefficient determinant must vanish. This condition results in the characteristic equation

$$2\,\omega^4 - 31\,\omega^2 + 13 = 0 \tag{9}$$

with roots $\omega_1^2 = 0.43$ and $\omega_2^2 = 15.07$.

The corresponding amplitude ratios ρ_1 and ρ_2 are given by

$$\rho_1 = \left(\frac{A_1}{A_2}\right)_1 = \frac{16}{13 - \omega_1^2} = 1.27\,,$$
$$\rho_2 = \left(\frac{A_1}{A_2}\right)_2 = \frac{16}{13 - \omega_2^2} = -7.73\,, \tag{10}$$

resulting in the solution

$$\bar{x}_1 = \rho_1 B_1 \cos{(\omega_1\tau + \beta_1)} + \rho_2 B_2 \cos{(\omega_2\tau + \beta_2)}\,,$$
$$\bar{x}_2 = \quad B_1 \cos{(\omega_1\tau + \beta_1)} + \quad B_2 \cos{(\omega_2\tau + \beta_2)}\,, \tag{11}$$

for small oscillations about the equilibrium position. The constants of integration $B_1, B_2, \beta_1, \beta_2$ are determined from the initial conditions.

1.2. (a) The equation of motion is given by

$$m\ddot{q} + 2c\left[1 - \frac{1 + \alpha}{\sqrt{\{1 + (q/l)^2\}}}\right]q = 0\,; \tag{12}$$

with $x = q/l, \tau = \sqrt{(2c/m)}\, t$ it takes on the form

$$x'' + \left(1 - \frac{1 + \alpha}{\sqrt{(1 + x^2)}}\right) x = 0 , \tag{13}$$

where the primes again denote a differentiation with respect to τ.

(b) The normalized restoring force

$$f(x) = \left(1 - \frac{1 + \alpha}{\sqrt{(1 + x^2)}}\right) x$$

is represented in Fig. 1 for various values of α.

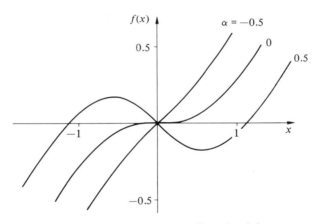

Fig. 1. Restoring force in Exercise 1.2.

A power-series expansion of the restoring force yields the equation of motion in the form

$$x'' - \alpha x + (1 + \alpha)\frac{1}{2} x^3 - (1 + \alpha)\frac{1 \cdot 3}{2 \cdot 4} x^5 + (1 + \alpha)\frac{1 \cdot 3 \cdot 5}{2 \cdot 4 \cdot 6} x^7 - \ldots = 0 . \tag{14}$$

It is immediately apparent that a linearization for $\alpha = 0$ certainly is not meaningful, since the linearized equation then has the form $x'' = 0$ and it is no longer even possible to make any statements about the stability or instability of the equilibrium position $x = 0$.

(c) The equilibrium positions are determined from the complete non-linear equation of motion with $x'' = 0$. As a result, one obtains $x_1 = 0$ and $x_{2,3}$

$= \pm \sqrt{\{\alpha(2 + \alpha)\}}$. Non-trivial, real equilibrium positions thus exist for only $\alpha < -2$ and for $\alpha > 0$. However, the natural length of the springs $s_0 = l(1 + \alpha)$ becomes negative for $\alpha < -1$ so that meaningful non-trivial real solutions actually exist only for $\alpha > 0$.

A time-independent first integral of the non-linear equation of motion is given by

$$x' = \pm \sqrt{\{2 (E - F(x))\}} \qquad (15)$$

with

$$F(x) = \frac{x^2}{2} - (1 + \alpha) \sqrt{(1 + x^2)}. \qquad (16)$$

The phase diagrams now may easily be constructed (Fig. 2). Because of symmetry, the diagrams are only sketched for the first quadrant.

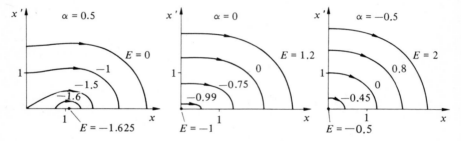

Fig. 2. Phase trajectories for Exercise 1.2.

1.3. The equation of motion is given by

$$m\ddot{z} = -f(z) + mg, \qquad (17)$$

where z is measured from the static equilibrium position of the system. The restoring force $f(z)$ is defined by

$$f(z) = 0 \qquad \text{for} \qquad z \leqslant -e,$$
$$\qquad\qquad\qquad\qquad\qquad\qquad (18)$$
$$f(z) = mg + cz \qquad \text{for} \qquad z \geqslant -e,$$

where $e = mg/c = g/\omega^2$ is the static elongation of the spring and where $\omega^2 = c/m$. Assume that the initial conditions are given by $\dot{z}(0) = 0$ and $z(0) = z_0 > 0$.

Two regions of motion must be distinguished:

(a) For $z_0 \leqslant e$ one obtains

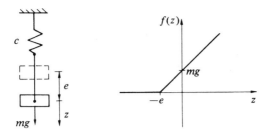

Fig. 3. Restoring force $f(z)$ for Exercise 1.3.

$$\ddot{z} + \omega^2 z = 0 \tag{19}$$

with corresponding phase trajectories specified by

$$\left(\frac{\dot{z}}{\omega e}\right)^2 + \left(\frac{z}{e}\right)^2 = \left(\frac{z_0}{e}\right)^2, \tag{20}$$

namely, circles in the $\dot{z}/\omega e$, z/e-plane.

(b) For $z_0 \geqslant e$, $f(z)$ becomes zero for part of the motion and the body then moves only under the influence of gravity.

(b$_1$) For $z \geqslant -e$ one has

$$\ddot{z} + \omega^2 z = 0 \tag{21}$$

and

$$\left(\frac{\dot{z}}{\omega e}\right)^2 + \left(\frac{z}{e}\right)^2 = \left(\frac{z_0}{e}\right)^2, \tag{22}$$

that is, the phase trajectories are again circles.

(b$_2$) For $z \leqslant -e$ one has

$$m\ddot{z} = mg, \tag{23}$$

with the parabolas

$$\frac{\dot{z}^2}{2} - g z = \frac{\dot{z}_1^2}{2} - g z_1 \tag{24}$$

as phase trajectories.

The constants of integration are determined from continuity conditions between corresponding circles and parabolas. For $z = z_1 = -e$, one has

$$\dot{z}^2 = \dot{z}_1^2 = \omega^2 e^2 \left\{ \left(\frac{z_0}{e}\right)^2 - 1 \right\},$$
(25)

which requires that the parabola be given by

$$\left(\frac{\dot{z}}{\omega e}\right)^2 - 2\frac{z}{e} = \left(\frac{z_0}{e}\right)^2 + 1 .$$
(26)

The resulting phase diagram is depicted in Fig. 4.

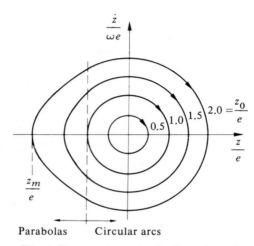

Fig. 4. Phase trajectories for Exercise 1.3.

It is easy to determine the period of oscillation, T. For small amplitudes $(z_0 < e)$, one simply has $T = 2\pi \sqrt{(m/c)}$. For large-amplitude motion on the circle, one has in the upper half-plane

$$\dot{z} = \omega \sqrt{(z_0^2 - z^2)}$$
(27)

and, hence,

$$\omega \int_0^{t_1} dt = \int_{-e}^{z_0} \frac{dz}{\sqrt{(z_0^2 - z^2)}}$$
(28)

resulting in

$$\omega t_1 = \arccos\left(-\frac{e}{z_0}\right).$$
(29)

For the motion on the parabolic arc (upper part), one has

$$\dot{z} = +\omega \sqrt{(z_0^2 + e^2 + 2\,ez)} \tag{30}$$

and

$$\int_{z_m}^{-e} \frac{dz}{\sqrt{(z_0^2 + e^2 + 2\,ez)}} = \omega \int_{t_0}^{t_2} dt . \tag{31}$$

follows. With $\dot{z}(z_m) = 0$ one obtains $2ez_m = -(z_0^2 + e^2)$ and, hence, $\omega\,(t_2) = \sqrt{\{(z_0/e)^2 - 1\}}$. In this case, the period of oscillation is given by

$$T = 2\,(t_1 + t_2) = 2 \sqrt{\left(\frac{m}{c}\right)} \left[\arccos\,(-e/z_0) + \sqrt{\left\{\left(\frac{z_0}{e}\right)^2 - 1\right\}} \right] \tag{32}$$

which has the approximation $(T/2\pi)\,\sqrt{(c/m)} \approx \frac{1}{2} + (z_0/\pi e)$ for large values of z_0/e. The period of oscillation as a function of the maximum deflection is represented in the diagram of Fig. 5.

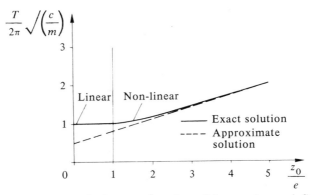

Fig. 5. Period of oscillation as a function of the maximum deflection.

Note that because of the asymmetry of the motion, the maximum deflection is not idential with the amplitude; the amplitdue is defined by $A = (z_{max} - z_{min})/2$.

1.4. (a) Use $\tau = \omega t, x = \mu y$ to transform the differential equation into

$$\omega^2 y'' + y + \mu y^2 = 0 \tag{33}$$

where $\omega/2\pi$ is the frequency of free oscillation which is to be determined and where μ is a small parameter which is chosen to be equal to the maximum deflection C.

(b) The substitution of

$$\omega = 1 + \mu\omega_1 + \mu^2\omega_2 + \ldots ,$$
$$y = y_0 + \mu y_1 + \mu^2 y_2 + \ldots \tag{34}$$

into the differential equation and a comparison of terms of the same order in μ yield the system

$$y_0'' + y_0 = 0 ,$$
$$y_1'' + y_1 = -2\,\omega_1 y_0'' - y_0^2 ,$$
$$y_2'' + y_2 = -2\,\omega_1 y_1'' - (\omega_1^2 + 2\,\omega_2)y_0'' - 2y_0 y_1 , \tag{35}$$

$$\ldots ,$$

which is solved recursively. With the initial conditions $y(0) = 1, y'(0) = 0$, one obtains $y_0(\tau) = \cos\tau$ as the first step.

As a consequence, the differential equation for $y_1(\tau)$ takes on the form

$$y_1'' + y_1 = 2\,\omega_1 \cos\tau - \cos^2\tau = 2\,\omega_1 \cos\tau - \frac{1}{2} - \frac{1}{2}\cos 2\tau . \tag{36}$$

A choice of $\omega_1 = 0$ is indicated to avoid resonance, so that

$$y_1(\tau) = C_1 \cos(\tau + \gamma_1) - \frac{1}{2} + \frac{1}{6}\cos 2\tau , \tag{37}$$

results. With the initial conditions $y_1(0) = 0, y_1'(0) = 0$ this becomes

$$y_1(\tau) = -\frac{1}{2} + \frac{1}{3}\cos\tau + \frac{1}{6}\cos 2\tau . \tag{38}$$

Substitution yields

$$y_2'' + y_2 = 2\,\omega_2 \cos\tau + \cos\tau - \frac{2}{3}\cos^2\tau - \frac{1}{3}\cos 2\tau \, \cos\tau$$

$$= -\frac{1}{3} + \left(2\,\omega_2 + \frac{5}{6}\right)\cos\tau - \frac{1}{3}\cos 2\tau - \frac{1}{6}\cos 3\tau , \tag{39}$$

as the equation for y_2. If resonance is to be avoided, then one must have $2\omega_2 + 5/6 = 0$ or $\omega_2 = -5/12$. The initial conditions $y_2(0) = 0$ and $y_2'(0) = 0$ then yield

$$y_2(\tau) = -\frac{1}{3} + \frac{29}{144}\cos\tau + \frac{1}{9}\cos 2\tau + \frac{1}{48}\cos 3\tau. \tag{40}$$

With $\mu = C$, one thus has

$$x(\tau) = -C^2\left(\frac{1}{2} + \frac{C}{3}\right) + C\left(1 + \frac{C}{3} + \frac{29}{144}C^2\right)\cos\tau +$$

$$+ C^2\left(\frac{1}{6} + \frac{C}{9}\right)\cos 2\tau + \frac{C^3}{48}\cos 3\tau + 0\,(C^4). \tag{41}$$

As was to be expected, the oscillations are not symmetrical with respect to $x = 0$. The circular frequency is given by $\omega = 1 - 5C^2/12$, that is, it decreases for an increasing maximum deflection.

(c) Note again that C is not identical with the amplitude due to the absence of symmetry; the amplitude is given by $A = (x_{\max} - x_{\min})/2$. From the expression for $x(\tau)$ one obtains

$$A = C\left(1 + \frac{C}{3} + \frac{29}{144}C^2 + \frac{C^2}{48}\right)$$

$$= C\left(1 + \frac{C}{3} + \frac{2}{9}C^2\right). \tag{42}$$

By expanding C in a power series

$$C = A + a_2 A^2 + a_3 A^3 + \cdots \tag{43}$$

and comparing coefficients, the relationship

$$C = A - \frac{1}{3}A^2 + 0\,(A^3) \tag{44}$$

is obtained. Consequently,

$$\omega = 1 - \frac{5}{12}\left(A^2 - \frac{2}{3}A^3\right). \tag{45}$$

The exact phase trajectories are obtained as a time-independent first integral of the original differential equation. Thus, they are represented by

$$\dot{x} = \pm \sqrt{\left\{ E_0 - 2 \left(\frac{x^2}{2} + \frac{x^3}{3} \right) \right\}} . \tag{46}$$

They are compared to the approximate solutions in Fig. 6.

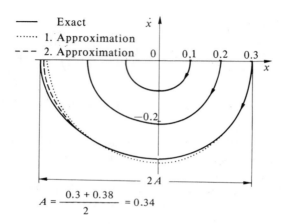

Fig. 6. Exact and approximate phase trajectories for Exercise 1.4.

1.5.   (a) With $\omega_0^2 = \tan \alpha$ the restoring force is given by

$$g(x) = \omega_0^2 x + P \operatorname{sgn} x . \tag{47}$$

As a result, one has to solve the differential equation

$$\ddot{x} + \omega_0^2 x = -P \operatorname{sgn} x . \tag{48}$$

In accordance with section 1.2.2, the equations for slowly-changing amplitude and phase are obtained as

$$\dot{a} = \frac{1}{2\pi\omega_0} \int_0^{2\pi} [-P \operatorname{sgn}\{a \sin(\theta + \psi)\}] \cos(\theta + \psi) \, d\theta ,$$

$$\dot{\psi} = \frac{1}{2\pi a\omega_0} \int_0^{2\pi} [-P \operatorname{sgn}\{a \sin(\theta + \psi)\}] \sin(\theta + \psi) \, d\theta , \tag{49}$$

where ψ and a on the right-hand side are treated as constants with respect to the integration. As a result, one has

$$\dot{a} = 0 ,$$

$$\dot{\psi} = \frac{4P}{2\pi a \omega_0}$$

(50

with solution

$$a = A ,$$

$$\psi = \frac{2P}{\pi \omega_0 A} t + \psi_0 .$$

(51)

If the initial conditions are chosen in such a way that $\psi_0 = \pi/2$, then one obtains the approximate solution

$$x = A \cos \left(\omega_0 + \frac{2P}{\pi \omega_0 A} \right) t .$$

(52)

The approximate period of oscillation, $\bar{T}$, is given by

$$\bar{T} = \frac{2\pi}{\omega_0 \left(1 + \frac{2P}{\pi \omega_0^2 A} \right)} .$$

(53)

There is no difficulty in determining the exact solution. With the initial conditions $x(0) = A > 0, \dot{x}(0) = 0$, one first has

$$x = -\frac{P}{\omega_0^2} + \left(A + \frac{P}{\omega_0^2} \right) \cos \omega_0 t ,$$

(54)

as long as x is positive. For $t = t_1 = (1/\omega_0)$ arc cos $\{1/(1 + A\omega_0^2/P)\}$, x becomes zero and one then is dealing with the solution of $\ddot{x} + \omega_2^0 x = +P$ with initial conditions $x(t_1) = 0, \dot{x}(t_1) = -\omega_0(A + (P/\omega_0^2)) \sin \omega_0 t$.

The phase trajectories are given by

$$\left(\frac{\dot{x}}{\omega_0} \right)^2 + x^2 + 2 \frac{P}{\omega_0^2} |x| = A^2 + 2 \frac{PA}{\omega_0^2} .$$

(55)

A comparison of exact and approximate phase trajectories is presented in Fig. 7.

The exact period of oscillation is obtained to be

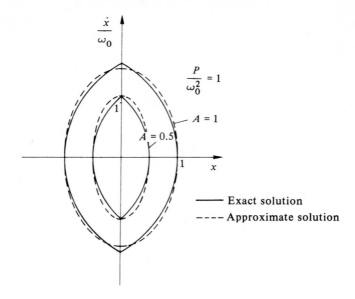

Fig. 7. Exact and approximate phase trajectories for Exercise 1.5(a).

$$T = \frac{4}{\omega_0} \arccos\left(1/(1 + A\omega_0^2/P)\right).\tag{56}$$

A comparison with the approximate expression reveals that $\lim_{A \to \infty} (\bar{T} - T) = 0$, that is, for $A \to \infty$, $\bar{T}$ approaches the limit of the exact expression, T. The relative error of the approximation is illustrated in Fig. 8.

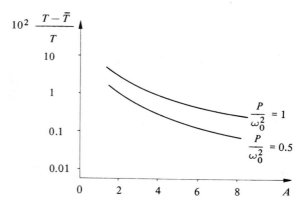

Fig. 8. Relative error in the approximate expression for the period of oscillation in Exercise 1.5(a).

(b) The restoring force now is given by

$$g(x) = \omega_0^2 (x - x_0), \qquad \text{for } x > x_0,$$

$$g(x) = 0, \qquad \text{for } -x_0 < x < x_0,$$

$$g(x) = \omega_0^2 (x + x_0), \qquad \text{for } x < -x_0, \qquad (57)$$

where $\omega_0^2 = \tan \alpha$, so that the differential equation

$$\ddot{x} + \omega_0^2 x = f(x) \qquad (58)$$

with

$$f(x) = \omega_0^2 x_0, \qquad \text{for } x > x_0,$$

$$f(x) = \omega_0^2 x, \qquad \text{for } -x_0 < x < x_0,$$

$$f(x) = -\omega_0^2 x_0, \qquad \text{for } x < -x_0 \qquad (59)$$

is to be solved. Since $f(x)$ is an odd function, $\dot{a} = 0$ follows from eqn (1.88). For $a = A$ one furthermore has

$$\dot{\psi} = -\frac{1}{2\pi\omega_0 A} \int_0^{2\pi} f(A \sin(\theta + \psi)) \sin(\theta + \psi) \, d\theta, \qquad (60)$$

with

$$f(\varphi) = \omega_0^2 A \sin \varphi, \qquad \text{for } 0 < \varphi < \varphi_1,$$

$$f(\varphi) = \omega_0^2 x_0, \qquad \text{for } \varphi_1 \leqslant \varphi \leqslant \varphi_2,$$

$$f(\varphi) = \omega_0^2 A \sin \varphi, \qquad \text{for } \varphi_2 \leqslant \varphi \leqslant \varphi_3,$$

$$f(\varphi) = -\omega_0^2 x_0, \qquad \text{for } \varphi_3 \leqslant \varphi \leqslant \varphi_4,$$

$$f(\varphi) = \omega_0^2 A \sin \varphi, \qquad \text{for } \varphi_4 \leqslant \varphi \leqslant 2\pi, \qquad (61)$$

where $\varphi = \theta + \psi$ and

$$\varphi_1 = \arcsin \frac{x_0}{A}, \qquad\qquad \varphi_2 = \pi - \varphi_1,$$

$$\varphi_3 = \pi + \varphi_1, \qquad\qquad \varphi_4 = 2\pi - \varphi_1. \qquad (62)$$

The integration over each section eventually yields

$$\dot{\psi} = -\frac{\omega_0}{2\pi} \left\{ 2\varphi_1 - \sin 2\varphi_1 + 4\frac{x_0}{A} \cos \varphi_1 \right\}, \tag{63}$$

so that the approximate period is given by

$$\overline{T} = \frac{2\pi}{\omega_0 + \dot{\psi}} = \frac{4\pi^2}{\omega_0 \left(2\pi - 2\varphi_1 + \sin 2\varphi_1 - 4\frac{x_0}{A} \cos \varphi_1\right)}. \tag{64}$$

Here also there is no difficulty in obtaining the exact solution corresponding to the initial conditions $x(0) = A > 0$, $\dot{x}(0) = 0$ (there are oscillations only for $A > x_0$). For $x > x_0$ one has

$$\ddot{x} + \omega_0^2 x = \omega_0^2 x_0 \tag{65}$$

with the solution

$$x = (A - x_0) \cos \omega_0 t + x_0 \tag{66}$$

and with phase trajectory

$$(x - x_0)^2 + \left(\frac{\dot{x}}{\omega_0}\right)^2 = (A - x_0)^2. \tag{67}$$

These equations are valid on the time interval $[0, t_1]$ with $t_1 = \pi/(2\omega_0)$. For $-x_0 < x < x_0$ one has $\ddot{x} = 0$; consequently, one obtains

$$x = x_0 + \frac{\pi}{2}(A - x_0) - \omega_0 (A - x_0) t, \tag{68}$$

where continuity conditions have been taken into consideration. This expression is valid for $t \in [t_1, t_2]$ with

$$t_2 = \frac{2 + \frac{\pi}{2}\left(\frac{A}{x_0} - 1\right)}{\omega_0 \left(\frac{A}{x_0} - 1\right)}.$$

Because of symmetry (see Fig. 9), the period of oscillation is given by

$$T = 2(t_1 + t_2) = \frac{4 + 2\pi\left(\dfrac{A}{x_0} - 1\right)}{\omega_0\left(\dfrac{A}{x_0} - 1\right)} .$$

(69)

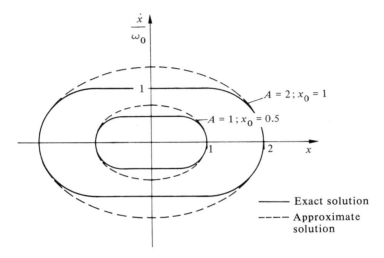

Fig. 9. Exact and approximate phase trajectories for Exercise 1.5(b).

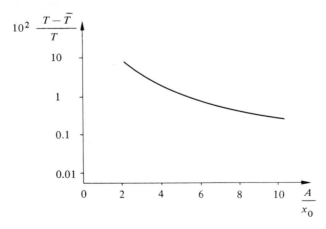

Fig. 10. Relative error in the approximate expression for the period of oscillation in Exercise 1.5(b).

The relative error in the approximate expression for T as a function of A/x_0 is shown in Fig. 10.

1.6. (a) Since $\ddot{x} + \rho\ \text{sgn}\ \dot{x} + g\ \text{sgn}\ x = 0$ is piecewise linear, the solution can be stated explicitly. In every quadrant of the phase-plane it is given by a different analytical expression (Fig. 11).

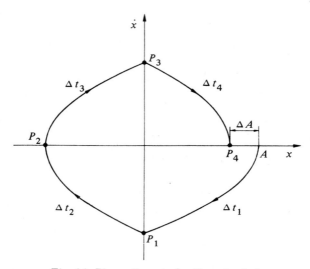

Fig. 11. Phase diagram for Exercise 1.6.

With the initial conditions $x(0) = A$, $\dot{x}(0) = 0$ the solution in the fourth quadrant is given by

$$\ddot{x} = -g + \rho\,,$$

$$\dot{x} = (-g + \rho)\,t\,,$$

$$x = \frac{1}{2}(-g + \rho)\,t^2 + A\,. \tag{70}$$

The trajectory reaches the $\dot{x}$-axis for $t = \Delta t_1$ at $\dot{x}_1$, where

$$\Delta t_1 = \sqrt{\left(\frac{2A}{g - \rho}\right)}, \quad \dot{x}_1 = -\sqrt{\{2A\,(g - \rho)\}}\,. \tag{71}$$

Next, there is a connecting motion in the third quadrant with the initial conditions $x(0) = 0, \dot{x}(0) = \dot{x}_1$ (the time measurement is begun anew). From the equation of motion

$$\ddot{x} = g + \rho \qquad (72)$$

there follows

$$\dot{x} = (g + \rho)t - \sqrt{\{2A(g - \rho)\}},$$

$$x = \frac{1}{2}(g + \rho)t^2 - \sqrt{\{2A(g - \rho)\}}t, \qquad (73)$$

and the trajectory reaches the x-axis at

$$x_2 = -A\frac{g - \rho}{g + \rho} \qquad (74)$$

after a time

$$t = \Delta t_2 = \frac{\sqrt{\{2A(g - \rho)\}}}{g + \rho}. \qquad (75)$$

In a similar manner, one obtains

$$\Delta t_3 = \sqrt{\left(\frac{2A}{g + \rho}\right)}, \qquad x_3 = (g - \rho)\sqrt{\left(\frac{2A}{g + \rho}\right)}, \qquad (76)$$

and

$$\Delta t_4 = \frac{g - \rho}{g + \rho}\sqrt{\left(\frac{2A}{g + \rho}\right)}, \qquad x_4 = A\frac{(g - \rho)^2}{(g + \rho)^2}. \qquad (77)$$

The period of oscillation thus is given by

$$T = \Delta t_1 + \Delta t_2 + \Delta t_3 + \Delta t_4$$

$$= \sqrt{(2A)}\, 2g\,\frac{(g + \rho)\sqrt{(g - \rho)} + (g - \rho)\sqrt{(g + \rho)}}{(g + \rho)^2(g - \rho)}, \qquad (78)$$

and the amplitude loss is

$$\Delta A = A - A\frac{(g - \rho)^2}{(g + \rho)^2} = A\frac{4\rho g}{(g + \rho)^2}. \qquad (79)$$

(b) For the approximate solution one obtains

$$\ddot{x} + \omega_0^2 x = \omega_0^2 x - \rho \, \text{sgn} \, \dot{x} - g \, \text{sgn} \, x \tag{80}$$

and, in accordance with section 1.2.2,

$$\dot{a} = \frac{1}{\omega_0 2\pi} \int_0^{2\pi} \{\omega_0^2 a \sin(\theta + \psi) - \rho \, \text{sgn} \cos(\theta + \psi) -$$

$$- g \, \text{sgn} \sin(\theta + \psi)\} \cos(\theta + \psi) \, d\theta \, ,$$

$$\dot{\psi} = -\frac{1}{\omega_0 2\pi} \int_0^{2\pi} \{\omega_0^2 a \sin(\theta + \psi) - \rho \, \text{sgn} \cos(\theta + \psi)$$

$$- g \, \text{sgn} \sin(\theta + \psi)\} \sin(\theta + \psi) \, d\theta \, , \tag{81}$$

where ω_0 still needs to be determined. An integration results in

$$\dot{a} = -\frac{2\rho}{\pi\omega_0} \, ,$$

$$\dot{\psi} = -\frac{\omega_0}{2} \left(1 - \frac{4g}{\pi a \omega_0^2}\right). \tag{82}$$

The first equation yields $a = A_0 - \dfrac{2\rho}{\pi\omega_0} t$. It is apparent from the expression for ψ that it is impossible to choose ω_0 in such a way that ψ remains small for large time intervals. However, if only the short time motion is of interest, then it is convenient to choose ω_0 in a way which assures $\dot{\psi}(0) = 0$. When this is done, one obtains

$$\omega_0 = \sqrt{\left(\frac{4g}{\pi A_0}\right)},$$

$$\psi = \psi_0 - \sqrt{\left(\frac{g}{\pi A_0}\right)} \left\{ t + \frac{\pi\omega_0 A_0}{2\rho} \ln\left(1 - \frac{2\rho}{\pi\omega_0 A_0} t\right) \right\} \tag{83}$$

and, eventually, with $\psi_0 = \dfrac{\pi}{2}$,

$$x(t) = \tag{84}$$

$$= \left(A_0 - \frac{2\rho}{\pi\omega_0} t\right) \sin\left[\omega_0 t + \frac{\pi}{2} - \frac{\omega_0}{2} \left\{ t + \frac{\pi\omega_0 A_0}{2\rho} \ln\left(1 - \frac{2\rho}{\pi\omega_0 A_0} t\right)\right\}\right].$$

1.7. (a) The normalization $\eta = \Omega/\omega_0, \tau = \omega_0 t, x = \omega_0^2 q/P, \mu = \beta P/\omega_0^2$ reduces the differential equation to the desired form,

$$x'' + x = \cos \eta\tau - \mu x^2 , \qquad (85)$$

and the formulation

$$x(\tau) = x_0(\tau) + \mu x_1(\tau) + \mu^2 x_2(\tau) + \ldots \qquad (86)$$

leads to

$$x_0'' + x_0 = \cos \eta\,\tau ,$$
$$x_1'' + x_1 = -x_0^2 ,$$
$$x_2'' + x_2 = -2 x_0 x_1 , \qquad (87)$$

. . . .

A solution with non-dimensional frequency η is to be obtained; for $\eta \neq 1$ the result is

$$x_0(\tau) = \frac{1}{1 - \eta^2} \cos \eta\,\tau . \qquad (88)$$

The equation for x_1 then takes on the form

$$x_1'' + x_1 = -\frac{1}{(1 - \eta^2)^2} \cos^2 \eta\,\tau$$

$$= -\frac{1}{2(1 - \eta^2)^2}(1 + \cos 2\eta\,\tau) \qquad (89)$$

with the periodic solution

$$x_1(\tau) = -\frac{1}{2(1 - \eta^2)^2} - \frac{1}{2(1 - \eta^2)^2(1 - 4\eta^2)} \cos 2\eta\,\tau , \qquad (90)$$

subject to $\eta \neq 1, \frac{1}{2}$. The corresponding equation for $q(t)$ is given by

$$q(t) = \frac{P}{\omega_0^2} \frac{1}{1 - \left(\frac{\Omega}{\omega_0}\right)^2} \cos \Omega t$$

$$- \beta \frac{P^2}{\omega_0^4} \frac{1}{2 \left\{1 - \left(\frac{\Omega}{\omega_0}\right)^2\right\}} \left\{1 + \frac{1}{1 - 4\left(\frac{\Omega}{\omega_0}\right)^2} \cos 2\Omega t\right\} + o(\beta).$$

(91)

This solution is a useful approximation as long as Ω is not too close to ω_0, that is, as long as one is sufficiently far removed from resonance (in addition, of course, it is required that $\Omega/\omega_0 \neq \frac{1}{2}$ be the case).

(b) Now an approximate solution is to be determined which yields good results for the case $\Omega = \omega_0$. The normalization $\eta = \Omega/\omega_0$, $\tau = \Omega t$, $x = \omega_0^2 q$, $\mu = \beta/\omega_0^2$, $P_0 = P/\mu$ leads to the differential equation

$$\eta^2 x'' + x = \mu (P_0 \cos \tau - x^2),$$

(92)

and the formulation (in accordance with Lindstedt 1883)

$$x(\tau) = x_0(\tau) + \mu x_1(\tau) + \mu^2 x_2(\tau) + \ldots,$$

$$\eta = 1 + \mu \eta_1 + \mu^2 \eta_2 + \ldots$$

(93)

yields

$$x_0'' + x_0 = 0,$$

$$x_1'' + x_1 = -2 \eta_1 x_0'' + P_0 \cos \tau - x_0^2,$$

$$x_2'' + x_2 = -2 \eta_1 x_1'' - (\eta_1^2 + 2 \eta_2) x_0'' - 2 x_0 x_1,$$

(94)

. . . .

The normalization for P_0 means that P has the same order of magnitude as μ. The general solution of the first differential equation is given by

$$x_0 = A_0 \cos \tau + B_0 \sin \tau,$$

(95)

which yields the following equation for $x_1(\tau)$,

$$x_1'' + x_1 = -\frac{1}{2}(A_0^2 + B_0^2) + (P_0 + 2\eta_1 A_0) \cos \tau + 2 \eta_1 B_0 \sin \tau +$$

$$+ \frac{1}{2}(-A_0^2 + B_0^2) \cos 2\tau - A_0 B_0 \sin 2\tau.$$

(96)

The requirement of the periodicity of the solution results in

$$P_0 + 2\eta_1 A_0 = 0, \qquad 2\eta_1 B_0 = 0, \tag{97}$$

that is,

$$\eta_1 = -\frac{P_0}{2A_0}, \qquad B_0 = 0, \tag{98}$$

so that the differential equation now becomes

$$x_1'' + x_1 = -\frac{1}{2}A_0^2 (1 + \cos 2\tau). \tag{99}$$

It has the periodic solution

$$x_1 = A_1 \cos \tau + B_1 \sin \tau - \frac{1}{2}A_0^2\left(1 - \frac{1}{3}\cos 2\tau\right). \tag{100}$$

The differential equation for $x_2(\tau)$ thus becomes

$$x_2'' + x_2 = \left(2\eta_1 A_1 + A_0 \,(\eta_1^2 + 2\eta_2) + \frac{5}{6}A_0^3\right) \cos \tau + 2\eta_1 B_1 \sin \tau +$$

$$+ \left(\frac{4}{3}\eta_1 A_0^2 - A_0 A_1\right) \cos 2\tau - \tag{101}$$

$$- A_0 B_1 \sin 2\tau - \frac{1}{6}A_0^3 \cos 3\tau - A_0 A_1.$$

The condition of periodicity again requires that the coefficients of $\sin \tau$ and $\cos \tau$ vanish, that is, one has the similtaneous equations

$$B_1 = 0 \qquad \text{and} \qquad 2\eta_1 A_1 + A_0 \,(\eta_1^2 + 2\eta_2) + \frac{5}{6}A_0^3 = 0, \tag{102}$$

resulting in

$$\eta_2 = -\frac{5}{12}A_0^2 - \frac{1}{2}\eta_1^2 - \eta_1 \frac{A_1}{A_0}. \tag{103}$$

It is a simple matter to obtain the periodic solution for $x_2(\tau)$; it is omitted here.

Until now, nothing has been said about the initial conditions. Instead of specifying general initial conditions for $x(\tau)$, $A_1 = 0$ will be used for simplicity, corresponding to the choice $C_1 = 0$ in section 1.1.1. With this choice, the approximate solution for the periodic oscillation $x(\tau)$ is given by

$$x(\tau) = A_0 \cos \tau + \mu \left(-\frac{1}{2} A_0^2 + \frac{1}{6} A_0^2 \cos 2\tau \right) + o(\mu),$$

$$\eta = 1 - \mu \frac{P_0}{2A_0} - \mu^2 \left(\frac{5}{12} A_0^2 + \frac{P_0^2}{8A_0^2} \right) + o(\mu^2),$$

(104)

resulting in

$$q(t) = \frac{A_0}{\omega_0^2} \cos \Omega t - \frac{\beta}{\omega_0^2} \left(-\frac{1}{2} A_0^2 + \frac{1}{6} A_0^2 \cos 2\Omega t \right) + o(\beta),$$

$$\frac{\Omega}{\omega_0} = 1 - \frac{P}{2A_0} \left(1 + \frac{P}{4A_0} \right) - \frac{\beta^2}{\omega_0^4} \frac{5}{12} A_0^2 + o(\beta^2).$$

(105)

Note that A_0 remains finite for $\Omega/\omega_0 \approx 1$.

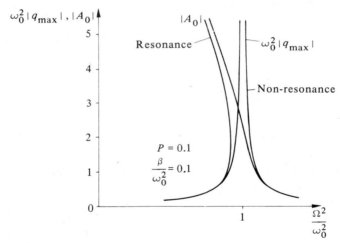

Fig. 12. Approximate resonance curves for Exercise 1.7.

In Fig. 12, A_0 given by the formula above (resonant case) is compared to the series expansion for $\omega_0^2 |q_{max}|$ in the non-resonance case. In the first approximation, both correspond to the amplitude of oscillation. In the vicinity of resonance, the series expansion of case (b) should be used; otherwise, that of case (a).

1.8. (a) The substitution of $x_1 = C \sin \Omega t$ into the right-hand side of

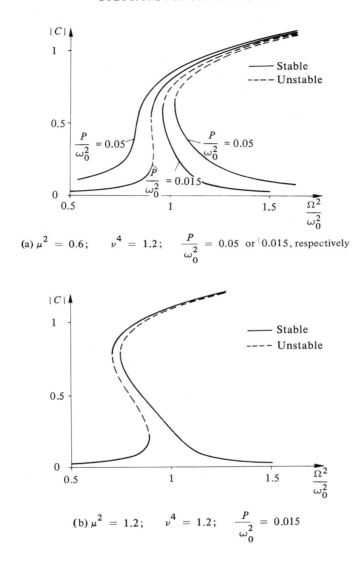

(a) $\mu^2 = 0.6$; $\quad \nu^4 = 1.2$; $\quad \dfrac{P}{\omega_0^2} = 0.05$ or 0.015, respectively

(b) $\mu^2 = 1.2$; $\quad \nu^4 = 1.2$; $\quad \dfrac{P}{\omega_0^2} = 0.015$

Fig. 13. Resonance curves for Exercise 1.8.

$$\ddot{x} = -\omega_0^2 (x - \mu^2 x^3 + \nu^4 x^5) + P \sin \Omega t \qquad (106)$$

and the subsequent transformation of the trigonometric terms result in

$$\ddot{x}_2 = \left(P - \omega_0^2 C + \frac{3}{4} \mu^2 \omega_0^2 C^3 - \frac{5}{8} \nu^4 \omega_0^2 C^5 \right) \sin \Omega t +$$

$$+ \left(-\frac{1}{4} \mu^2 \omega_0^2 C^3 + \frac{5}{16} \nu^4 \omega_0^2 C^5 \right) \sin 3\Omega t - \frac{1}{16} \nu^4 \omega_0^2 C^5 \sin 5\Omega t . \qquad (107)$$

Two integrations together with the assumption of periodicity of the solution yield

$$x_2 = \frac{1}{\Omega^2} \left(-P + \omega_0^2 C - \frac{3}{4} \mu^2 \omega_0^2 C^3 + \frac{5}{8} \nu^4 \omega_0^2 C^5 \right) \sin \Omega t$$

$$+ \frac{1}{\Omega^2} \left(\frac{1}{36} \mu^2 \omega_0^2 C^3 - \frac{5}{144} \nu^4 \omega_0^2 C^5 \right) \sin 3\Omega t \qquad (108)$$

$$+ \frac{1}{400} \nu^4 \frac{\omega_0^2}{\Omega^2} C^5 \sin 5\Omega t .$$

In accordance with the method of Duffing in section 1.3.2, one now imposes the equality of the factors of $\sin \Omega t$ in $x_1(t)$ and $x_2(t)$. One hence obtains the condition

$$\frac{\Omega^2}{\omega_0^2} = 1 - \frac{P}{\omega_0^2 C} - \frac{3}{4} \mu^2 C^2 + \frac{5}{8} \nu^4 C^4 . \qquad (109)$$

(b) $|C|$ as a function of Ω^2/ω_0^2 is plotted in Fig. 13. It is apparent that there is a jump in the amplitude for changes in the frequency ratio in a neighbourhood of resonance.

1.9. In Exercise 1.7, approximate periodic solutions with circular frequency Ω were determined for the differential equation

$$\ddot{q} + \omega_0^2 (q + \beta q^2) = P \cos \Omega t . \qquad (110)$$

Periodic solutions with circular frequency $\Omega/2$ will now be obtained. Since the restoring force here is not an odd function, the formulation

$$q = q_0 + A \cos \frac{\Omega}{2} t \qquad (111)$$

is used. Substitution in the preceding differential equation results in

$$-\frac{1}{4}\Omega^2 A \cos\frac{\Omega}{2}t + \omega_0^2 q_0 + \omega_0^2 A \cos\frac{\Omega}{2}t +$$

$$+ \beta\omega_0^2\left(q_0^2 + 2q_0 A \cos\frac{\Omega}{2}t + \frac{1}{2}A^2 + \frac{1}{2}A^2 \cos\Omega t\right) = P\cos\Omega t ; \tag{112}$$

this equation becomes an *identity in t* if

$$\omega_0^2 q_0 + \omega_0^2 \beta q_0^2 + \frac{1}{2}\omega_0^2 \beta A^2 = 0 ,$$

$$-\frac{1}{4}A\Omega^2 + \omega_0^2 A + 2\beta\omega_0^2 q_0 A = 0 , \tag{113}$$

$$\frac{1}{2}\beta\omega_0^2 A^2 = P$$

holds. Based on the last of these equations, one obtains

$$A = \sqrt{\left(\frac{2P}{\beta\omega_0^2}\right)} , \tag{114}$$

whose substitution in the first equation yields

$$q_0 = -\frac{1}{2\beta} \pm \frac{1}{2}\sqrt{\left(\frac{1}{\beta^2} - \frac{4P}{\beta\omega_0^2}\right)} . \tag{115}$$

Finally, the second equation provides

$$\Omega^2 = 4\omega_0^2(1 + 2\beta q_0) ; \tag{116}$$

from this it follows that only the upper sign is valid in the expression for q_0 and that one has

$$\Omega/\omega_0 = 2\sqrt[4]{(1 - 4\beta P/\omega_0^2)} \tag{117}$$

as a consequence. Hence, the present formulation yields a solution only for $4\beta P < \omega_0^2$.

Thus, for a certain frequency ratio Ω/ω_0 a subharmonic solution has been found which is an *exact* description of a purely harmonic oscillation of the type $q = q_0 + A \cos(\Omega t/2)$. Subharmonic oscillations also may exist for other frequency ratios. They may be determined approximately by using the method of harmonic balance together with a formulation of the type

$$q = q_0 + \sum_{k=1}^{n} \left(A_k \cos \frac{k\Omega}{2} t + B_k \sin \frac{k\Omega}{2}.t \right). \tag{118}$$

2.1. (a) The linearization of

$$\dot{x}_1 = -(x_1 - 3x_2)(1 - 2x_1^2 - 4x_2^2),$$

$$\dot{x}_2 = -(x_1 + x_2)(1 - 2x_1^2 - 4x_2^2) \tag{119}$$

yields

$$\dot{x}_1 = -x_1 + 3x_2,$$

$$\dot{x}_2 = -x_1 - x_2, \tag{120}$$

and the formulation $\mathbf{x} = \mathbf{a}\, e^{\lambda t}$ results in the characteristic equation

$$\begin{vmatrix} \lambda + 1 & -3 \\ 1 & \lambda + 1 \end{vmatrix} = \lambda^2 + 2\lambda + 4 \tag{121}$$

with $\lambda_{1,2} = -1 \pm i\sqrt{3}$. The trivial solution of the non-linear system thus is asymptotically stable.

In accordance with the direct method,

$$V(x_1, x_2) = x_1^2 + 3x_2^2 \tag{122a}$$

yields

$$\dot{V}(x_1, x_2) = -2(x_1^2 + 3x_2^2)(1 - 2x_1^2 - 4x_2^2), \tag{122b}$$

and the asymptotic stability again follows immediately from the negative definiteness of $\dot{V}(x_1, x_2)$. With this Liapounov function, it also follows that Ω_l: $x_1^2 + 3x_2^2 < l = 1/2$ is contained in the domain of attraction of the trivial solution. In fact, from $x_1^2 + 3x_2^2 < 1/2$ follows $1 - 2x_1^2 - 4x_2^2 > 0$ and, hence, $\dot{V} < 0$. One may easily convince oneself that all of the hypotheses of Krasovskii's theorem are satisfied.

(b) The linearization of

$$\dot{x}_1 = -x_1^3 - 3x_2,$$

$$\dot{x}_2 = 3x_1 - 5x_2^3 \tag{123}$$

yields the eigenvalues $\lambda_{1,2} = \pm 3i$. This is a critical case and the linearized equations thus may not be used to obtain statements concerning the stability of the non-linear system.

The function $V = x_1^2 + x_2^2$ results in $\dot{V} = -2(x_1^4 + 5x_2^4)$. Thus, the trivial solution is asymptotically stable and the domain of attraction consists of the whole phase plane. Such a case is referred to as asymptotic stability *in the large* or as *global* asymptotic stability.

(c) The linearization of

$$\dot{x}_1 = x_1^2 + x_2,$$

$$\dot{x}_2 = x_1 + x_2^2 \tag{124}$$

yields $\lambda_{1,2} = \pm 1$. The trivial solution of the non-linear system thus is unstable. The same result is obtained with

$$V = \frac{x_1^3}{3} + 2x_1 x_2 + \frac{x_2^3}{3} \tag{125}$$

and

$$\dot{V} = 2(x_1^2 + x_2^2) + 3x_1 x_2 (x_1 + x_2) + x_1^4 + x_2^4, \tag{126}$$

since $\dot{V}$ is positive definite and V is indefinite.

(d) For

$$\dot{x}_1 = x_1^2 - x_2^2,$$

$$\dot{x}_2 = -2x_1 x_2 \tag{127}$$

one has $\lambda_{1,2} = 0$, a critical case. The function $V = 3x_1 x_2^2 - x_1^3$ yields

$$\dot{V} = -3(x_1^2 - x_2^2)^2 - 12x_1^2 x_2^2, \tag{128}$$

and it follows that the trivial solution is unstable.

(e) The linearization of

$$\dot{x}_1 = x_2,$$

$$\dot{x}_2 = -a_1 x_1 - a_2 x_2 - (b_1 x_2 + b_2 x_1)^2 x_2 \tag{129}$$

results in the characteristic equation $\lambda^2 + a_2 \lambda + a_1 = 0$. For $a_1, a_2 > 0$ only roots with negative real part exist. The trivial solution of the non-linear system thus is asymptotically stable.

With $V = a_2 x_1^2 + x_2^2$ one obtains $\dot{V} = -2x_2^2 \{a_1 + (b_1 x_2 + b_2 x_1)^2\}$ and the (weak) stability of the trivial solution follows from the first stability theorem. However, $\dot{V} = 0$ yields $x_2 = 0$ and $\dot{x}_2 \equiv 0$ implies $x_1 = 0$ as obtained from the equations of motion; hence, Krasovskii's theorem here even guarantees global asymptotic stability.

(f) Now, assume that a_1, a_2, b_1, b_2 in the differential equations above are functions of time. With

$$V = a_2 x_1^2 + x_2^2 \tag{130}$$

one obtains

$$\dot{V} = \dot{a}_2 x_1^2 - 2x_2^2 \{a_1 + (b_1 x_2 + b_2 x_1)^2\}. \tag{131}$$

If there exists a constant $\bar{a}_2$ such that

$$a_2(t) \geqslant \bar{a}_2 > 0, \qquad \dot{a}_2(t) \leqslant 0, \qquad \forall t \geqslant t_0 \tag{132}$$

are satisfied, then stability follows from the first stability theorem. If, further-more, there exist constants $\bar{\bar{a}}_2 > 0$ and a* < 0 such that

$$\bar{\bar{a}}_2 \geqslant a_2(t) \geqslant \bar{a}_2 > 0, \qquad a* < \dot{a}_2(t) \leqslant 0, \qquad \forall t \geqslant t_0 \tag{133}$$

are satisfied, then the second stability theorem even guarantees asymptotic stability.

2.2.   The Liapounov function

$$V = \{1 + e^{-\beta t}(2 - \sin \Omega t)\}(x_1^2 + x_2^2) +$$
$$+ (x_1 + y_2^4)^2 + (x_2 + y_1)^2 \tag{134}$$

together with

$$\dot{x}_1 = 2(x_2 + y_1),$$
$$\dot{x}_2 = 8(x_1 + y_2^4)y_2^3,$$
$$\dot{y}_1 = -2\{1 + e^{-\beta t}(2 - \sin \Omega t)\}x_1 - 2(x_1 + y_2^4),$$
$$\dot{y}_2 = -2\{1 + e^{-\beta t}(2 - \sin \Omega t)\}x_2 - 2(x_2 + y_1) \tag{135}$$

leads to

$$\dot{V} = e^{-\beta t} \left(-2\beta + \beta \sin \Omega t - \Omega \cos \Omega t \right) (x_1^2 + x_2^2) . \tag{136}$$

However, for

$$2\beta > \sqrt{(\beta^2 + \Omega^2)}, \tag{137}$$

that is, for $\Omega^2 < 3\beta^2$, the time-dependent term is most certainly negative. The first stability theorem then guarantees the stability of the trivial solution, since V is positive definite and $\dot{V}$ is negative semi-definite.

Note that the second stability theorem is not applicable with the function V which was used here. For, although $V(x_1, x_2, y_1, y_2, t)$ is uniformly small, $\dot{V}$ is no longer negative definite (see the definition of definiteness for time-dependent functions).

Here, $\dot{V}$ may be determined with very little computational effort if one first notes that the differential equations are of the Hamiltonian type (see Chapter 4). The function V which was chosen here corresponds to the Hamiltonian, and $\dot{V}$ to the partial derivative $\partial V/\partial t$ since all of the other terms vanish.

2.3. It is easy to check that

$$\dot{x}_1 = x_2 , \tag{138}$$
$$\dot{x}_2 = -x_2 - x_1^3$$

represents a critical case so that linearization leads nowhere. Let

$$\text{grad } V = \mathbf{k}(\mathbf{x}) = \begin{pmatrix} k_1 \\ \\ k_2 \end{pmatrix} = \begin{pmatrix} ax_1 + bx_2 \\ \\ cx_1 + ex_2 \end{pmatrix} , \tag{139}$$

with $a, b, c,$ and e as unknown functions of x_1, x_2.

The derivative $\dot{V}$ then becomes

$$\dot{V} = k_1 x_2 + k_2 (-x_2 - x_1^3)$$
$$= -cx_1^4 - (e - b)x_2^2 + (a - c - ex_1^2)x_1 x_2 . \tag{140}$$

This expression is negative definite if b, c, e are chosen constant with $c > 0$, $e > b$, and $a = c + ex_1^2$. The integrability condition

$$\frac{\partial k_2}{\partial x_1} = \frac{\partial k_1}{\partial x_2} \tag{141}$$

yields

$$c + x_1 \frac{\partial c}{\partial x_1} + x_2 \frac{\partial e}{\partial x_1} = x_1 \frac{\partial a}{\partial x_2} + b + x_2 \frac{\partial b}{\partial x_2} , \tag{142}$$

which is satisfied for $b = c$. One thus has

$$e > b = c > 0 \quad \text{and} \quad a = c + ex_1^2 . \tag{143}$$

$V(\mathbf{x})$ now may be determined by integration:

$$V(\mathbf{x}) = \int_0^{\mathbf{x}} \mathbf{h}(\mathbf{x}) \, d\mathbf{x}$$

$$= \int_0^{x_1} \int_0^{x_2} [(ax_1 + bx_2) \, dx_1 + (cx_1 + ex_2) \, dx_2] \tag{144}$$

$$= \frac{c}{2} x_1^2 + cx_1 x_2 + \frac{e}{2} x_2^2 + \frac{e}{4} x_1^4 .$$

It is easy to check that one actually has $\mathbf{h}(\mathbf{x}) = \text{grad } V$. With V_i as the ith-order term in the Taylor series expansion of V, V_2 and $V = V_2 + V_4$ are positive definite as long as $e > c$ is used, a condition which conforms to those which were derived above. The second stability theorem thus assures the asymptotic stability of the trivial solution and even global asymptotic stability in conjunction with Krasovskii's theorem. This could also have been deduced by means of the function $V = x_1^4 + 2x_2^2$, for example.

2.4.   The equations of motion are obtained from

$$\frac{d}{dt} \frac{\partial L}{\partial \dot{\varphi}_i} - \frac{\partial L}{\partial \varphi_i} = Q_i - \frac{\partial D}{\partial \dot{\varphi}_i} , \qquad i = 1, 2 , \tag{145}$$

with $L = T - U$, where

$$T = \frac{ml^2}{2} \{3\dot{\varphi}_1^2 + \dot{\varphi}_2^2 + 2\dot{\varphi}_1 \dot{\varphi}_2 \cos(\varphi_1 - \varphi_2)\},$$

$$U = \frac{c}{2} (2\varphi_1^2 - 2\varphi_1 \varphi_2 + \varphi_2^2) . \tag{146}$$

The function D is the dissipation function

$$D = \frac{1}{2} b_1 \dot{\varphi}_1^2 + \frac{1}{2} b_2 (\dot{\varphi}_1 - \dot{\varphi}_2)^2 ,$$ (147)

and

$$Q_1 = Pl \sin (\varphi_1 - \varphi_2) ,$$

$$Q_2 = 0$$ (148)

are the generalized forces which do not have a potential and which also are not included in the dissipation function.

With this in mind, the linearized equations of motion are given by

$$3ml^2 \ddot{\varphi}_1 + (b_1 + b_2)\dot{\varphi}_1 - (Pl - 2c)\varphi_1 + ml^2 \ddot{\varphi}_2 - b_2 \dot{\varphi}_2 + (Pl - c)\varphi_2 = 0 ,$$ (149)

$$ml^2 \ddot{\varphi}_1 - b_2 \dot{\varphi}_1 - c\varphi_1 + ml^2 \ddot{\varphi}_2 + b_2 \dot{\varphi}_2 + c\varphi_2 = 0 .$$

With the normalization

$$F = Pl/c, \quad B_i = \frac{b_i}{l\sqrt{(cm)}} \ (i = 1, 2) \text{ and } t = \sqrt{\left(\frac{ml^2}{c}\right)} \tau ,$$

one eventually obtains the characteristic equation

$$a_0 \lambda^4 + a_1 \lambda^3 + a_2 \lambda^2 + a_3 \lambda + a_4 = 0$$ (150)

with

$$a_0 = 2 ,$$

$$a_1 = B_1 + 6 B_2 ,$$

$$a_2 = 7 - 2F + B_1 B_2 ,$$ (151)

$$a_3 = B_1 + B_2 ,$$

$$a_4 = 1 .$$

In the undamped case $(B_1 = B_2 = 0)$ the characteristic equation is biquadratic and it is easy to show that the trivial solution is unstable for $F > \frac{7}{2} - \sqrt{2} = F_e$

$\cong 2.086$; $F < F_e$ corresponds to a critical case. For the damped case, the Hurwitz criterion implies that the condition

$$F < \frac{4\beta^2 + 33\beta + 4}{2(\beta^2 + 7\beta + 6)} + \frac{1}{2}B_1B_2 \,, \quad F < \frac{5(\beta + 8)}{2(\beta + 6)} + \frac{1}{2}B_1B_2$$

$$F < \frac{7}{2} + \frac{1}{2}B_1B_2$$

must be satisfied for $R_e\lambda_i < 0$, $i = 1, 2, 3, 4$, where $\beta = B_1/B_2$. This result is simplified if the product B_1B_2 becomes small in comparison to the other term in the inequality. Namely, then, one may determine the manner in which the critical value F_d of F depends on β (see Fig. 14). It is worth noting that for small linear damping, the critical load may become larger than in the undamped case!

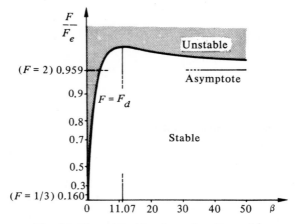

Fig. 14. The critical load as a function of β

2.5. A use of the method of slowly-changing phase and amplitude yields the equations (see section 1.3.3, eqn (1.128)):

$$\dot{a} = -\frac{P}{2\Omega} \sin \psi - \delta a ,$$

$$\dot{\psi} = -\frac{P}{2\Omega a} \cos \psi - \frac{1}{2\Omega} (\Omega^2 - \omega_0^2) + \frac{3}{8} \frac{\mu}{\Omega} a^2 \tag{152}$$

with the stationary solution $a \equiv a_{st} = C$, $\psi = \psi_{st}$ defined by

$$P^2 = C^2 \left\{ 4\delta^2\Omega^2 + \left(\omega_0^2 - \Omega^2 + \frac{3}{4}\mu C^2 \right)^2 \right\} ,$$

$$\sin \psi_{st} = \frac{-2\delta\Omega C}{P} ,$$

$$\cos \psi = \frac{-c\left(\Omega^2 - \omega_0^2\right) + \frac{3}{4}\mu c^3}{P} \qquad (153)$$

Here C is the amplitude of the forced oscillations. With $a = C + \bar{a}$, $\psi = \psi_{st} + \bar{\psi}$ one then obtains

$$\dot{\bar{a}} = -\frac{P}{2\Omega}\sin\left(\psi_{st} + \bar{\psi}\right) - \delta\left(C + \bar{a}\right),$$

$$\dot{\bar{\psi}} = -\frac{P\cos\left(\psi_{st} + \bar{\psi}\right)}{2\Omega\left(C + \bar{a}\right)} - \frac{1}{2\Omega}\left(\Omega^2 - \omega_0^2\right) + \frac{3}{8}\frac{\mu}{\Omega}\left(C + \bar{a}\right)^2, \qquad (154)$$

with corresponding linearized equations

$$\dot{\bar{a}} = -\delta\bar{a} + \frac{C}{2\Omega}\left(\Omega^2 - \omega_0^2 - \frac{3}{4}\mu C^2\right)\bar{\psi},$$

$$\dot{\bar{\psi}} = \frac{1}{2\Omega C}\left(\omega_0^2 - \Omega^2 + \frac{9}{4}\mu C^2\right)\bar{a} - \delta\bar{\psi}. \qquad (155)$$

The usual exponential formulation of the form $\bar{a} = e_1 e^{\lambda t}$, $\bar{\psi} = e_2 e^{\lambda t}$ results in the characteristic equation

$$\lambda^2 + 2\delta\lambda +$$

$$+ \frac{1}{4\Omega^2}\left\{4\Omega^2\delta^2 + \left(\omega_0^2 - \Omega^2 + \frac{9}{4}\mu C^2\right)\right\}\left(\omega_0^2 - \Omega^2 + \frac{3}{4}\mu C^2\right) = 0. \qquad (156)$$

The stability behaviour thus depends only on the sign of

$$S = \left\{4\Omega^2\delta^2 + \left(\omega_0^2 - \Omega^2 + \frac{9}{4}\mu C^2\right)\right\}\left(\omega_0^2 - \Omega^2 + \frac{3}{4}\mu C^2\right) \qquad (157)$$

(see also eqn (2.86)). If $S > 0$ is the case, then the real parts of $\lambda_{1,2}$ are negative, that is, the stationary solution $a = C$, $\psi = \psi_{st}$ is asymptotically stable. For $S < 0$, one eigenvalue has a positive real part so that the stationary solution becomes unstable. The stability boundary in the parameter plane is given by $S = 0$. This corresponds to eqn (1.122), and for the resonance curve it corresponds to the points with vertical tangents (Fig. 1.18).

Similar considerations may be used to show that the stability behaviour of the stationary solutions of Exercise 1.8 has been correctly represented in the figures. If the restoring force is given by a more complicated function than $\omega_0^2 x + \mu x^3$, then eqn (1.120b) is changed; eqn (1.120a), however, always remains biquadratic in Ω^2/ω_0^2 so that it may always be solved for Ω^2/ω_0^2. It is easy to show that the left branch of the resonance curve (corresponding to the lower sign in eqn (1.120b) is stable for $dC/d(\Omega^2/\omega_0^2) < 0$ and unstable for $dC/d(\Omega^2/\omega_0^2) > 0$ (see Forbat 1966, p. 183 ff.).

2.6. For $\epsilon = 0$, the equations

$$\dot{x} = \left(-\frac{1}{2} + \epsilon a \cos 2t\right) x + (1 - \epsilon a \sin 2t) y,$$

$$\dot{y} = (-1 - \epsilon a \sin 2t) x + \left(-\frac{1}{2} - \epsilon a \cos 2t\right) y \tag{158}$$

simplify to

$$\dot{x} = -\frac{1}{2} x + y,$$

$$\dot{y} = -x - \frac{1}{2} y, \tag{159}$$

and $V = \frac{1}{2}(x^2 + y^2)$ leads to $\dot{V} = -\frac{1}{2}(x^2 + y^2)$. Thus, the trivial solution is asymptotically stable in this case and it may be expected that this result will still be valid for sufficiently small $|\epsilon|$.

The use of the same Liapounov function for $\epsilon \neq 0$ yields

$$\dot{V} = -\left(\frac{1}{2} - \epsilon a \cos 2t\right) x^2 - 2(\epsilon a \sin 2t)xy -$$

$$- \left(\frac{1}{2} + \epsilon a \cos 2t\right) y^2. \tag{160}$$

For negative definiteness,

$$\dot{V} < -\delta x^2 - \delta y^2 \tag{161}$$

must be valid for some constant $\delta > 0$. Based on Sylvester's theorem, this requires

$$(a_{11} - \delta)(a_{22} - \delta) - a_{12}^2 > 0 \tag{162}$$

with

$$a_{11} = \frac{1}{2} - \epsilon a \cos 2t,$$

$$a_{21} = a_{12} = \epsilon a \sin 2t, \qquad\qquad (163)$$

$$a_{22} = \frac{1}{2} + \epsilon a \cos 2t,$$

resulting in the condition

$$\frac{1}{4} - \epsilon^2 a^2 > \delta (1 - \delta). \qquad\qquad (164)$$

A positive δ which fulfills this inequality may always be found as long as $|\epsilon| < 1/2a$ holds. Then the second stability theorem guarantees asymptotic stability. For $|\epsilon| = 1/2a$ only the hypotheses of the first stability theorem are satisfied and one can deduce only stability and not asymptotic stability, although the system still may or may not be asymptotically stable. For $|\epsilon| > 1/2a$ no statements based on the present choice of the function V can be made.

2.7. The linearization of

$$\dot{x} = y - xf(x, y, t),$$
$$\qquad\qquad (165)$$
$$\dot{y} = -x - yf(x, y, t)$$

yields

$$\dot{x} = y,$$
$$\qquad\qquad (166)$$
$$\dot{y} = -x$$

with corresponding eigenvalues given by $\lambda_{1,2} = \pm i$. This is a critical case and the stability behaviour thus is determined by the non-linear terms. With

$$V = \frac{1}{2} (x^2 + y^2),$$
$$\qquad\qquad (167)$$
$$\dot{V} = -(x^2 + y^2)f(x, y, t)$$

one obtains the following statements concerning the stability of the trivial solution:

(a) $f(x, y, t) \geqslant 0$, $\forall t \geqslant t_0$ in a neighbourhood of $x = 0, y = 0 \Rightarrow$ stability;

(b) $f(x, y, t) > \delta$, $\forall t \geqslant t_0$ for a given $\delta > 0$ in a neighbourhood of $x = 0$, $y = 0 \Rightarrow$ asymptotic stability;

(c) for every $t \geqslant t_0$, every neighbourhood of $x = 0, y = 0$ contains a point $\bar{x}, \bar{y}$ such that $f(\bar{x}, \bar{y}, t) < 0 \Rightarrow$ instability.

2.8. When written as a system of first-order equations

$$\dot{x} = y,$$
$$\dot{y} = -2bx - ay - 3x^2, \tag{168}$$

the differential equation has the critical points $(0,0)$ and $(-\frac{2}{3}b, 0)$. Linearization with respect to $(0,0)$ results in

$$\dot{x} = y,$$
$$\dot{y} = -2bx - ay \tag{169}$$

with characteristic equation

$$\begin{vmatrix} -\lambda & 1 \\ -2b & -a-\lambda \end{vmatrix} = \lambda^2 + a\lambda + 2b = 0, \tag{170}$$

and with

$$\lambda_{1,2} = -\frac{a}{2} \pm \sqrt{\left(\frac{a^2}{4} - 2b\right)} \tag{171}$$

as the corresponding eigenvalues. Both eigenvalues always have a negative real part so that $(0,0)$ is asymptotically stable. For $a^2 < 8b$ they are conjugate complex (stable focus), for $a^2 > 8b$ they are real (stable node).

For the investigation of the stability of $(-\frac{2}{3}b, 0)$ one writes

$$\bar{x} = x + \frac{2}{3}b,$$
$$\bar{y} = y, \tag{172}$$

resulting in the differential equations

$$\dot{\overline{x}} = \overline{y} ,$$

$$\dot{\overline{y}} = -a\overline{y} - 3\overline{x}\left(\overline{x} - \frac{2}{3}b\right) .$$

(173)

The linearized system

$$\dot{\overline{x}} = \overline{y} ,$$

$$\dot{\overline{y}} = 2b\overline{x} - a\overline{y} ,$$

(174)

has the characteristic equation

$$\begin{vmatrix} -\lambda & 1 \\ 2b & -a-\lambda \end{vmatrix} = \lambda^2 + a\lambda - 2b = 0$$

(175)

with roots

$$\lambda_{1,2} = -\frac{a}{2} \pm \sqrt{\left(\frac{a^2}{4} + 2b\right)} .$$

(176)

Both eigenvalues are real and they have opposite signs; it follows that $(-\frac{2}{3}b,0)$ is a saddle-point.
   With

$$V = bx^2 + \frac{1}{2}y^2 + x^3$$

(177)

and with derivative

$$\dot{V} = -ay^2$$

(178)

one may construct an approximation for the domain of attraction of $(0,0)$. Since $\dot{V} \leqslant 0$ and $\dot{V} \equiv 0$ holds only for $(0,0)$ and for $(-\frac{2}{3}b,0)$ one would choose the region

$$\Omega_l : V(x, y) = bx^2 + \frac{1}{2}y^2 + x^3 < l$$

(179)

so small that the point $(-\frac{2}{3}b,0)$ is no longer contained in Ω_l. For

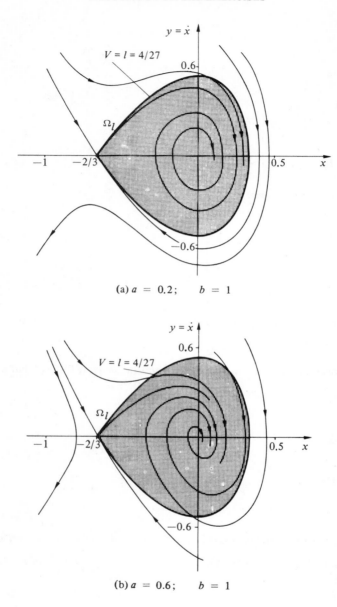

(a) $a = 0.2;$ $b = 1$

(b) $a = 0.6;$ $b = 1$

Fig. 15. Phase diagram and region Ω_l for Exercise 2.8.

$$l = V\left(-\frac{2}{3}b, 0\right) = b\left(-\frac{2}{3}b\right)^2 + \left(-\frac{2}{3}b\right)^3 = \frac{4}{27}b^3 \qquad (180)$$

this is just barely still the case. In accordance with Lasalle's theorem (or also Krasovskii's theorem), the region Ω_l defined in this manner belongs to the domain of attraction of (0,0) and it is depicted in Fig. 15. Note that Ω_l does not depend on the value of a, although the phase trajectories themselves and hence the domain of attraction are strongly influenced by a (note also, however, that Ω_l is only a part of the domain of attraction!).

2.9. In Example 1.9, the exact harmonic solution

$$q = q_0 + A \cos\frac{\Omega}{2} t \qquad (181)$$

was determined for

$$\ddot{q} + \omega_0^2 (q + \beta q^2) = P \cos \Omega t \qquad (182)$$

for $\beta > 0$, with

$$A = \sqrt{\left(\frac{2P}{\beta\omega_0^2}\right)},$$

$$q_0 = -\frac{1}{2\beta} + \frac{1}{2}\sqrt{\left(\frac{1}{\beta^2} - \frac{4P}{\beta\omega_0^2}\right)}, \qquad (183)$$

$$\Omega = 2\omega_0 \sqrt[4]{\left(1 - \frac{4\beta P}{\omega_0^2}\right)}.$$

This may be written in the form

$$q_0 = \frac{1}{2\beta}\left\{-1 + \left(\frac{\Omega}{2\omega_0}\right)^2\right\},$$

$$\qquad (184)$$

$$A = \frac{1}{\beta}\sqrt{\left[\frac{1}{2}\left\{1 - \left(\frac{\Omega}{2\omega_0}\right)^4\right\}\right]}$$

(one always has $\Omega/2\omega_0 < 1$). For the stability investigation, the formulation

$$q = q_0 + A \cos \frac{\Omega}{2} t + \bar{q} , \tag{185}$$

is used. The original differential equation now takes on the form

$$\ddot{q} + 2\beta\omega_0^2 (q_0 + A \cos \frac{1}{2} \Omega t)\bar{q} + \omega_0^2 (\bar{q} + \beta\bar{q}^2) = 0$$

whose linearization yields the Mathieu equation

$$\ddot{q} + \omega_0^2 (1 + 2\beta q_0) (1 + \frac{2\beta A}{1 + 2\beta q_0} \cos \frac{1}{2} \Omega t)\bar{q} = 0 \tag{186}$$

(see also eqn (2.121)). The stability behaviour of the trivial solution of this equation follows from section 2.5 (Example 1): in view of $\omega_0^2 (1 + 2\beta q_0)$ $= (\Omega/2)^2$ the trivial solution is unstable!

2.10. The substitution of the cited solution in eqn (1.139) results in

$$(\omega_0^2 - \frac{\Omega^2}{9}) + \frac{3}{4}\mu A^2 = 0$$

$$-\frac{1}{4}\mu A^3 = P, \tag{187}$$

that is, $A^3 = -4P/\mu$ and the amplitude has the same sign as P for $\mu < 0$ and the opposite sign for $\mu > 0$. A necessary and sufficient condition for the existence of this subharmonic oscillation thus is given by

$$(\omega_0^2 - \frac{\Omega^2}{9}) + \frac{3}{4}\mu \left(\frac{4P}{\mu}\right)^{2/3} = 0. \tag{188}$$

The substitution of $x = A \sin \frac{1}{3} \Omega t + \bar{x}$ in the Duffing equation and the subsequent linearization with respect to $\bar{x}$ yields the Mathieu equation

$$\bar{x}'' + (\bar{\lambda} + \bar{\mu} \cos \tau) \bar{x} = 0 \tag{189}$$

with $\tau = \frac{2}{3}\Omega t$, $\bar{\lambda} = \frac{1}{2} - \frac{9}{4\eta^2}$, $\bar{\mu} = -\frac{1}{2} + \frac{9}{2\eta^2}$, $\eta = \frac{\Omega}{\omega_0}$, where the prime denotes the derivative with respect to the non-dimensional time. As a consquence of the definitions of $\bar{\lambda}$ and $\bar{\mu}$ one obtains the linear relation

$$4\bar{\lambda} + 2\bar{\mu} = 1. \tag{190}$$

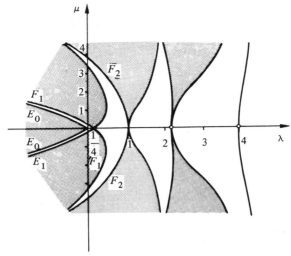

(a) Instability regions in the parameter plane

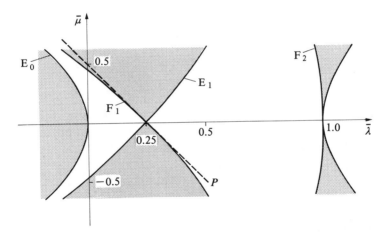

(b) Determination of the stabililty boundary for Exercise 2.10

Fig. 16. Stability diagram for the Mathieu equation.

For the investigation of the stability of this solution, the results of section 2.5 (Example 1) cannot be used, since $\bar{\lambda}$ now may also be negative. Instead, the usual stability diagram shown in Fig. 16 (see Forbat 1966, p. 87) is used, where the shaded areas correspond to instability regions whose boundaries are given by E_i and F_i ($i = 0, 1, 2, \ldots$). Note that the straight line $4\bar{\lambda} + 2\bar{\mu} = 1$ is tangent to the curve F_1 at $\bar{\lambda} = 0.25$. Because of $\bar{\lambda} = \frac{1}{2} - (9/4\eta^2)$ only the region $\bar{\lambda} < \frac{1}{2}$

makes sense. Thus, the subharmonic solution is stable for $\bar{\mu} < 0$ (corresponding to $\eta^2 > 9$ or, equivalently, $\mu > 0$ in (1.139)), and it is unstable for $\bar{\mu} > 0$ (that is, $\eta^2 < 9$ or, equivalently, $\mu < 0$ in (1.139)).

3.1. By writing

$$\ddot{x} + (1 - |x|)\dot{x} + x = 0 \tag{191}$$

in the form

$$\ddot{x} + x = (|x| - 1)\dot{x} \tag{192}$$

one obtains

$$\dot{a} = \frac{1}{2\pi} \int_0^{2\pi} (a\,|\sin\theta| - 1)\, a \cos^2\theta \; d\theta \,,$$

$$\tag{193}$$

$$\dot{\psi} = -\frac{1}{2\pi a} \int_0^{2\pi} (a\,|\sin\theta| - 1)\, a \sin\theta \cos\theta \; d\theta$$

in accordance with (3.57), and, eventually,

$$\dot{a} = \frac{2a^2}{3\pi} - \frac{a}{2} \,,$$

$$\tag{194}$$

$$\dot{\psi} = 0 \,.$$

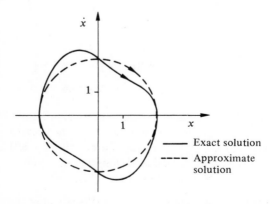

Fig. 17. Limit cycle for the equation of the Lewis regulator.

With these, the stationary solution is given as $a = a_{st} = \dfrac{3\pi}{4} \approx 2.36$, $\psi_{st} = 0$, and a linearization of the equation for $\dot{a}$ about a_{st} shows that the limit cycle is unstable. However, for values of a as large as those in the equation under consideration, it becomes difficult to assert that $a(t)$ is slowly changing. Still, a comparison of the present approximation with the exact limit cycles shows that the amplitudes correspond rather well (Fig. 17).

3.2. With the transformation

$$
\begin{aligned}
x_1 &= x, \\
x_2 &= \dot{x} + F(x), \qquad F(x) = \int_0^x f(\bar{x})\, \mathrm{d}\bar{x}
\end{aligned}
\tag{195}
$$

the equation $\ddot{x} + f(x)\dot{x} + g(x) = 0$ takes on the form

$$
\begin{aligned}
\dot{x}_1 &= x_2 - F(x_1), \\
\dot{x}_2 &= -g(x_1).
\end{aligned}
\tag{196}
$$

The choice of

$$
V(x_1, x_2) = \frac{x_2^2}{2} + \int_0^{x_1} g(x)\, \mathrm{d}x = \frac{x_2^2}{2} + G(x_1),
\tag{197}
$$

as a Liapounov function yields

$$
\dot{V} = x_2 \dot{x}_2 + g(x_1)\dot{x}_1 = -g(x_1) F(x_1)
\tag{198}
$$

for its derivative. If $xg(x) > 0$, $\forall x \neq 0$ is satisfied, then V is positive definite and the differential equation furthermore has no non-trivial critical points. That region Ω_l: $V \leqslant l$, in which $\dot{V} = -g(x_1) F(x_1) \leqslant 0$ is valid, in accordance with the theorems due to Lasalle or Krasovskii, then is a part of the domain of attraction of the asymptotically stable trivial solution, insofar as there are no non-trivial solutions in Ω_l with $\dot{V} \equiv 0$. In addition, any possible limit cycles must contain Ω_l in their interior.

3.3. For the Van der Pol equation

$$
\ddot{x} + \mu(x^2 - 1)\dot{x} + x = 0,
\tag{199}
$$

an application of the transformation of Exercise 3.2 yields

$$x_1 = x,$$
$$x_2 = \dot{x} + \mu \left(\frac{x^3}{3} - x \right) \tag{200}$$

and, eventually,

$$\dot{x}_1 = x_2 - F(x_1) , \tag{201}$$
$$\dot{x}_2 = -x_1$$

with $F(x_1) = \mu(\frac{1}{3} x_1^3 - x_1)$, $G(x_1) = \frac{1}{2} x_1^2$. The Liapounov function

$$V(x_1, x_2) = \frac{1}{2} x_2^2 + G(x_1) = \frac{1}{2}(x_1^2 + x_2^2) \tag{202}$$

has the derivative

$$\dot{V}(x_1, x_2) = -\mu x_1^2 \left(\frac{x_1^2}{3} - 1 \right) \tag{203}$$

with $\mu < 0$. For $x_1^2 \leqslant 3$ one has $\dot{V} \leqslant 0$ and this is certainly assured for $V = \frac{1}{2}(x_1^2 + x_2^2) \leqslant 3/2$. A non-trivial solution with $\dot{V} \equiv 0$ does not exist. However, a choice of $l = 3/2$ ensures that a limit cycle must surround the 'circle' $x_1^2 + x_2^2 = x^2 + \{\dot{x} + \mu(\frac{1}{3} x^3 - x)\}^2 \leqslant 3$. In Fig. 18, it is apparent that this is quite a good bound for the limit cycle.

For the equation of the Lewis regulator

$$\ddot{x} + (1 - |x|)\dot{x} + x = 0 \tag{204}$$

the trivial solution is also asymptotically stable. With

$$x_1 = x,$$
$$x_2 = \dot{x} - \frac{1}{2} x|x| + x \tag{205}$$

one obtains

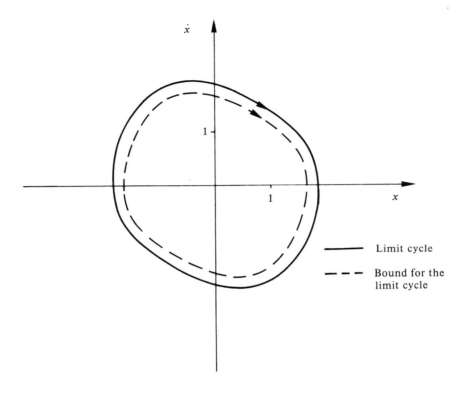

Fig. 18. Approximation of the limit cycle of the Van der Pol equation ($\mu = -0.3$).

$$\dot{x}_1 = x_2 + \frac{1}{2} x_1 |x_1| - x_1,$$

$$\dot{x}_2 = -x_1,$$

(206)

and $F(x_1) = x_1 - \frac{1}{2} x_1 |x_1|$, $G(x_1) = \frac{1}{2} x_1^2$, where the same notation as that of Exercise 3.2 has been used. From $V = \frac{1}{2}(x_1^2 + x_2^2)$ follows $\dot{V} = -x_1^2\left(1 - \frac{1}{2}|x_1|\right)$. Furthermore, $\dot{V} \leq 0$ holds for $|x_1| \leq 2$, which in turn is assured as long as $V = (x_1^2 + x_2^2)/2 \leq 2$ is the case. The limit cycle must contain the 'circle' $x_1^2 + x_2^2 = x^2 + \left(\dot{x} - \frac{1}{2}x|x| + x\right)^2 \leq 4$ in its interior. It is apparent from Fig. 19 that this is indeed a bound for the limit cycle.

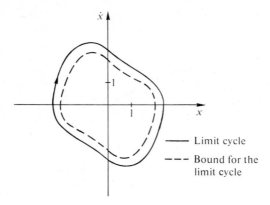

Fig. 19. Estimate of the limit cycle for the equation of the Lewis regulator.

3.4.   (a) The singular points of

$$\dot{x}_1 = x_2 + x_1 f(r^2),$$
$$\dot{x}_2 = -x_1 + x_2 f(r^2),$$

$$(207)$$

with $f(r^2) = \alpha + 2r^2 - r^4, r^2 = x_1^2 + x_2^2$ must satisfy the equations

$$0 = x_2 + x_1 f(r^2),$$
$$0 = -x_1 + x_2 f(r^2).$$

$$(208)$$

It follows that one must have

$$(x_1^2 + x_2^2) f(r^2) = 0,$$

$$(209)$$

and that $x_1 = 0, x_2 = 0$ obviously is the only critical point. Linearization of the equations results in

$$\dot{x}_1 = \alpha x_1 + x_2,$$
$$\dot{x}_2 = -x_1 + \alpha x_2$$

$$(210)$$

with corresponding eigenvalues

$$\lambda_{1,2} = \alpha \pm \sqrt{\left(-\frac{1}{2}\right)}.$$

$$(211)$$

The trivial solution thus is asymptotically stable (stable focus) for $\alpha < 0$ and it is unstable (unstable focus) for $\alpha > 0$. For $\alpha = 0$ one has a critical case (the linearized system has a centre).

(b) A closer scrutiny of the differential equation shows that approximation methods are superfluous here, since the equations may be solved exactly in terms of polar coordinates. With $x_1 = r \cos \phi$, $x_2 = r \sin \phi$ one obtains

$$\dot{r} = r(\alpha + 2r^2 - r^4),$$

$$r(1 + \dot{\phi}) = 0.$$

$$(212)$$

With $\dot{r} = 0$, the stationary solutions (limit cycles) follow as

$$r_1 = \sqrt{\{1 + \sqrt{(1 + \alpha)}\}}, \qquad r_2 = \sqrt{\{1 - \sqrt{(1 + \alpha)}\}}. \qquad (213)$$

Clearly, there are values of α for which r_1 and r_2 are not real. The following three cases are possible:

(1) $\alpha < -1$. r_1 and r_2 are imaginary; no limit cycles exist. The domain of attraction of the asymptotically stable equilibrium position consists of the whole phase plane.

(2) $-1 < \alpha < 0$. There are two limit cycles and the equilibrium position is asymptotically stable.

(3) $\alpha > 0$. There now is only one limit cycle, since r_2 is imaginary. The equilibrium position is unstable.

A linearization of the differential equation $\dot{r} = r(\alpha + 2r^2 - r^4)$ about the stationary values of r shows that the limit cycle with $r = r_1$ is stable but that the one with $r = r_2$ is unstable.

Until now, the special cases $\alpha = -1$ and $\alpha = 0$ have not yet been considered. For $\alpha = -1$ one has $r_1 = r_2 = 1$ and the limit cycle is semi-stable (the equilibrium position is asymptotically stable). For $\alpha = 0$ only the limit cycle with $r_1 = \sqrt{2}$ exists and the linearization shows that it is stable. It follows that the equilibrium position must be unstable for $\alpha = 0$. This result also may easily be deduced from $\dot{r} = r^3(2 - r^2)$ by using the Liapounov function $V(r) = r^4$, for example.

3.5. First write the equations in the form

$$\dot{x}_1 = P(x_1, x_2),$$

$$\dot{x}_2 = Q(x_1, x_2),$$

$$(214)$$

where $P(x_1, x_2) = x_2 + x_1 f(r^2)$, $Q(x_1, x_2) = -x_1 + x_2 f(r^2)$. With $f(r^2) = \alpha + 2r^2 - r^4$, $r^2 = x_1^2 + x_2^2$ one then obtains

$$\frac{\partial P}{\partial x_1} + \frac{\partial Q}{\partial x_2} = 2(\alpha + 4r^2 - 3r^4);\qquad (215)$$

and this expression has the zeros

$$z_{1,2} = \frac{2 \pm \sqrt{(4 + 3\alpha)}}{3}. \qquad (216)$$

For $\alpha \geqslant 0$ the expression $(\partial P/\partial x_1) + (\partial Q/\partial x_2)$ is positive inside the region $r^2 < z_1(\alpha)$ where z_1 corresponds to the upper sign in front of the radical. This region thus cannot contain a limit cycle. A comparison of this estimate with the limit cycle specified in terms of $r_1(\alpha)$ in Exercise 3.4 shows that $z_1(\alpha)$ indeed provides a lower bound for $r_1^2(\alpha)$ (Fig. 20).

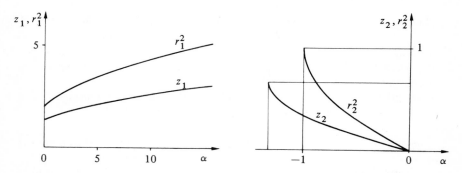

Fig. 20. Lower bounds for the radii of the limit cycles in Exercise 3.5.

For $\alpha < 0$, the expression $(\partial P/\partial x_1) + (\partial Q/\partial x_2)$ is negative inside the region $r^2 < z_2(\alpha) = \frac{1}{3}\{2 - \sqrt{(4 + 3\alpha)}\}$; for $-\frac{4}{3} \leqslant \alpha < 0$, the expression is positive and real, and for such values of α there can be no limit cycle within $r^2 < z_2(\alpha)$. In fact, $z_2(\alpha)$ is a lower bound for the $r_2^2(\alpha)$ obtained in Exercise 3.4 (see Fig. 20).

For $\alpha < -4/3$, the expression $(\partial P/\partial x_1) + (\partial Q/\partial x_2)$ is negative in the whole phase plane; hence, there can be no limit cycle (actually, it is known from Exercise 3.4 that there are no limit cycles for $\alpha < -1$).

3.6.   (a) With $\dot{x} = 0$, the critical points of the differential equation

$$\ddot{x} - \left(\frac{1}{10} - \frac{10}{3}\dot{x}^2\right)\dot{x} + x - x^3 = 0 \tag{217}$$

follow from $x - x^3 = 0$ as $(0,0)$, $(1,0)$, and $(-1,0)$. Clearly, the point $(0,0)$ corresponds to an unstable focus.

The stability of $(1,0)$ is investigated by writing $x = 1 + \bar{x}$, $\dot{x} = \dot{\bar{x}}$, and thereafter considering the linearized differential equation in $\bar{x}$ and $\dot{\bar{x}}$,

$$\ddot{\bar{x}} - \frac{1}{10}\dot{\bar{x}} - 2\bar{x} = 0 . \tag{218}$$

The roots

$$\lambda_{1,2} = \frac{1}{20} \pm \sqrt{\left(\frac{1}{400} + 2\right)} \tag{219}$$

of the characteristic equation indicate that $(1,0)$ is a saddle-point. Hence, the equilibrium position $(1,0)$ is unstable.

With $x = -1 + \bar{x}$, $\dot{x} = \dot{\bar{x}}$, one eventually obtains the roots

$$\lambda_{1,2} = \frac{1}{20} \pm \sqrt{\left(\frac{1}{400} + 2\right)}, \tag{220}$$

indicating that $(-1,0)$ also is a saddle-point and hence is unstable.

(b) From eqn (3.83), the index of a possible limit cycle follows as

$$j = 1 = F - S, \tag{221}$$

where F and S denote the number of foci and saddle-points, respectively, located within the limit cycle. Since one has only one focus and two saddle-points here, it follows that the limit cycle must surround the focus $(0,0)$; the saddle-points $(1,0)$ and $(-1,0)$, however, must lie outside the limit cycle.

The differential equation is written as a first-order system of the form

$$\dot{x}_1 = P(x_1, x_2),$$
$$\dot{x}_2 = Q(x_1, x_2), \tag{222}$$

with $P(x_1, x_2) = x_2$ and

$$Q(x_1, x_2) = \left(\frac{1}{10} - \frac{10}{3}x_2^2\right)x_2 - x_1 + x_1^3 . \tag{223}$$

An application of Bendixson's negative criterion with

$$\frac{\partial P}{\partial x_1} + \frac{\partial Q}{\partial x_2} = \frac{1}{10} - 10 x_2^2 , \tag{224}$$

indicates that any possible limit cycle must intersect the straight lines $x_2 = \pm \dfrac{1}{10}$ in the $x_1 x_2$-plane.

For a final estimate of the limit cycle, the method of equivalent linearization will be used. The introduction of $x = C \sin \omega t$ and $\dot{x} = \omega C \cos \omega t$ in the differential equation yields the result

$$- C\omega^2 \sin \omega t - \frac{1}{10} C\omega \cos \omega t +$$

$$+ \frac{10}{3} \omega^3 \left(\frac{1}{4} \cos 3\omega t + \frac{3}{4} \cos \omega t \right) C^3 + C \sin \omega t - \tag{225}$$

$$- C^3 \left(\frac{3}{4} \sin \omega t - \frac{1}{4} \sin 3\omega t \right) = 0 .$$

A coefficient comparison for the lowest harmonics yields

$$- C\omega^2 + C - \frac{3}{4} C^3 = 0 ,$$

$$\tag{226}$$

$$- \frac{1}{10} C\omega + \frac{10}{4} \omega^3 C^3 = 0$$

or, equivalently,

$$1 - \omega^2 = \frac{3}{4} C^2 ,$$

$$\tag{227}$$

$$\frac{10}{4} C^2 \omega^2 - \frac{1}{10} = 0 .$$

The elimination of ω results in the equation

$$C^4 - \frac{4}{3} C^2 + \frac{16}{300} = 0 \tag{228}$$

with the positive roots $C_1 = 0.203$ and $C_2 = 1.290$. Since it is known, however, that the limit cycle may not enclose the saddle-points, it is clear that C_2 certainly does not provide an estimate for a limit cycle. With $C_1 = 0.203$ one obtains $\omega = 0.985$ and it may be shown that this limit cycle is stable. The limit cycle is shown in Fig. 21. The approximate solution here is so good that the approximate and the exact solutions coincide in the phase diagram within the accuracy of the drawing.

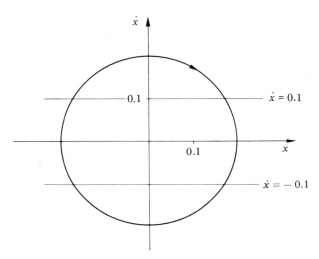

Fig. 21. Limit cycle for Exercise 3.6.

4.1. Since the transformation

$$q^* = \alpha_1 q + \beta_1 p,$$
$$p^* = \alpha_2 q + \beta_2 p \tag{229}$$

is time-independent, it is advisable to look for a principal function which is also independent of t. In eqn (4.38) p and p^* are replaced by

$$p = \frac{q^*}{\beta_1} - \alpha_1 \frac{q}{\beta_1},$$
$$p^* = (\alpha_2 \beta_1 - \alpha_1 \beta_2) \frac{q}{\beta_1} + \beta_2 \frac{q^*}{\beta_1}, \tag{230}$$

with corresponding expressions for $\dot{p}$, $\dot{p}^*$ in terms of $\dot{q}$, $\dot{q}^*$. In view of the identity

$$H^*\left(q^*\left(q, p\right), p^*\left(q, p\right)\right) = cH\left(q, p\right)$$

one then obtains

$$c\left(\frac{q^*}{\beta_1} - \alpha_1 \frac{q}{\beta_1}\right)\dot{q} = \left\{\left(\alpha_1\beta_1 - \alpha_1\beta_2\right)\frac{q}{\beta_1} + \beta_2\frac{q^*}{\beta_1}\right\}\dot{q}^* +$$

$$+ \frac{d}{dt}\phi_1\left(q, q^*\right),$$

(231)

which may also be written as

$$c\left(q^* - \alpha_1 q\right)\dot{q} + \left\{\left(\alpha_1\beta_2 - \alpha_2\beta_1\right)q - \beta_2 q^*\right\}\dot{q}^* =$$

$$= \beta_1 \frac{d}{dt}\phi_1\left(q, q^*\right).$$

(232)

If the left-hand side is to be an exact differential, it is necessary and sufficient that

$$\frac{\partial}{\partial q^*}c\left(q^* - \alpha_1 q\right) = \frac{\partial}{\partial q}\left\{\left(\alpha_1\beta_2 - \alpha_2\beta_1\right)q - \beta_2 q^*\right\}$$

(233)

be satisfied, and it follows that one must have $c = \alpha_1\beta_2 - \alpha_2\beta_1$. An integration then yields

$$\phi_1 = \frac{c}{\beta_1}\left(q^* q - \frac{1}{2}\alpha_1 q^2 - \frac{\beta_2}{2c}q^{*2}\right).$$

Thus, the given transformation is canonical; generally, however, subject to the restriction $c \neq 1$ (see also p. 163). One may easily convince oneself that the function $\phi_1(q, q^*)$ obtained here actually generates the given transformation in accordance with eqns (4.41) and (4.42).

4.2. A simple application of the conditions (4.63) indicates that the transformations given by (b) and (c) are canonical. The transformation (a), however, is not canonical.

4.3. Since

$$H_0^* = \frac{3}{2l\sqrt{(2c)}}\alpha_2\sqrt{(\alpha_1)}\sin\omega_1\left(\beta_1 - \beta_2\right)$$

(234)

does not contain the time explicitly, $H_0^* = c_1$ is a first integral of the equations of motion,

$$\dot{\alpha}_1 = \frac{3\omega_1}{2l\sqrt{(2c)}} \alpha_2 \sqrt{(\alpha_1)} \cos \omega_1 (\beta_1 - \beta_2),$$

$$\dot{\alpha}_2 = -\frac{3\omega_1}{2l\sqrt{(2c)}} \alpha_2 \sqrt{(\alpha_1)} \cos \omega_1 (\beta_1 - \beta_2),$$

$$\qquad (235)$$

$$\dot{\beta}_1 = -\frac{3}{4l\sqrt{(2c)}} \frac{\alpha_2}{\sqrt{(\alpha_1)}} \sin \omega_1 (\beta_1 - \beta_2),$$

$$\dot{\beta}_2 = -\frac{3}{2l\sqrt{(2c)}} \sqrt{(\alpha_1)} \sin \omega_1 (\beta_1 - \beta_2).$$

In addition, the first two differential equations yield $\dot{\alpha}_1 + \dot{\alpha}_2 = 0$ so that another first integral is given by

$$\alpha_1 + \alpha_2 = c_2. \qquad (236)$$

The squaring of the differential equation for $\dot{\alpha}_2$ and the elimination of $\cos^2 \omega_1(\beta_1 - \beta_2)$ by means of $H_0^* = c_1$ yield

$$\dot{\alpha}_2^2 = \omega_1^2 \left\{ \frac{9}{8l^2c} (c_2 - \alpha_2) \alpha_2^2 - c_1^2 \right\}. \qquad (237)$$

This differential equation may be solved analytically. The solution is obtained in terms of elliptic functions in a manner and form similar to those which arose in the solution of the Duffing equation. Note also that $\alpha_2(t)$ generally is a periodic function. From $\alpha_1(t) + \alpha_2(t) = c_2$ it furthermore follows that the energy wanders back and forth between the two eigenmodes of the linearized problem. For any further details of the solution, the reader is referred to Kane and Kahn (1968).

However, the instability of the vertical oscillations with $\alpha_1 = c_2 \neq 0, \alpha_2 = 0$ is immediately apparent. In this connection, it suffices to scrutinize motions with $c_1 = 0$. From

$$\dot{\alpha}_2^2 = \omega_1^2 \frac{9}{8l^2c} (c_2 - \alpha_2) \alpha_2^2 \qquad (238)$$

it then follows that arbitrarily small perturbations $\alpha_{20} \neq 0$ in the initial conditions always lead to motions for which one eventually has $\alpha_2 = c_2$. Thus, the deviations from the vertical oscillation always become large, independent of how small one has chosen the disturbance in the initial conditions.

4.4. With

$$\dot{q} = p ,$$

$$\dot{p} = -(\omega_0^2 + \mu \cos 2t)\, q \qquad (239)$$

the differential equation

$$\ddot{q} + (\omega_0^2 + \mu \cos 2t)\, q = 0 \qquad (240)$$

is described by the Hamiltonian

$$H = \frac{1}{2}(p^2 + \omega_0^2 q^2) + \frac{1}{2}\mu q^2 \cos 2t , \qquad (241)$$

and with

$$H_0 = \frac{1}{2}(p^2 + \omega_0^2 q^2) ,$$

$$H_1 = \frac{1}{2}\mu q^2 \cos 2t , \qquad (242)$$

H may be written in the form $H = H_0 + H_1$. In Example 1 of section 4.5, it was shown that

$$q = \frac{\sqrt{(2\alpha)}}{\omega_0}\sin \omega_0 (t - \beta) ,$$

$$p = \sqrt{(2\alpha)}\cos \omega_0 (t - \beta) \qquad (243)$$

is a solution of the 'truncated' system given by H_0, with α, β as the canonical constants of integration. Consequently, one has

$$H^*(\alpha, \beta, t) = H_1\,(q\,(\alpha, \beta, t)\,,\, p\,(\alpha, \beta, t))$$

$$= \frac{\mu\alpha}{\omega_0^2}\cos 2t \sin^2 \omega_0 (t - \beta)$$

$$= \frac{\mu\alpha}{2\omega_0^2}\left[\cos 2t - \frac{1}{2}\cos 2\{(\omega_0 + 1)t - \omega_0\beta\} - \right.$$

$$\left. - \frac{1}{2}\cos 2\{(\omega_0 - 1)t + \omega_0\beta\}\right] . \qquad (244)$$

Note that the temporal mean of H^* is zero, with the exception of when $|\omega_0 - 1|$ ≈ 0 (or, more precisely, when $\omega_0 - 1 = O(\mu)$). For $\omega_0 \gg 1$ and $\omega_0 \ll 1$, α and β are approximately constant, for $\omega_0 - 1 = O(\mu)$ they are not. In that case,

$$H_0^* = -\frac{\mu\alpha}{4\omega_0^2} \cos 2\{(\omega_0 - 1)t + \omega_0\beta\} \tag{245}$$

is used as a first approximation to $H^*(\alpha, \beta, t)$. With $\dot{\alpha} = (\partial H_0^*/\partial\beta)$ and $\dot{\beta} = -\partial H_0^*/\partial\alpha$ this leads to

$$\dot{\alpha} = \frac{\mu\alpha}{2\omega_0} \sin 2\{(\omega_0 - 1)t + \omega_0\beta\},$$

$$\dot{\beta} = \frac{\mu}{4\omega_0^2} \cos 2\{(\omega_0 - 1)t + \omega_0\beta\}. \tag{246}$$

As long as one has $-(\omega_0 - 1)/\omega_0 = [\mu/(4\omega_0^2)] \cos 2\beta_0$, the second equation has a solution of the form $\beta = \beta_0 - t(\omega_0 - 1)/\omega_0$. Such a β_0 may always be found, provided

$$|\omega_0 - 1| < \frac{\mu}{4\omega_0} \tag{247}$$

is satisfied. For the differential equation one then obtains $\dot{\alpha} = [\mu\alpha/(2\omega_0)]$ $\sin 2\beta_0$ and, since β_0 may always be chosen in such a way as to satisfy $\sin 2\beta_0 > 0$, there exist initial values for which $\alpha(t)$ becomes unbounded. It thus follows that the trivial solution of the original differential equation is unstable for $1 - \frac{1}{4}\mu < \omega_0 < 1 + \frac{1}{4}\mu$. This corresponds to the results expressed in eqns (2.137) and (2.138) of Chapter 2.

4.5. Since the Hamiltonian

$$H(r, \theta, p_r, p_\theta) = \frac{1}{2m} \left(p_r^2 + \frac{p_\theta^2}{r^2} \right) + U(r) \tag{248}$$

does not contain the time explicitly, the solution of the Hamilton–Jacobi equation

$$\frac{1}{2m} \left\{ \left(\frac{\partial S}{\partial r}\right)^2 + \frac{1}{r^2} \left(\frac{\partial S}{\partial \theta}\right)^2 \right\} + U(r) + \frac{\partial S}{\partial t} = 0 \tag{249}$$

is assumed in the form $S = -ht + W(r, \theta)$ in accordance with expression (4.82). One then obtains the new partial differential equation

$$\frac{1}{2m} \left\{ \left(\frac{\partial W}{\partial r} \right)^2 + \frac{1}{r^2} \left(\frac{\partial W}{\partial \theta} \right)^2 \right\} + U(r) = h. \tag{250}$$

An assumed separation of variables for W in the form $W = F(r) + \alpha_1 \theta$ leads to the ordinary differential equation

$$\frac{1}{2m} \left\{ \left(\frac{dF}{dr} \right)^2 + \frac{\alpha_1^2}{r^2} \right\} + U(r) = h. \tag{251}$$

Solving for dF/dr leads to

$$\frac{dF}{dr} = \sqrt{\left\{ 2m(h - U(r)) - \alpha_1^2/r^2 \right\}}, \tag{252}$$

and to

$$F(r) = \int_{r_0}^{r} \sqrt{\left\{ 2m(h - U(r)) - \alpha_1^2/r^2 \right\}} \, dr \tag{253}$$

upon integration. The function $W(r, \theta)$ thus is given by

$$W = \alpha_1 \theta + \int_{r_0}^{r} \sqrt{\left\{ 2m(h - U(r)) - \alpha_1^2/r^2 \right\}} \, dr \tag{254}$$

with constants α_1 and h. The use of eqns (4.85) - (4.87) yields

$$\beta_1 = -\frac{\partial W}{\partial \alpha_1} = -\theta + \int_{r_0}^{r} \frac{\alpha_1 \, dr}{r^2 \sqrt{\{2m(h - U) - \alpha_1^2/r^2\}}},$$

$$-t + \beta_2 = -\int_{r_0}^{r} \frac{m \, dr}{\sqrt{\{2m(h - U) - \alpha_1^2/r^2\}}}, \tag{255}$$

$$p_\theta = \alpha_1,$$

$$p_r = \sqrt{\{2m(h - U) - \alpha_1^2/r^2\}}.$$

The generalized momentum p_θ is constant. This also could have been deduced from H directly, since θ does not appear explicitly and hence is a *cyclic* coordinate. In fact, a separation of variables together with a linear formulation for one of the variables is always successful if that coordinate is cyclic.

4.6. First, write the differential equation

$$\ddot{x} + x + \mu\dot{x}^3 = 0 \tag{256}$$

as a first-order system:

$$\dot{x}_1 = x_2 ,$$
$$\dot{x}_2 = -x_1 - \mu x_2^3 . \tag{257}$$

Now, use the additional 'adjoint' variables y_1, y_2 to define the Hamiltonian

$$H(x_1, x_2, y_1, y_2) = y_1 x_2 + y_2(-x_1 - \mu x_2^3) . \tag{258}$$

Then, with $\dot{x}_1 = \partial H/\partial y_1$, $\dot{x}_2 = \partial H/\partial y_2$ one again obtains the original first-order system and, in view of $\dot{y}_1 = -\partial H/\partial x_1$, $\dot{y}_2 = -\partial H/\partial x_2$, the adjoint differential equations

$$\dot{y}_1 = y_2 ,$$
$$\dot{y}_2 = -y_1 + 3\mu y_2 x_2^2 . \tag{259}$$

In this manner, the original second-order differential equation which was not of Hamiltonian type has been embedded in a fourth-order Hamiltonian system. There is no simple visualization of the 'momenta' y_1 and y_2.

By writing

$$H = H_0 + H_1 ,$$
$$H_0 = y_1 x_2 - y_2 x_1 , \tag{260}$$
$$H_1 = -\mu y_2 x_2^3 ,$$

the usual approach of canonical perturbation theory may be used to obtain an approximate solution for the fourth-order system and hence for the original differential equation. With $H = H_0$ one obtains

$$\dot{x}_1 = x_2, \qquad \dot{y}_1 = y_2,$$

$$\dot{x}_2 = -x_1, \qquad \dot{y}_2 = -y_1. \tag{261}$$

A solution of this system can be cited without difficulty. However, for the application of canonical perturbation theory as described in Chapter 4, it is required that the integration constants α_1, α_2 and β_1, β_2 in the general solution be adjoints of one another. Such a solution is given by

$$x_1 = \alpha_1 \sin (t + \alpha_2),$$

$$x_2 = \alpha_1 \cos (t + \alpha_2),$$

$$y_1 = \beta_1 \sin (t + \alpha_2) + \frac{\beta_2}{\alpha_1} \cos (t + \alpha_2), \tag{262}$$

$$y_2 = \beta_1 \cos (t + \alpha_2) - \frac{\beta_2}{\alpha_1} \sin (t + \alpha_2),$$

for example. It is easy to see that this is a solution of the differential equations. The fact that $(\alpha_1, \alpha_2, \beta_1, \beta_2, t) \rightarrow (x_1, x_2, y_1, y_2, t)$ is a canonical transformation may easily be checked with the conditions (4.63) for the Poisson brackets, for example. The expressions for y_1, y_2 may also be obtained by beginning with the equations $x_1 = \alpha_1 \sin (t + \alpha_2)$, $x_2 = \alpha_1 \cos (t + \alpha_2)$ and considering the transformation equations for the corresponding point transformation in accordance with eqns (4.57) – (4.61).

For $H^*(\boldsymbol{\alpha}, \boldsymbol{\beta}, t)$ one obtains $H^*(\boldsymbol{\alpha}, \boldsymbol{\beta}, t) = H_1 (q(\boldsymbol{\alpha}, \boldsymbol{\beta}, t), p(\boldsymbol{\alpha}, \boldsymbol{\beta}, t))$ or

$$H^*(\alpha_1, \alpha_2, \beta_1, \beta_2, t) = -\mu \{ \beta_1 \cos (t + \alpha_2) -$$

$$-\frac{\beta_2}{\alpha_1} \sin (t + \alpha_2) \} \alpha_1^3 \cos^3 (t + \alpha_2)$$

$$\tag{263}$$

$$= -\frac{\mu}{8} \beta_1 \alpha_1^3 (\cos 4\gamma + 4 \cos 2\gamma + 3) +$$

$$+ \frac{\mu}{8} \beta_2 \alpha_1^2 (-\sin 2\gamma + \sin 4\gamma + 3 \sin 2\gamma),$$

where $\gamma = t + \alpha_2$. Since there are some difficulties in solving the differential equation corresponding to H^*, H^* is written in the form $H^* = H_0^* + H_1^*$ where H_0^* consists of those terms which are independent of γ. With

$$H_0^* = -\frac{3}{8} \mu \beta_1 \alpha_1^3 , \tag{264}$$

there follows

$$\dot{\alpha}_1 = \frac{\partial H_0^*}{\partial \beta_1} = -\frac{3}{8} \mu \alpha_1^3 , \qquad \dot{\beta}_1 = -\frac{\partial H_0^*}{\partial \alpha_1} = \frac{9}{8} \mu \alpha_1^2 \beta_1 ,$$

$$\tag{265}$$

$$\dot{\alpha}_2 = \frac{\partial H_0^*}{\partial \beta_2} = 0 , \qquad \dot{\beta}_2 = -\frac{\partial H_0^*}{\partial \alpha_2} = 0 ,$$

with solution

$$\alpha_1(t) = \frac{1}{\sqrt{\left(\dfrac{1}{\alpha_{10}^2} + \dfrac{3}{4} \mu t\right)}} , \qquad \alpha_2(t) \equiv \alpha_{20} , \tag{266}$$

for the first two differential equations. The procedure will be truncated here; thus, it will not be necessary to obtain the solutions $\beta_1(t), \beta_2(t)$ since these do not appear in the expressions for $x_1(t), x_2(t)$. Eventually, one obtains

$$x(t) = x_1(t) \approx \frac{1}{\sqrt{\left(\dfrac{1}{\alpha_{10}^2} + \dfrac{3}{4} \mu t\right)}} \sin(t + \alpha_{20}) \tag{267}$$

as an approximate solution for the original differential equation, α_{10} and α_{20} being constants of integration.

5.1.   The equations of motion are

$$\dot{x}_1 = v \cos \theta , \tag{268}$$

$$\dot{x}_2 = v \sin \theta ,$$

where the velocity is given by $v = \sqrt{(v_0^2 + 2gx_2)}$ and where θ represents the control function. The Hamiltonian is given by

$$H = -1 + y_1 v \cos \theta + y_2 v \sin \theta ,$$
(269)

and the required maximization of H with respect to θ yields

$$\sin \theta = \frac{y_2}{\sqrt{(y_1^2 + y_2^2)}} , \qquad \cos \theta = \frac{y_1}{\sqrt{(y_1^2 + y_2^2)}} .$$
(270)

The first integral $H = 0$ then implies the relation $1/v = \sqrt{(y_1^2 + y_2^2)}$. The adjoint equations are given by

$$\dot{y}_1 = 0 ,$$
(271)
$$\dot{y}_2 = -g \frac{y_1}{v} \cos \theta - g \frac{y_2}{v} \sin \theta = -g (y_1^2 + y_2^2) .$$

Since y_1 is constant, the last equation results in

$$\frac{dy_2}{y_1^2 + y_2^2} = -g dt,$$
(272)
$$\frac{1}{y_1} \arctan \frac{y_2}{y_1} = -gt - \frac{\alpha}{y_1} ,$$

and, finally, in

$$y_2 = -y_1 \tan (y_1 gt + \alpha),$$
(273)

where α is a constant of integration. This expression, together with $v^2 = v_0^2 + 2gx_2 = 1/(y_1^2 + y_2^2)$ then yields

$$x_2 (t) = -\frac{v_0^2}{2g} + \frac{1}{4g y_1^2} \{ 1 + \cos 2(y_1 gt + \alpha) \}.$$
(274)

Now, the differential equation for x_1 may also be integrated. With $\dot{x}_1 = v^2 y_1$ one obtains

$$\dot{x}_1 = \frac{1}{y_1} \cos^2 (y_1 gt + \alpha) ,$$
(275)

which may be integrated to give

$$x_1(t) = \frac{1}{2y_1} t + \frac{1}{4y_1^2 g} \sin 2(y_1 gt + \alpha) + a, \ \alpha = \text{const.} \quad (276)$$

The boundary conditions $x_1(0) = 0$, $x_2(0) = 0$, and $x_1(t_B) = x_{1B}$ may then be used to determine the constants y_1, α, and a, as well as the time, t_B. From the expressions for $x_1(t)$ and $x_2(t)$ it is apparent that the trajectory is a cycloid.

For the special case $v_0 = 0$ the boundary conditions $x_2(0) = 0$ and $x_1(0) = 0$ imply $\alpha = \frac{1}{2}\pi$ and $a = 0$ so that the optimal solution is given by

$$x_1(t) = \frac{t}{2y_1} - \frac{1}{4gy_1^2} \sin 2y_1 gt,$$

$$(277)$$

$$x_2(t) = \frac{1}{4gy_1^2} (1 - \cos 2y_1 gt).$$

If one assumes, for example, that the point B has the coordinates $(\pi/8g, 1/2g)$, then one obtains $y_1 = 1$ and $t_B = \pi/4g$ (here, all of the variables were taken to be non-dimensional).

5.2. With

$$u(x_1, x_2) = -w \frac{x_2}{h},$$

$$(278)$$

$$v(x_1, x_2) \equiv 0,$$

eqns (5.38) become

$$\dot{x}_1 = w \cos \varphi - w \frac{x_2}{h},$$

$$(279)$$

$$\dot{x}_2 = w \sin \varphi.$$

Equation (5.45) yields

$$\frac{\cos \varphi}{w - w \frac{x_2}{h} \cos \varphi} = \text{const.} = \frac{\cos \varphi_e}{w}, \quad (280)$$

where φ_e is the value of the control at the end-point, that is, at the point $x_1 = 0$, $x_2 = 0$. It is advantageous to use the angle φ instead of the time as the independent variable in the equations of motion. The function $x_2(\varphi)$ is already known:

$$\frac{x_2}{h} = \frac{1}{\cos \varphi} - \frac{1}{\cos \varphi_e} . \tag{281}$$

Based on eqn (5.44), one has

$$\dot{\varphi} = \frac{w}{h} \cos^2 \varphi , \tag{282}$$

or, equivalently,

$$\frac{dt}{d\varphi} = \frac{h}{w} \frac{1}{\cos^2 \varphi} , \tag{283}$$

which results in

$$\frac{w}{h} (t_e - t) = \tan \varphi_e - \tan \varphi \tag{284}$$

This relationship may now be used to write the first equation of motion in the form

$$\frac{dx_1}{d\varphi} = \frac{h}{\cos^3 \varphi}\left(\cos^2 \varphi + \frac{\cos \varphi}{\cos \varphi_e} - 1\right) \tag{285}$$

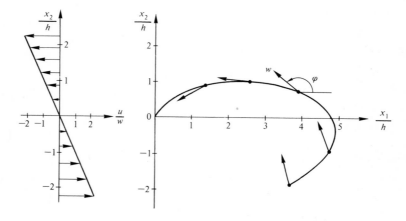

(a) Flow field   (b) Optimal trajectory

Fig. 22. Exercise 5.2.

with solution

$$
x_1 = -\frac{h}{2} \left\{ \sec \varphi_e \left(\tan \varphi_e - \tan \varphi \right) - \right.
$$
$$
\left. - \tan \varphi \left(\sec \varphi_e - \sec \varphi \right) + \ln \frac{\tan \varphi_e + \sec \varphi_e}{\tan \varphi + \sec \varphi} \right\}. \tag{286}
$$

If one introduces the initial conditions $x_1 = 3.66h$, $x_2 = -1.86h$, and $\varphi = \varphi_0$, then the expressions for $x_1(\varphi)$ and $x_2(\varphi)$ yield algebraic equations for the two unknowns φ_0 and φ_e. This approach eventually results in $\varphi_0 = 105°$ and $\varphi_e = 240°$. The corresponding optimal trajectory is represented in Fig. 22.

5.3. The equations of motion

$$
\dot{x}_1 = w \cos \theta,
$$
$$
\dot{x}_2 = w \sin \theta, \tag{287}
$$
$$
\dot{\theta} = \frac{w}{\rho}
$$

are subject to the condition $-1 \leqslant R/\rho \leqslant 1$ and it is furthermore assumed that the driver may instantaneously change the radius of curvature, ρ. Therefore, $u = R/\rho$ is chosen as control and the system now is written in the form

$$
\dot{x}_1 = w \cos \theta,
$$
$$
\dot{x}_2 = w \sin \theta, \tag{288}
$$
$$
\dot{\theta} = \frac{w}{R} u, \qquad -1 \leqslant u \leqslant 1.
$$

The Hamiltonian

$$
H = -1 + y_1 w \cos \theta + y_2 w \sin \theta + y_3 \frac{w}{R} u \tag{289}
$$

is used to generate the adjoint equations

$$
\dot{y}_1 = 0,
$$
$$
\dot{y}_2 = 0, \tag{290}
$$
$$
\dot{y}_3 = y_1 w \sin \theta - y_2 w \cos \theta.
$$

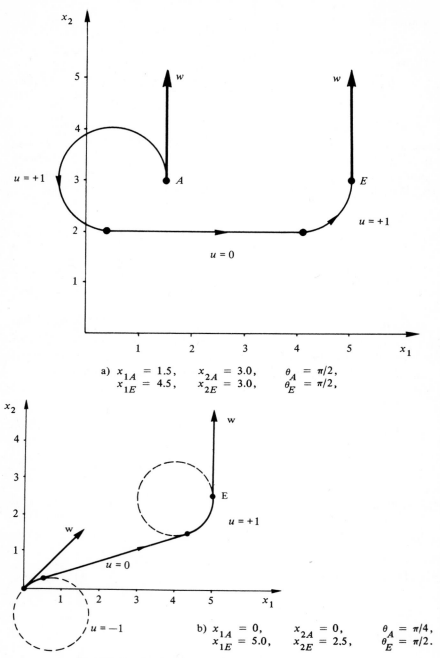

a) $x_{1A} = 1.5,$ $x_{2A} = 3.0,$ $\theta_A = \pi/2,$
    $x_{1E} = 4.5,$ $x_{2E} = 3.0,$ $\theta_E = \pi/2,$

b) $x_{1A} = 0,$ $x_{2A} = 0,$ $\theta_A = \pi/4,$
    $x_{1E} = 5.0,$ $x_{2E} = 2.5,$ $\theta_E = \pi/2.$

Fig. 23. Optimal trajectories for Exercise 5.3 ($R = 1$).

In addition, an application of the maximum principle implies

$$u = \operatorname{sgn} y_3 \quad \text{for} \quad y_3 \neq 0 . \tag{291}$$

In the $x_1 x_2$-plane, the trajectories for $u = +1$ and $u = -1$ consist of circular arcs of radius R (they are orthogonal projections of the trajectories in state space).

The case $y_3 \equiv 0$ must be investigated independently. From

$$0 = y_1 w \sin \theta - y_2 w \cos \theta \tag{292}$$

one obtains

$$\tan \theta = \frac{y_2}{y_1} , \tag{293}$$

indicating that θ remains constant. The differential equation $\dot{\theta} = (\omega/R) u$ then implies $u = 0$ and the corresponding trajectories obviously are straight lines in the $x_1 x_2$-plane.

Thus, all optimal trajectories here are composed of circular arcs with radius R and of straight lines! In Fig. 23, two examples of optimal trajectories have been indicated. The initial and final values of θ here are given by the angle between the arrows and the x_1-axis. The optimal trajectories can be conveniently represented in the $x_1 x_2$-plane, which naturally should not be confused with the three-dimensional state space.

5.4. With $\dot{x} = x + u$ and $J = \dfrac{1}{4} \displaystyle\int_0^1 u^4 \, \mathrm{d}t$ the Hamiltonian may be written in the form

$$H = -\frac{1}{4} u^4 + y (x + u) \tag{294}$$

with corresponding adjoint equation

$$\dot{y} = -y . \tag{295}$$

The maximum principle implies $\partial H / \partial u = y - u^3 = 0$ as a necessary condition and, hence,

$$u = \sqrt[3]{y} . \tag{296}$$

Since $y = Ce^{-t}$ is the solution of the adjoint equation, the state equation now takes on the form

$$\dot{x} = x + \sqrt[3]{(Ce^{-t})} \tag{297}$$

and, finally,

$$x(t) = x_0 e^t - \frac{3}{4} \sqrt[3]{C} \left(e^{-t/3} - e^t \right). \tag{298}$$

The terminal condition $x(1) = 0$ results in

$$\sqrt[3]{C} = \frac{4}{3} x_0 \left(e^{-4/3} - 1 \right)^{-1}, \tag{299}$$

and it follows that the optimal control is given by

$$u = \frac{4}{3} x_0 \left(e^{-4/3} - 1 \right)^{-1} e^{-t/3}. \tag{300}$$

The corresponding optimal trajectory then is

$$x = x_0 \left\{ e^t - \frac{e^{-t/3} - e^t}{e^{-4/3} - 1} \right\}. \tag{301}$$

It is an easy matter here to check that H is constant along the optimal trajectory but that this constant is not zero. This was to be expected, since the time interval was specified.

5.5. The motion in the $x_1 x_2$-plane is described by the equations

$$\dot{x}_1 = v \cos \theta,$$

$$\dot{x}_2 = v \sin \theta,$$

$$m\dot{v} = S \cos \delta. \tag{302}$$

$$m \frac{v^2}{\rho} = S \sin \delta.$$

Here, x_1 and x_2 are the coordinates of the particle, v is its velocity, θ is the angle between the velocity vector and the x_1-axis, m is the mass, S is

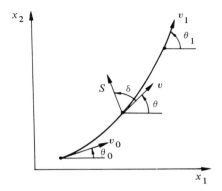

Fig. 24. The equations of motion for Exercise 5.5.

the absolute value of the thrusting force, δ is the angle between the velocity vector and the thrust vector, and ρ is the radius of curvature of the path (Fig. 24). With $s = S/m$ as the acceleration due to the thrust, $\rho\dot\theta = v$, as well as $\theta = x_3$ and $v = x_4$, these equations may be rewritten in the form

$$\dot{x}_1 = x_4 \cos x_3 ,$$

$$\dot{x}_2 = x_4 \sin x_3 ,$$

$$\dot{x}_3 = \frac{s}{x_4} \sin \delta ,$$

$$\dot{x}_4 = s \cos \delta ,$$

(303)

where $s(s \leqslant \bar{s} = S_{max}/m)$ and δ are the control variables. Without loss of generality, the initial conditions are chosen as $x_1(0) = 0, x_2(0) = 0, x_3(0) = \theta_0$, $x_4(0) = v_0$, and the terminal conditions are given by $x_3(t_1) = \theta_1, x_4(t_1) = v_1$, with t_1 as the free terminal time, and with $x_1(t_1), x_2(t_1)$ arbitrary.

The Hamiltonian

$$H = -1 + y_1 x_4 \cos x_3 + y_2 x_4 \sin x_3 + \frac{y_3 s}{x_4} \sin \delta + y_4 s \cos \delta \quad (304)$$

yields the adjoint equations

$$\dot{y}_1 = 0 ,$$

$$\dot{y}_2 = 0 ,$$

$$\dot{y}_3 = y_1 x_4 \sin x_3 - y_2 x_4 \cos x_3 , \qquad (305)$$

$$\dot{y}_4 = -y_1 \cos x_3 - y_2 \sin x_3 + y_3 \frac{s}{x_4^2} \sin \delta ,$$

with $y_1 \equiv y_{10}$ and $y_2 \equiv y_{20}$. With $x_1 (t_1)$ and $x_2 (t_1)$ unspecified, the transversality conditions imply

$$y_1 (t_1) = 0 , \qquad (306)$$

$$y_2 (t_1) = 0 ,$$

resulting in $y_{10} = 0$ and $y_{20} = 0$. The Hamiltonian thus takes on the simplified form

$$H = -1 + \frac{s}{x_4} (y_3 \sin \delta + x_4 y_4 \cos \delta) , \qquad (307)$$

and the adjoint equations are reduced to

$$\dot{y}_3 = 0 ,$$

$$\dot{y}_4 = y_3 \frac{s}{x_4^2} \sin \delta , \qquad (308)$$

with $y_3 \equiv y_{30}$. In accordance with the maximum principle, the optimal control is given by $s = \bar{s}$ with

$$\sin \delta = \frac{y_3}{\sqrt{(y_3^2 + x_4^2 y_4^2)}} ,$$

$$\qquad (309)$$

$$\cos \delta = \frac{x_4 y_4}{\sqrt{(y_3^2 + x_4^2 y_4^2)}}$$

(the expression enclosed in parentheses in H may be viewed as the inner product of the vectors $(\sin \delta, \cos \delta)$ and $(y_3, x_4 y_4)$; the scalar product takes on a maximum when the two vectors are parallel).

The condition $H = 0$ then yields

$$\sqrt{(y_{30}^2 + x_4^2 y_4^2)} = \frac{x_4}{\bar{s}} \tag{310}$$

and

$$x_4 y_4 = \pm \sqrt{\left(\frac{x_4^2}{\bar{s}^2} - y_{30}^2\right)}, \tag{311}$$

resulting in

$$\sin \delta = \frac{y_{30} \bar{s}}{x_4}, \qquad \cos \delta = \pm \frac{1}{x_4} \sqrt{(x_4^2 - y_{30}^2 \bar{s}^2)}. \tag{312}$$

With these expressions, the differential equations for x_3 and x_4 may be written in the form

$$\dot{x}_3 = y_{30} \frac{\bar{s}^2}{x_4^2}, \tag{313}$$

$$\dot{x}_4 = \pm \frac{\bar{s}}{x_4} \sqrt{(x_4^2 - y_{30}^2 \bar{s}^2)}.$$

This last equation, together with the initial condition $x_4(0) = v_0$ result in

$$x_4(t) = \sqrt{[y_{30}^2 \bar{s}^2 + \{\bar{s} t \pm \sqrt{(v_0^2 - y_{30}^2 \bar{s}^2)}\}^2]}, \tag{314}$$

and the function $\delta(t)$ then also is known up to a constant of integration y_{30}. When the time is eliminated between the two differential equations, one obtains

$$\pm dx_3 = y_{30} \bar{s} \frac{dx_4}{x_4 \sqrt{(x_4^2 - y_{30}^2 \bar{s}^2)}}, \tag{315}$$

with the solution

$$\pm x_3 + C = \arccos \frac{y_{30} \bar{s}}{x_4}, \tag{316}$$

which becomes

$$\pm x_3 = \arccos \frac{y_{30} \bar{s}}{x_4} - \arccos \frac{y_{30} \bar{s}}{v_0} \tag{317}$$

upon use of the conditions $x_3(0) = 0$, $x_4(0) = v_0$. Thus, $x_3(t)$ is also known. The boundary conditions $x_3(t_1) = \theta_1$, $x_4(t_1) = v_1$ lead to a system of algebraic equations in t_1 and y_{30} from which y_{30} is obtained in the form

$$y_{30} = \frac{v_0 v_1 \sin\theta_1}{\overline{s}\ \sqrt{(v_0^2 + v_1^2 - 2v_0 v_1 \cos\theta_1)}}. \tag{318}$$

It may also be shown that

$$\delta(t) = \arcsin\frac{y_{30}\overline{s}}{v_0} - x_3 \tag{319}$$

is satisfied for the optimal control. Additional integrations then yield $x_1(t)$ and $x_2(t)$.

5.6.   The introduction of the new variable $x_1 = x - c$, where c is to be determined later, in the differential equation

$$\ddot{x} + \omega_0^2 x + ax^3 = u, \qquad |u| \leqslant 1, \tag{320}$$

results in

$$\ddot{x}_1 + \Omega^2 x_1 + 3\,acx_1^2 + ax_1^3 + l = 0 \tag{321}$$

with

$$\Omega^2 = \omega_0^2 + 3\,ac^2,$$
$$l = ac^3 + \omega_0^2 c - u. \tag{322}$$

When written as a first-order system, this differential equation becomes

$$\dot{x}_1 = x_2,$$
$$\dot{x}_2 = -\Omega^2 x_1 - 3\,acx_1^2 - ax_1^3 - l. \tag{323}$$

The corresponding Hamiltonian is given by

$$H = -1 + y_1 x_2 - y_2 (\Omega^2 x_1 + 3\,acx_1^2 + ax_1^3 + l). \tag{324}$$

It is immediately apparent that one is dealing with 'bang-bang' control in the form $u = \text{sgn}\, y_2$ so that the differential equation need only be solved for $u = \pm 1$.

For the determination of the switching points, however, the adjoint equations

$$\dot{y}_1 = y_2 (\Omega^2 + 6acx_1 + 3ax_1^2),$$

$$\dot{y}_2 = -y_1$$

(325)

must also be solved.

One possibility of applying canonical perturbation theory consists of separating the given Hamiltonian into a sum $H = H_0 + H_1$ in the usual manner and beginning the approximation procedure by first solving the equations corresponding to H_0. However, the differential equations for x_1 and x_2 here are themselves of Hamiltonian type and they contain neither the adjoint variables nor the time (as long as u remains constant). With $q = x_1$ and $p = x_2$ they may be derived from

$$\bar{H} = \frac{p^2}{2} + lq + \frac{\Omega^2}{2} q^2 + acq^3 + \frac{a}{4} q^4 .$$

(326)

With $\bar{H} = \bar{H}_0 + \bar{H}_1$, where

$$\bar{H}_0 = \frac{p^2}{2} + lq + \frac{\Omega^2}{2} q^2 ,$$

$$\bar{H}_1 = acq^3 + \frac{a^4}{4} q^4 ,$$

(327)

the Hamilton–Jacobi equation for $\bar{H}_0$ eventually yields

$$S = -\beta\Omega t + \int \sqrt{(2\beta\Omega - \Omega^2 q^2 - 2lq)} \, dq ,$$

(328)

resulting in

$$q = -\frac{l}{\Omega^2} + \frac{\sqrt{(2\beta\Omega + l^2/\Omega^2)}}{\Omega} \sin(\Omega t + \alpha)$$

(329)

$$p = \sqrt{(2\beta\Omega + l^2/\Omega^2)} \cos(\Omega t + \alpha) .$$

With these, one obtains

$$\bar{H}^* = \bar{H}_1(q\,(\alpha, \beta, t)\,,\, p\,(\alpha, \beta, t)\,)$$

$$= \frac{a}{4}\left(-6\,c\,A^2\,L - 4\,c\,L^3 + L^4 + \frac{3}{8}A^4 + 3\,A^2\,L^2\right) +$$

$$+ \frac{a}{4}\left(L^2\,A\,(12\,c - 4\,L) + 3\,A^3\,(c - L)\,\sin\gamma\right) - \tag{330}$$

$$- \frac{a}{4}A^3\,(c - L)\,\sin 3\,\gamma -$$

$$- \frac{a}{8}\{LA^2\,(-12\,c + 6\,L) + A^4\}\cos 2\,\gamma + \frac{a}{32}A^4\cos 4\,\gamma ,$$

where

$$A = \frac{1}{\Omega}\sqrt{(2\,\beta\Omega + l^2/\Omega^2)}, \quad L = l/\Omega^2 , \quad \gamma = \Omega t + \alpha . \tag{331}$$

If only the terms independent of γ are considered, then one obtains

$$\dot{\alpha} = \frac{a}{4\Omega^3}\left\{3\,\beta\Omega + l\left(\frac{15}{2}\frac{l}{\Omega^2} - 12\,c\right)\right\},$$

$$\dot{\beta} = 0 , \tag{332}$$

whose solution is given by

$$\alpha = \alpha_0 + \frac{a}{4\Omega^3}\left\{3\,\beta\Omega + l\left(\frac{15}{2}\frac{l}{\Omega^2} - 12\,c\right)\right\}t ,$$

$$\beta = \beta_0 . \tag{333}$$

Thus, an approximate solution of the equations of motion for a time interval in which u and, consequently, l remain constant, is given by

$$x_1 = q = -\frac{l}{\Omega^2} + \frac{1}{\Omega}\sqrt{(2\,\beta_0\Omega + l^2/\Omega^2)} \cdot \sin\{(\Omega + \dot{\alpha}(\beta_0))t + \alpha_0\} , \tag{334}$$

$$x_2 = p = \sqrt{(2\,\beta_0\Omega + l^2/\Omega^2)}\,\cos\{(\Omega + \dot{\alpha}(\beta_0))t + \alpha_0\} .$$

For the determination of the switching points, one still needs the function $y_2\,(t)$. Toward this purpose, one again considers the complete Hamiltonian system with the variables x_1, x_2, y_1, y_2. However, the functions $x_1(\alpha_0, \beta_0, t)$, $x_2(\alpha_0, \beta_0, t)$ obtained from the 'reduced' system, determine a 'point trans-formation' in the complete system. In accordance with the results from section 4.2 (eqns (4.57) – (4.60)), one then calculates the functions $y_1(t), y_2(t)$. They are obtained in the form

$$y_1 = \left(-\frac{3aA}{4\Omega} t \sin \gamma + \frac{1}{A} \cos \gamma\right) \lambda_\alpha + (A\Omega \sin \gamma) \lambda_\beta ,$$

$$y_2 = -\left(\frac{3aA}{4\Omega^2} t \cos \gamma + \frac{1}{A\Omega} \sin \gamma\right) \lambda_\alpha + (A \cos \gamma) \lambda_\beta ,$$

(335)

where λ_α and λ_β are constants of integration which correspond to the 'new momenta'. The switching points may now be deduced from $y_2(t)$.

It must be noted that other than the constants of integration, the functions $x_1(t)$, $x_2(t)$, $y_1(t)$, $y_2(t)$ contain the still undetermined parameter c. It is convenient to determine it in such a way that the coefficient of $\sin \gamma$ vanishes in the expression for $\bar{H}^*$.† Note, furthermore, that the constants of integration as well as c must be determined anew for the succeeding time interval at every switching point for a constant u.

†See the literature in connection with Chapter 5, in particular, Hagedorn (1978).

NAME INDEX

Amaldi, V., 180
Andronov, A. A., 53, 111, 150
Athans, M., 206

Bell, D. J., 206
Bellman, R., 71, 110, 206
Bendixson, J., 139
Bernoulli, James, 208
Bernoulli, John, 208
Birkhoff, G. D., 1, 180
Blaquière, A., 15, 53, 124, 125, 149, 150
Böhm, F., 151
Bogoliubov, N. N., 26, 54, 151
Bolotin, V. V., 111
Boltiansky, V. G., 206
Brouwer, L. E. J., 30
Bryson, A. E., 206, 208

Cesari, L., 11, 53
Chaikin, S. E., 53, 111, 150
Chetayev, N. G., 80, 90, 110
Cole, J. D., 53
Conti, R., 35
Cooper, C. A., 207
Coulomb, C. A. de, 21, 120

Delaunay, C. E., 2
Den Hartog, J. P., 127, 151
Dirichlet, P. G., 60
Djukic, D. J. S., 207
Dubey, R. N., 151
Duffing, G., 5, 35, 36, 52

Eminhizer, C. R., 54
Euler, L., 76, 94, 111, 158

Falb, P. L., 206
Floquet, G., 97
Forbat, N., 30, 33, 35, 151, 181, 251
Fraeijs de Veubeke, B., 206

Galerkin, B. G., 14
Gamkrelidze, R. V., 206
Gantmacher, F., 65, 76, 77, 86, 92, 110, 180
Garrick, I. E., 127
Giacaglia, G. E. O., 54, 180
Graham, D., 54, 110, 142, 151

Hagedorn, P., 77, 110, 111, 115, 202, 207, 283
Hagedorn, R., 181
Hahn, W., 64, 66, 77, 92, 110
Halanay, A., 110
Hale, J. K., 53, 54
Hamel, G., 182
Hamilton, W. R., 155, 180
Hayashi, Ch. 12, 54, 151
Heinbockel, J. H., 180, 181
Hellemann, R. H. G., 54
Helmholtz, H., 53
Herrmann, G., 112, 115
Hill, G. W., 98
Hine, M. G. N., 181
Ho, Y. C., 206, 208
Hurwitz, A., 90, 97, 105

Isaacs, R., 206

Jacobi, C. G. J., 180
Jacobson, D. H., 206
Jong, I. C., 112, 115

Kahn, M. E., 180, 181, 263
Kane, T. R., 180, 181, 263
Kappel, F., 53, 98, 185, 206
Kármán, T. von, 128, 151
Kauderer, H., 49, 53, 145, 151
Kielhöfer, H., 111
Klotter, K., 53, 151
Knobloch, H. W., 53, 98, 185, 206
Krasovskii, N. N., 80, 82, 109, 110

Lagrange, J. L., 60
Landvogt, G. F., 150
La Salle, J., 77, 82, 110, 116
Lawden, D. F., 206
Lee, E. B., 199, 201, 202, 206, 209
Lefschetz, S., 77, 82, 84, 110, 116
Legendre, A. M., 163
Leibniz, G. W., 208
Leipholz, H., 111
Levi-Civita, T., 180
Levinson, N., 53, 139
Lewis, J. B., 142, 152, 252, 254, 256
L'Hospital, G.-F.-A. de, 208
Lie, S. 180
Liénard, A. 91, 117, 153

Lindstedt, A., 9, 53
Liapounov, A. M., 1, 60, 61, 97
Longman, R. W., 207
Lur'é, L., 77, 177, 180

Magnus, K., 53, 54, 125, 151
Malkin, I. G., 53, 74, 80, 93, 98, 111, 145, 151
Mansour, W. M., 146, 151
Markus, L., 199, 201, 202, 206, 209
Mathieu, E., 98, 102, 183, 250, 251
Mc Ruer, D., 54, 110, 142, 151
Mc Shane, E. J., 206
Mettler, E., 110, 181
Mikhlin, S. G., 54
Minorsky, N., 124
Mischenko, E. F., 206
Mitropolski, J. A., 26, 54, 151
Mizohata, S., 33
Montroll, E. W., 54
Moser, J., 54, 110, 180, 181
Müller, P. C., 187

Nayfeh, A. H., 1, 11, 54, 151, 180
Newcomb, S., 53
Newton, I., 208

Otterbein, S., 206
Ozgoren, M. K., 207

Painlevé, P., 77
Pars, L. A., 160, 180
Plaut, R. H., 111
Poincaré, H., 1, 53, 54, 68, 139, 141, 180
Poisson, S. D., 165, 183, 268
Pontryagin, L. S., 53, 86, 96, 187, 190, 206

Rauscher, M., 49
Risito, C., 110
Ritz, W., 12, 14
Rizzi, P., 112

Rocard, Y., 128, 151
Rodrigues, H. M., 54
Rosenberg, R. M., 146

Sagirow, P., 206
Sansone, G., 35
Schiehlen, W. O., 187
Schmidt, G., 111
Schoch, A., 181
Schräpel, H. D., 64, 111
Schwinger, J., 181
Sethna, P. R., 180
Siegel, C. L., 180
Simonyi, K., 150
Smith, O. K., 139
Snell, W., 198
Stoker, J. J., 38, 49, 53, 124, 151
Struble, R. A., 53, 151, 180, 181
Sylvester, J. J., 71, 79, 244

Teschner, W., 165
Theodorchik, K. F., 149, 150, 151
Tolle, H., 206
Tondl, A., 54, 151
Tong, K. N., 146

Van der Pol, B., 124, 150
Van Dyke, M., 53

Walter, W., 31, 53
Whittaker, E. T., 180
Willems, J. L., 110, 114
Witt, A. A., 53, 111, 150

Yamaguti, S., 33
Yoshizawa, T., 110
Young, L. C., 206

Zeipel, H. von, 180
Zubov, V. I., 111

SUBJECT INDEX

abnormal problem, 189
absorber, 146
adhesive force, 25
admissible control function, 187
angular momentum integral, 78
artificial satellite, 63
asymptotically stable, 64, 69
attractive solutions, 64
augmented state space, 61
autonomous system, 26

backbone curve, 38, 40, 52
bang-bang control, 196
Bellman's equation, 202
Bendixson's negative criterion, 142
Bendixson's theorem, 141
Bessel function (k-th order, first kind), 16
brachistochrone, 208

canonical transformation, 161
celestial mechanics, 8, 53
centre, 85, 86, 141
characteristic exponents, 98
characteristic number, 109
Chetayev's theorem, 81
combination frequencies, 52, 53
combination oscillation, 30
complete
    controllability, 185
    dissipation, 75
    elliptic integral, 20
    solution, 168
completely damped, 187
conservative, 155
conservative system, 21, 60
contact transformation, 161
contraction, 31
control
    closed loop, 193
    feedback, 193
    function, 184
    open loop, 193
    optimal, 155, 168, 184, 278, 280
    synthesis of optimal, 193
controllable, 184
convergence (L_2-norm), 14
convergent (uniformly), 9
cost functional, 187

Coulomb friction, 21, 120, 128
cyclic coordinate, 75

damped
    forced oscillation, 29
    completely, 187
damping
    Coulomb, 22, 24, 25, 27, 28, 29, 130
    laws, 21, 22
    linear, 21, 23, 40
    negative, 124, 128
    quadratic, 22
definite
    positive, 70, 71, 73
    positive semi-definite, 70, 73
    form, 72
    indefinite, 70, 72, 73
    indefinite form, 72
    semi-definite form, 72
definiteness
    negative, 70
    positive, 71
detuning, 144
dimensionless time, 132
direct method, 61
disturbed motion, 63
disturbed phase trajectory, 63
domain of attraction, 81, 82
dominant stability behaviour, 93
double pendulum (with follower force), 115
drag
    coefficient, 126
Duffing equation, 5, 42, 46, 49, 54, 116
    with simultaneous harmonic excitation,
        52
Duffing's method, 43

elastic pendulum, 171
elliptic integral, 18
    of the first kind, 20
energy
    diagram, 17
    diagram (of self-excited oscillations),
        118
    integral, 21, 78
equilibrium positions, 5, 17
    stable, 60
    unstable, 60

equivalent linearization, 14, 54, 136
Euclidian norm, 61
Euler angles, 94
Euler equations, 65
Euler-Lagrange equations, 158
extremal, 190

first approximation (method of), 84
first integral, 21, 75
first stability theorem, 74, 75
fixed point, 30, 32
    theorem, 30, 31, 32, 35
flutter oscillation, 125
focus, 141
    stable, 85, 86
    unstable, 85, 86
follower force, 115
form of order m, 71
friction coefficient, 120
fundamental matrix, 96

galloping oscillations, 127, 147
generalized
    coordinates, 156
    momenta, 75, 156
    phase plane, 31
    velocities, 75
generating function, 162
gyroscopic
    forces, 75
    terms, 75, 160

Hamilton's
    equations, 156
    principle, 157, 174
Hamilton-Jacobi partial differential
    equation, 168
Hamilton-Jacobi-Bellman equation,
    168
Hamiltonian, 75, 154, 155, 159, 160
    differential equations, 154
harmonic balance (method of) 11, 12, 40,
    47, 49, 54, 143
higher harmonics, 12
Hill's equation, 99
Hurwitz criterion, 97, 105
Hurwitz' theorem, 90

impulsively excited systems, 128
index
    of a closed curve, 140
    of a critical point, 139
infinitesimal disturbances, 66
initial manifold 198
inner resonance 54
instability of equilibrium, 76
isolated periodic solution, 117, 122

Jacobi elliptic function, 20
Jordan curve, 33
Jordan normal form, 86
jump phenomenon, 39, 41, 42

K-transformation, 54
Karman vortices, 128
kinetic energy, 17
Krasovskii's theorem, 75, 82, 142

L-unstable, 66, 68
La Salle's theorem, 82
Lagrange multipliers, 157
Lagrange's theorem, 74
Lagrangian, 74, 155, 160
    equations, 157
Lagrange-Dirichlet stability theorem, 60, 75
Legendre transformation, 163
Levinson-Smith theorem, 142
Lewis regulator, 142
Liapounov
    function, 77
    stability, 60
Liapounov's
    characteristic numbers, 109
    direct method, 79, 70
    first method, 69
    second method, 33, 69, 70
    stability theorem, 74
Liénard-Chipart crtierion, 91
lift coefficient, 126
limit cycle, 82, 83, 84, 117
    semi stable, 119
    stable, 119, 125
Lindstedt's perturbation methods, 100, 132
linearization theorems, 93, 98, 109

Mathieu equation, 99
    with additional non-linear terms, 102
mean square error, 13
mechanical
    energy, 22
    hysteresis, 22
    total mechanical energy, 157

natural mechanical system, 155
node, 141
    stable, 85, 86
    unstable, 85, 86
non-linear
    capacitor, 16
    electric circuit, 5, 125, 150
non-stationary oscillations, 41
normal modes (for a non-linear system), 146

optimal
    linearization method, 15

solution, 187
orbital stability, 63, 64, 66
orbitally stable, 64, 119

parametrically excited oscillation, 99
pendulum
    mathematical, 3, 18, 19, 21, 28, 62
    rotating, 18, 19
    undamped, free oscillation, 3
pentodes, 124
periodic solutions, existence of, 29, 35
perturbation,
    methods, 5
    theory, 49, 53, 54
pervasive damping, 75, 187
phase diagram, 17, 18, 28, 29, 45, 46,
    62, 83
    cylindrical, 19
    of impulsively excited system, 128, 130
    of self-excited oscillation, 118
phase plane, 18, 62
phase space, 64
phase trajectory, 17, 18, 62
point transformation, 164
Poisson brackets, 165
Pontryagin maximum principle, 188
practical stability, 66, 68
practically
    stable, 66, 68
    unstable, 68
principal function, 175

quasi-harmonic, 117
quasi-periodic, 145
quasi-statically, 40

Rauscher's method, 38
relaxation oscillations, 123
resonance
    curves, 37, 38, 40, 41, 42, 43, 47,
    51, 144
    diagram, 38, 43
restoring
    force, 25
    term (nonlinear), 15
Robinson's oscillator, 125

saddle point, 85, 86, 139, 141
scleronomic, 157
second stability theorem, 74
secular terms, 9, 10, 54
self-excited oscillations, 117
self-excitation
    hard, 118, 119
    soft, 118, 119
separatrix, 18

singular differential equation, 149
slowly changing
    parameters, 117
    phase and amplitude, 25, 26, 43, 135
small denominators, 54
Snell's law, 198
stability
    of a rocket, 78
    of periodic solution, 63
    of static equilibrium of pendulum, 63
stable
    differential equation, 61
    solution, 61, 62
    system, 61
    trajectory, 63, 64
state variable, 184
stationary
    oscillations, 40, 41
    plane flow, 125, 127
subharmonic, 52
    oscillations, 30, 49
    resonances, 51, 52
sublinear spring, 16
superlinear spring, 16
Sylvester's theorem, 71
synchronization (theory of), 145

terminal manifold, 198
time optimal control, 194
transient motions, 45
transversality conditions, 198
trivial solution, 66

ultraharmonic oscillations, 30
undisturbed motion, 63
uniform asymptotic stability, 109
uniformly
    asymptotically stable, 109
    continuous dependence, 61
    small, 74
    stable, 109
unstable
    periodic solutions, 62
    solution, 61

vacuum tubes, 124
Van der Pol
    equation, 83, 124, 131, 135, 142,
    143, 153
    planes, 45, 46
variable gradients (method of), 114
variation of constants, 177

weakly stable, 69
Wronskian determinant, 99